THE TIGRESS AND
THE ROSE

THE TIGRESS AND THE ROSE

Eleanor of Aquitaine and the Fair Rosamond

Richard Cameron Low

The Book Guild Ltd
Sussex, England

First published in Great Britain in 2003 by
The Book Guild Ltd
25 High Street,
Lewes, Sussex
BN7 2LU

Typesetting in Baskerville by
Keyboard Services, Luton, Bedfordshire

Printed in Great Britain by
Bookcraft (Bath) Ltd, Avon

A catalogue record for this book is
available from the British Library

ISBN 1 85776 705 5

To Sheila, my inspiration for this book

CONTENTS

ACKNOWLEDGEMENTS

My thanks go to Mr and Mrs Philip Watkins of Flaxley Abbey, Mrs Henrietta Clifford and Mr and Mrs Rollo Clifford of Frampton and Professor Tom Beaumont James amongst many others for all their support, encouragement and kindness whilst I was writing this book.

PRELUDE: CHRISTMAS EVE 1143

The Vale of Castiard in the weak midday sunshine of a winter's morning. Two harts had come out of the Flaxley Woods and were grazing by the stream. One of them raised its head and warily sniffed the air. It remained poised ready for flight. Suddenly the second also stopped grazing.

Out of sight on the higher ground and obscured by the thickets were three young horsemen – waiting. Lower down and upwind from the harts two more and very experienced huntsmen were closing in cleverly using the tree cover. Within seconds two arrows were intended to be winging on their way to provide venison for the Earl of Hereford's Christmas table at Gloucester Castle on the morrow. Then an arrow was loosed, whirring fast and true towards its target. The harts fled towards the safety of the adjacent forest. Milo, Earl of Hereford, toppled gently off his horse, mortally wounded. As he fell the last words spoken to him by Sibilla, his countess, as he left their solar before dawn, flashed through his dying brain.

'I beseech you, Milo, my lord, I beseech you again and again not to go hunting today. You know that I have heard whisperings in corners here and alcoves there; men turn away so that I cannot see who speaks; there are comings and goings to and from the Abbey; I trust not that Abbot Foliot or any of those canons of his. There's trouble afoot. Go not for the love that you bear me.'

Milo's companion, Ernulph de Mandeville, turned his horse towards their waiting squires. He gave terse instructions to Mahel, the Earl's youngest son, William de Tracy and his own attendant, young Reginald FitzUrse. These were immediately carried out.

Later that evening Reginald noticed that his master's quiver was lacking one arrow shaft.

The attention span of the freckled tawny-haired Prince Henry FitzEmpress was limited as he mused and listened to Bishop Foliot's threnody during the magnificent service of consecration and dedication for the Cistercian Abbey of Flaxley. The high altar was on that very spot where the Earl Milo had been assassinated nearly eight years before. A huge and finely arrayed concourse of nobles, bishops, clergy and the leading powerful local families had gathered in the new Abbey to pay tribute to the memory of Earl Milo who had fought with such skill and tenacity to secure the throne for his mother, the Empress Maud. It was vital that the eighteen-year-old prince should see and be seen, and play a full part in all these ceremonies, and he fully intended to enjoy himself. Although it did rather all go on.

Sitting in the crossing in the front of the transept was an astonishingly good-looking girl. A quiff of blonde hair peeked from beneath her coif and beguiling curls had escaped and were visible round her neck. Their eyes locked together for a split second and they both looked down at the self same moment – and that was that.

'One more thought and that is this … the last point that I am making…' On and on he goes, the prince thought, and this is the last point that Bishop Foliot has made for the third time. Henry was a congenital fidgeter at the best of times.

He looked at those sitting in the seats that mattered. There was Milo's dowager Sibilla, small, dark, intense and always brooding, very handsome still and very Welsh too. Her daughters: Berthe, once betrothed to Ernulph de Mandeville and now married to William de Braose; Margery, who had married Humphrey de Bohun; and Lucy, who had recently wed the widowed Herbert FitzHerbert. Herbert's first wife had been his grandfather's concubine who had by then been well past childbearing age. Perhaps Lucy would produce an heir for the Lord Herbert. Milo's girls were all good-looking and had married well. His younger sons were sitting by their mother and were lightweight, not a patch on their famous father. Sitting next to Henry was Roger, Milo's eldest son, who had succeeded as Earl of Hereford. The bishop was also a kinsman of Milo and, when Abbot of Gloucester, had not behaved as properly as he should have done when Milo had been killed. Quite a family gathering. In the chancel sat the young, able and darkly handsome Thomas Becket, whose flashing eyes missed nothing.

Henry glanced towards the girl in the crossing. She was sitting between a handsome knight and a lovely, relaxed and serene lady who were obviously her parents. Again the youngsters' eyes locked together – and disengaged.

He nudged Roger and asked in a loud whisper, 'Who are those three sitting in the front row over there?' He pointed. 'With that very pretty girl in the middle?'

'Lord Walter Clifford, your highness, a border lord with a castle on the vital Herefordshire borders with Wales. And his wife the Lady Margaret, a daughter of Ralph de Toeney whom your highness may recall.'

'And the girl?' The Prince was irritated: his question had been evaded and his grey eyes began to smoulder – a dangerous sign. The bishop paused in mid-sentence and glanced down. He was not tolerant of being distracted, even by his future king.

'Their eldest daughter Jane, sire.'

'*Rosamunda pulcherrima*,' muttered Henry – the most beautiful rose in all the world. Henry was, from that very moment, smitten, and Jane was on the edge of an abyss. But it was as Rosamond the Fair that she was to be known as their two lives became inextricably entwined.

1

Events leading up to 1143

Milo FitzWalter was born in 1080 and brought up initially in the Conqueror's court. His father, Walter, came across to England in the second wave of the Norman invasion and was primarily an engineer and builder of castles – essentially, an expert in defensive warfare. King William needed to dominate England as quickly as possible following his astonishingly rapid success at the Battle of Hastings – before the defeated Saxons could regroup and retaliate.

Walter rebuilt and strengthened the Tower of London and then built Rochester Castle. He was then dispatched to the troublesome West Country with particular instructions to dominate the Welsh princes, who never stopped their incursions into Shropshire and Herefordshire. He built the major strongholds at Bristol, Gloucester and finally Hereford as well as many secondary forts, including the vital crossing point between Wales and the Forest of Dean at St Briavels. His final promotion was to be Constable of all England, a most singular honour.

In Walter's declining years he founded and handsomely endowed the monastery in the Welsh mountains known initially as Llanthony and later called Llanthony Prima for reasons that will soon become obvious. Walter retired to Llanthony, becoming a Canon Regular and was buried in the Chapter House about 1130.

Milo became a trusted and faithful supporter of the Conqueror's third son, who to all intents and purposes usurped the throne in 1100, becoming Henry I. Milo was appointed counsellor as well as inheriting his father's appointment of Constable of all England. King Henry realised that diplomacy was as valuable as warfare in stabilising his kingdom and arranged in 1121 that

Milo should marry Sibilla. Sibilla had had an interesting upbringing and, as it turned out, a lucky one too. Her father was Bernard, Earl of Brecknock, and her mother was Nesta, the daughter of the most powerful Welsh Prince Griffydd ap Llewellyn. Mahel, Nesta's eldest son, interrupted a love tryst of his mother and, besides thrashing the erring gentleman, told his mother what he thought of her. Nesta's revenge was to denounce her son to the king as being illegitimate and not the heir to her husband, Bernard. Consequently Mahel was disinherited and Sibilla became the Brecknock heir, to the huge financial advantage of Milo, quite apart from the direct access that he now enjoyed with the immensely complex princely relationships in Wales. Quite apart from this, Sibilla's great grandmother was the celebrated and original Lady Godiva, so Milo's wife certainly had some sparkling genes in her bloodline.

Shrewdly, Henry had made a diplomatic marriage with Matilda, daughter of the Scottish king and a granddaughter of Edmund Ironside. This move consolidated his position on the throne by combining the old and much respected English royal family, the Scottish neighbours and his own Norman inheritance. Henry had been present in the New Forest when his brother William Rufus was shot and killed by an arrow dispatched by an unknown assassin in circumstances not dissimilar to Milo's later death. Henry promptly claimed the throne despite the fact that his eldest brother, Robert (called Curthose or Shortsocks) had a prior claim. Presumably he was, in today's politically correct language, vertically challenged or in the vernacular a shortarse. But Robert was miles away and when he got round to returning to England he was captured and imprisoned at Bristol Castle for the remaining twenty-eight years of his life.

Henry, nicknamed Beauclerc, was a scholar, a fine administrator and had a legal brain far in advance of his time. He gave a valuable stability to the country after the earlier turmoil and the depredations suffered under brother Rufus. Peace and prosperity were returning to England and Henry was not going to tolerate any usurpation, interference or rivalry from Robert Curthose. He was nothing if not ruthless. Henry's eldest son, Robert, was illegitimate and born in 1090. The King was fortunate in having such an outstanding, albeit unambitious, son of astonishing ability to give him support, so he made Robert Earl of Gloucester and entrusted him with the responsibility for the safe custody of his uncle at Bristol Castle.

Henry had two legitimate children but the elder, William, was sadly drowned in 1120 when the *White Ship* sank with all hands whilst sailing with a drunken captain and crew from France to England. This left his daughter, also another Matilda but mercifully called Maud in most histories, as his successor. The Salic Law did not pertain in England but for a princess to succeed in these turbulent times was difficult and of course the realm extended to Normandy, which was always jealously watched by the French king, to whom allegiance was owed.

There was a further contender for the throne – Henry's sister Adela had married the Count of Blois and their son, Stephen, was a grandchild of William the Conqueror as too was his cousin, Maud. Stephen had the great advantage that he was male in a male dominated world.

In 1126 Henry obtained sworn allegiance at Windsor from his archbishops, bishops, abbots and nobility to acknowledge Maud as his successor and was alleged to have guaranteed that she would not remarry outside the realm. Maud, by then, was a widow and childless. Henry, ever the diplomat, realised that he had landed himself in a trap. He still had no heir in the second generation and probably no suitable son-in-law in prospect. Earl Robert of Gloucester was sent to arrange a marriage between Maud and the fifteen-year-old Geoffrey, heir to the Count of Anjou. In 1128 Maud and her boyish bridegroom were married and, in the following year, Geoffrey succeeded his father and promptly quarrelled with Maud and sent her back to dad. The Norman nobles in the Henrician court had no time for the upstart Angevins and this arrogance from the new count was a bad omen for the future. In 1132 some *rapprochement* was achieved since a son was born in the following year, also called Henry, and this child grew into the founder of the Plantagenet dynasty of England.

A fresh allegiance, which included Stephen's fealty, was sworn towards Maud's accession with reversion to the infant Henry, but the arrangements were now transparently uneasy and fragile and were further rocked by Maud siding with Geoffrey in a blazing row between her father and her husband.

Two months later, on 1 December 1135, Henry died from a

surfeit of lampreys – a great delicacy of small eels, probably what the Spanish call *anguillas*. Henry had been an astute king and had kept England at peace for thirty-five years, although he had the morals of an alley cat, with thirty-five mistresses and twenty surviving bastards – nine boys and eleven girls. But his legacy was catastrophic and the proverbial began to hit the fan.

Stephen was in France when the news broke and straightway went to London to claim the throne. The steward of the royal household, Hugh Bigod, swore before the Archbishop of Canterbury that Henry had disinherited Maud on his deathbed and nominated Stephen as his successor. The Bishop of Salisbury opined that the original allegiance given by the clergy and nobles had been vitiated by their lack of approval to Maud's marriage. The behaviour of Geoffrey and Maud had not endeared them to the English court and the potential antipathy towards the expected influx of upstart Angevins was dreaded. Bishop Henry of Winchester, Stephen's brother, secured that city and, more importantly, the Treasury for which he was responsible. The London aldermen and citizens, in a significant development for democracy, threw their support behind Stephen. Possession was nine-tenths of the law – Maud was still abroad and Stephen was at hand. He *seemed*, incidentally, a very courteous, civil and amiable gentleman.

The hitherto reluctant William, Archbishop of Canterbury, then agreed to crown Stephen on 26 December. The die was cast, but there were many who were absolutely appalled and so the nation broke into two factions.

King David of Scotland, Maud's great uncle, invaded England and was bought off by heavy bribes. Rebellions in Norwich, Bampton and Exeter were crushed. Normandy was more than edgy and was also bought off. Stephen relied on Flemish mercenaries who were immensely greedy, violent and unpopular. Stephen also had character defects which rapidly became apparent – he did not attract affection, inspire awe or command obedience and he transparently lacked security. He was lavish with his promises regarding afforestation abuses and Church rights and reallocated properties from those he mistrusted to those who were currying favour.

The crunch came when he fell out with Earl Robert and Milo in 1138. Robert had hitherto tried his best to keep excesses in

8

check and could see no value in plunging the country into end-less turmoil after all the prosperity and peace enjoyed through-out his father's reign. Maud had meantime kept a low profile and when it became apparent that Stephen was losing his initial sup-port, Robert threw in his lot with his half-sister for the sake of the country and its people. In 1139 Maud returned to the coun-try and was besieged at Arundel. Here, Stephen's quixotic nature manifested itself when he allowed safe conduct for his cousin to join Earl Robert at his power base at Bristol. The West Country nobility rallied round Maud and she moved her headquarters to Milo's castle at Gloucester.

Stephen's campaign disintegrated despite his own personal val-our and bravery and he was captured and brought to Gloucester. Maud then displayed the most appalling insensitivity by sending him in chains to Bristol, despite Stephen's earlier chivalry to her. Maud travelled in triumph first to Winchester where Stephen's own brother, the bishop, threw in his lot with her. Earl Robert, a wise and sensible adviser, was now utterly ignored by his sister. Maud went to London where she prematurely announced herself as queen before being crowned. In her charters then she described herself as 'Matilda the Empress, King Henry's daugh-ter' as well as 'Queen of the English'. So it was that her son became known as Henry FitzEmpress for the time being anyway.

Matters went rapidly from bad to worse. Maud treated the most charming and sensitive wife of Stephen (yet another Matilda) with utter contempt and contumely. She behaved with even greater ruthlessness in the confiscation of lands and property than ever Stephen had. She offended the barons who came to do her homage and insulted the citizens of London to such an extent that they took up arms and drove her ignominiously from the capital.

Maud fled to Oxford where she made Milo Earl of Hereford in recognition of his faithful services. Meanwhile, Bishop Henry revoked his allegiance – he, after all, had the nation's money under his control. This reverse tempted Maud to besiege the bishop in his castle at Wolvesey, but she in turn was besieged at Winchester by forces led by Stephen's wife. With incredible brav-ery and accompanied by the Earls Robert and Milo, they forced their way out, but Robert was himself captured in a rearguard action covering their flight. Maud and Milo reached safety at

Gloucester, half starved and in rags. But she still had the King, and they had Robert, so complex bargaining began for an exchange which was eventually completed by late 1141.

Maud then tried to get her husband Geoffrey to join in, but he had problems of his own and declined to help. However, the solution to all this now became apparent to Robert: Maud was no longer a viable option. Stephen was a disaster but was at least the crowned sovereign. The country needed to recover. Stephen's eldest son was not good news and his younger sons were unlikely to be a problem. Maud's son, Henry, was only nine years old but had potential and a powerful claim to the throne – thus fulfilling Henry I's wishes.

Thus in 1142, Robert removed the father's hated Angevin influence, fetched the young Henry from Normandy and undertook, at Bristol, the training necessary for kingship. Robert now bent his mind around the negotiations required to achieve his goal, and it cannot be said that these were going to be easy.

* * *

Before we come to the events of 1143, we shall tidy up some of the affairs of the other main characters.

Milo had followed very much in the footsteps of his father. Perhaps it may seem odd that he did not marry until he was forty-one years of age. There is no evidence of an earlier marriage. With the example of his king before him he may have found comfort elsewhere of an impermanent nature. But his main activities revolved round castle building. The first Norman castles had been put up very quickly and were full of defects in structure and planning. He reconstructed his own base at Gloucester and made considerable revisions to St Briavels, which vastly improved the defences of this vital crossing point into England from Wales. He took on responsibility for the castle at Hereford and his duties were then extended to Staffordshire. Thus Milo had control of the entire southern Welsh frontier from Gloucester to the borders of Cheshire. Like Walter, his father, he was a defence expert and with his marriage to Sibilla his possessions in Brecknockshire gave him vast territories in mid-Wales quite apart from invaluable family contacts across those borders.

The Marcher lords right on the borders were independent fiefdoms, with virtually complete independence from royal inter-

10

ference. One such was Lord Richard FitzPonce who had married Maud of Gloucester, a daughter of Milo's father, Walter. Hence Richard and Milo were brothers-in-law and Milo would have been an adviser in the construction of Clifford's Castle near Hay-on-Wye. Richard's son, Walter, was later to be Lord Clifford and the father of Rosamond. Milo was thus a great uncle of Rosamond. Walter married Margaret de Toeney in about 1136 and succeeded his father a year later. Their eldest child was baptised Jane, later known as Rosamond and was born in either 1137 or 1138.

Geoffrey de Mandeville was created Earl of Essex by Stephen, the document witnessed by Richard FitzUrse and others. Maud endeavoured to lure de Mandeville to her cause by reconfirming her father's honours and privilege but also adding the hereditary office of sheriff of London, Middlesex and Hertfordshire with its responsibilites of jurisprudence and, more importantly, the valuable perquisites. His support for Maud does not seem to have been enthusiastic and his tactics were now primarily aimed at his own advantage as he waited to see who would emerge on top of the slippery pole.

In 1137 the fifteen-year-old Eleanor, Duchess of Aquitaine, married Louis, heir to the French throne, thus bringing all her extensive lands in south-west France under the suzerainty of that kingdom. Within a month of her wedding, her husband succeeded his father as Louis VII. France had achieved a major triumph against the English/Norman power group.

Thomas Becket had just joined the household of Theobald, Archbishop of Canterbury, as a personal assistant. In other words, he was being groomed for stardom and knew everything that was going on at the top level. The young Reginald FitzUrse, Richard's son, had joined the de Mandeville household as a squire. The family had property at Williton in Somerset and at Barham in Kent. The Tracy family had considerable properties in both Gloucestershire and in Bovey in Devonshire, the latter place subsequently becoming known as Bovey Tracy. Young William Tracy also joined the Milo household as a squire.

*　　*　　*

Milo, as his father had done before him, now paid attention to his soul and to what might happen to him when he died. The monks at Llanthony, where his father was buried, were under

11

continual threat from the marauding Welsh who surrounded them. They were being continually hounded and harried and frequently had to be evacuated over the border. Milo decided to build a new and safer monastery for them on his own land just outside the walls of Gloucester and in honour of his patron, Henry I, and this was dedicated in 1136. This new venture he called Llanthony Secunda and the original foundation of his father was henceforth called Llanthony Prima.

Milo's kinsman, Gilbert Foliot, had been achieving a rising reputation as prior first of Cluny and then Abbeville and Milo persuaded his friend Betune, the Bishop of Hereford, to nominate Gilbert to the vacant abbacy of Gloucester. This turned out to be a mixed blessing. The monks at Gloucester had gained much revenue from pilgrimages to the tomb of Robert Curthose who had finally died in 1134. The new monastery at their gates in honour of Robert's brother who had usurped the throne was an insult, quite apart from the competition in prestige and, more importantly, the resultant reduction in alms. Gilbert, despite his familial connection, supported his monks and therein lay the seeds of future controversy.

Milo was also having financial problems. For one thing he had boasted that he had paid all Maud's expenses, and this is generally accepted. Royalty down the ages expect to live free. He had just been made an earl and his commitments and responsibilities were considerable and continuing to grow. He had three handsome daughters who needed substantial dowries and deserved husbands of equivalent status to their own enhanced position. The endowments of Milo's monastery reduced his income – his insurance policy against eternal damnation. He was expecting to contribute towards a commitment which would stand him in even better stead. And his troops needed paying. So he had a go at the Church and demanded that they should put their hands in their pockets – after all, he was providing a safe haven for them. He also claimed the traditional Saxon right as Earl of Hereford to levy such taxes. His erstwhile friend Bishop Betune refused, so Milo seized what he wanted. The bishop then excommunicated him. Milo's insurance policy was in danger of being voided. Abbot Foliot interceded with Betune on the grounds that the Pope's legate had not been consulted, but matters remained tense between Milo and the Church.

* * *

Whilst Maud was at Oxford and during the time Earl Robert was in Anjou, Stephen stormed the city and then besieged the castle. The garrison was reduced to virtual starvation and nigh to surrender. However, one night just before Christmas, Maud and three intrepid knights clad in white robes lowered themselves over the walls onto the frozen river and crept across the snow unseen and unheard through Stephen's lines, making their way via Abingdon and Wallingford to safety. This astonishing and daring escapade saved the Empress from disaster.

The civil war then continued on a much reduced scale in 1143 and Maud returned to Bristol to be with her son. Henry's regimen was supervised by a monk named Matthew from St James in Bristol. Henry was to be imbued with letters and instructed in all good manners beseeming a youth of his rank. His uncle also made certain that Henry should have a good grounding in the law and that his education should follow not only that of Henry I but also the wide scholarship of Robert himself. Henry was also learned in the science of verse.

Milo had been most concerned with the way that the campaigns had stumbled during the previous years and he had begun to understand that there was a vital shortcoming in their supply problems, which had prejudiced their tactics. So he arranged a meeting with Earl Robert during the summer of 1143 at Bristol to suggest a solution.

'I take your point, my old friend,' said the Earl, once they had settled the preliminary courtesies and were relaxing in the Earl's anteroom. 'We have always been constrained for lack of swords, arrowheads, shields and armour, not to mention continually being at our wits' end for repairs and replacements. How many times have we failed to follow up our initial successes?'

'And, sire,' replied Milo, 'how many times have our cavalry been unable to pursue their advantage for lack of spare horseshoes and nails? We simply lack adequate and regular supplies of iron. And so we lose our initial impetus and hence the success that was there.'

'And we could put more troops into the field. We have enough support from the west and we know more will rally to us if we

13

could achieve better results. And your solution lies in the Forest of Dean? Tell me more.'

'Sire,' said Milo, 'I have as you know that forest under my commission and have rebuilt St Briavels to make that border safe. I have hunted the area often and know the land well. We have Newnham Castle to the south of the forest to give protection from any river crossing. The Romans had iron smelting works at a tiny hamlet called Flaxley in the valley there. It is still working but it is out of date and has very primitive processes; in fact it has hardly changed since Roman times. There are considerable deposits of ore in the forest area, easily extractable and the forest will give us an inexhaustible supply of wood to convert to charcoal. This charcoal will fire the furnaces which will smelt the ore. We must modernise the plant and processes and make them really efficient. It will, of course, require a considerable investment. But it will solve our essential supply problem.'

'What about communications? Isn't it pretty inaccessible and remote?'

'Not too bad, sire. The old Roman road comes through from Newnham to Mitcheldean, which could be much improved to come up to present-day standards. The main road from Gloucester to Newnham, which leads on to Chepstow, you will know well. There is a passable track off that to Flaxley via Blaisdon and another very primitive one about a mile further on, and that too could be much improved.'

'As always you have done your homework, Milo. I would not expect it otherwise.' The Earl paused, then added, 'But carts taking the iron ingots would soon chew up the roads. I take it that you are thinking of these going to Gloucester rather than Bristol where our main armourers are?'

'There is a passable harbour at Newnham and good river traffic facilities there. But there is an extremely nice little deep-water river fishing harbour at Broad Oak, three miles nearer to Gloucester by river and, more importantly, three miles nearer to Flaxley. And there is no reason why the boats should not go straight to Bristol with their cargoes if we think it better.'

They were interrupted by a squat tow-headed little boy bursting in and throwing himself into the lap of the earl, who rumpled his hair. The boy then noticed Milo and said, 'Uncle, I had no idea that you were busy.' He turned to Milo. 'Sir, please forgive my manners and for my disturbing you.'

For a prince to apologise for his discourtesy impressed Milo. Milo was still rather out of his depth in his new rank, for when he had first been ennobled he had addressed his fellow earl, Robert of Gloucester, with more familiarity than he had ever done before and been reminded that some earls are more royal than others. Now a prince was begging his pardon. Robert told Henry that they were talking about an interesting new idea and were indeed rather involved.

'Uncle, if it is something new, then should I be told about it? I would like to know more, if I may, as it could, I suppose, affect my own future.' The boy was astonishingly self-possessed and had matured immensely since he had been under his uncle's tutelage. Robert told him the gist of their discussion. 'How would you get people in who can bring the furnaces up to today's standards?' the boy asked.

Milo was taken aback at this most perceptive question from one so young. 'We have an iron industry in both Gloucester and Bristol and we will put a team in from there to modernise the business.'

'So it is important then. Let's go to Flaxley and see for ourselves. You and Lord Hereford could do some hunting too. And I can join in. What about going tomorrow? Uncle? Please?'

'Steady on lad! Who said that I *was* going?' Milo smiled. He knew that Robert was itching to go, and would insist on some hunting too. 'And who said that you could come? What would Brother Matthew say if you took a week off from your books? Flaxley is over forty miles away. No, not this time, Henry. Another time.'

'It's not too far, uncle, honestly. I've ridden fifty miles in a day, heaps of times. Ask Mama or Matthew. One day to get there – isn't there a castle on the river near there where we could stay? A day at Flaxley and I could join in the chase too. And back in one day – isn't there a ferry across the river near there? That would cut a corner on the way back. Matthew says I have been so good that I need a break. Three days, that's all. Please Uncle Robert. Please, Lord Milo, tell him I'll be good.'

It was quite astonishing how the boy knew his own mind, knew how to get his way, knew so much about the lie of the land. And

15

it turned out that he was as tough as he claimed to be. Thus they all went. They had a splendid trip and the prince kept on asking sensible questions and taking everything in. The party stayed overnight at Newnham Castle. On the way back they took the little ferry at Broad Oak across the Severn to the Arlingham peninsula. Lord Walter Clifford met them and lent them horses to ride along the old Roman causeway leading to his property. As they trotted along for the final stage of their ride they crossed a small river where a flaxen-haired child, with her handmaiden, was playing with sticks which she was dropping over the edge of the old Saxon bridge which spanned the River Frome at that point. She was rushing from side to side to see which stick came out first and clapping her hands. Henry dismounted and joined in the game. Lord Clifford introduced the little girl as his elder daughter, Jane. The two children larked about for a while before the main party repaired to the Clifford house.

Clifford's family had owned the land at Frampton for nigh on seventy-five years and he had just completed a fine new house in the modern style just by the church. The house was stoutly built of timber on good dry foundations with a fine screens passage and a gracious hall overlooked by the family solar on the first floor.

They were greeted by Walter's wife, the Lady Margaret, and amply fed by a splendid repast. Jane had meantime returned from her play by the river and with modesty and decorum insisted on serving the young prince. Lady Margaret had realised that perhaps the young Henry was more tired than he was prepared to let on, so she made a fuss of him and suggested that he have a rest and a lie down in their fine new solar. The two children had a well-earned nap before Henry's party had to wend onwards to join the Bristol road. The whole journey took only three days.

Robert authorised Milo to pursue his project and report back. There was one problem. Robert was not too keen on financing it himself, or at any rate only for a modest amount, and Milo did not wish to divulge that he still had not solved all his cashflow problems. The Church was still not being too cooperative either.

* * *

Mrs Henriette Clifford, the present chatelaine of Frampton Court, told us of three verbal legends handed down through her family concerning the Henry/Rosamond story. This branch of the Clifford family has been in Frampton in continuous succession since 1087 and has a direct descent from Rosamond's younger brother, Richard. It has to be explained that Mrs Clifford's late husband changed his name to Clifford upon marriage, so the line comes directly through Mrs Clifford. She has been brought up on these stories and has always understood them to have been handed down from the twelfth century.

Henry is said to have met Rosamond on three separate occasions when they were quite young. The first was on the nearby River Frome, very close to Frampton. The second was an occasion when Rosamond served Henry at table. Both these I have described in this chapter. The third occurrence apparently happened when they were being taught together by a tutor assigned to them both, an episode described later in this chapter.

There are an extraordinary number of coincidences in these tales from Mrs Clifford. In the first place the tutor story firmly establishes that Rosamond was, as Lord Clifford's book on the Cliffords says, not that much younger than the prince. Secondly, it is clear that they met as children. Thirdly, both the Frome and the serving at table stories are more likely to have occurred whilst the pair of them were quite young.

It is also extremely probable that the leading families in the Maud/Henry/Earl Robert faction would have been in constant touch with each other as well as their children, so the Prince and Jane/Rosamond probably met each other on a reasonably regular basis. Children do not necessarily have clear memories of these early meetings, but these threads are often recalled in later life.

Mrs Clifford does not recall meeting or being in touch with Baden Watkins, but she has certainly read his book on Flaxley. So where does Baden get his story from? It certainly ties in with these tales from Frampton.

Now we tell of the final coincidences. During the initial drafts of this book, I had described Henry and Rosamond meeting as children at Bristol in 1143 when the Prince threw a tantrum and she comforted him. So all that was now necessary was to add the tutoring episode. This first draft also described the meeting at Frampton when the Earls Robert and Milo, with Henry, stopped off there. It then only remained for the addition of the Frome and serving at table episodes to add verisimilitude to both this tale and the Frampton legends. These three stories are in no way contradictory but are cumulative evidence that

17

these two met very much earlier on than the official histories suggest.
Verbal legends should be listened to, never rejected or discounted.

*   *   *

Milo decided to go to London in the late summer of 1143 to pursue a number of personal affairs. Sibilla was not at all easy in her mind. Her husband was slowing down considerably and definitely showing his age. That stupidly rushed visit from Bristol to Flaxley and back hadn't done him any good either – he had been utterly worn out after it, but was better now. Not only were his financial affairs of concern but the spiritual interdict was hanging over him like a sword of Damocles. Milo was a self-made man, admittedly in the second generation, who had achieved a rank that had never seemed possible when his father was alive. The family in Normandy had been humble – they were just above artisan class, originally modest builders, and had never had land or territorial affiliations. They were not 'of' somewhere like the de Bohuns or de Mandevilles, and this rankled. It also meant that Milo was not used to handling his estates, and the income that could be derived therefrom was not as much as it should have been compared with that of other barons, who had grown up with such responsibilities – so this too was contributory to his problem. He should have been better off than he was. Milo was a proud, difficult and most ambitious man albeit with wide knowledge and a very practical streak. He was not very good at delegation but this iron business was right up his street.

Milo took both his daughter Berthe and his squire William Tracy with him, and they stayed at his house at Westminster which had been granted to him by Maud in 1141 and which was once used by Gregory the Sewer. He needed to visit the Lord Mayor of London and his sheriffs to make diplomatic comments about the progress being made by the young prince. They were much impressed by what he told them and he had broad discussions about how he and Earl Robert wished the future to be fulfilled. The City Fathers were most receptive and cooperative and appreciated the mutual frankness, but both sides realised that there was much prejudice to be overcome since the disastrous impression made by the prince's mother. After all, the City had once acclaimed Stephen and been sorry, and had welcomed and then dispossessed Maud.

18

Milo then floated the idea of some financial support for his iron ore project and this was less enthusiastically received as the City Fathers were sick and tired of conflict. However, Milo cleverly stressed the non-military aspects, as well as stressing the probable profits, which appealed to their traditional sense of cupidity. He knew and they knew that traders had recently arrived in London from Lombardy who specialised in activities of this nature. Milo was relieved that that door was left open for further discussions later on.

He wondered whether he had not been too open and brought them too much into his confidence, but he felt that, on balance, it was more advisable to be frank as it would pay off in the long term. However, Stephen was known to have his supporters everywhere.

But all this was not Milo's primary purpose of coming to London. Geoffrey de Mandeville, the recently created Earl of Essex, had recently made preliminary overtures with a view to a betrothal between Berthe and his eldest son, Ernulph. Milo could not but be dazzled at this prospect which would combine the power and wealth of old money and position with the strength of his new money and vigour. It would also join the de Mandeville strengths in eastern England with his broad acres in the west and would be a most valuable consolidation for the cause of Maud and the young prince. Until recently Geoffrey had been most firmly in the Stephen camp but the empress had increased his power base so considerably that he was now much beholden to Maud and her cause. The de Mandevilles were a landed family from Magnavil in Normandy. They had been in the first wave and fought at Senlac with the Conqueror. Milo had not hitherto been accepted into the de Mandeville circle and he had always thought him to be one whom you would prefer to face rather than show him your back. Nevertheless he could not do better for Berthe financially or socially. Apart from a negotiated substantial settlement, which was admittedly somewhat inopportune, the match would remove a commitment to one of Milo's daughters – to everyone's advantage.

He had sent Tracy to the de Mandeville quarters in the Tower of London to advise him of his arrival and to await the pleasure of his company. That evening, to his surprise, de Mandeville and his son appeared at Milo's house in Westminster and their meeting was immensely affable. Ernulph seemed a most pleasant and mannerly young man and was genuinely and enthusiastically respectful to Milo. Milo did not wish to force his middle daughter into an arrangement about which she might not be happy, so he suggested that the two young people should retire to an ante-room.

The two earls exchanged news.

'The Earl Robert, I hear, has arranged a marvellous regimen for Henry FitzEmpress, and the boy is responding well. This is good news for us all in this ensaddened land of ours,' said de Mandeville.

How does he know? wondered Milo. He said, 'The boy is very bright, like his grandfather. We are all most impressed and hopeful for the future.'

'He has a temper though, I hear, like his mother, and I hope he has not too much of his father's arrogance, which does not go down well with us here – but you know that as well as I do, my dear Milo. We are all of one mind to ensure that the succession for this land of ours is wisely ordered, but there are many rocks ahead. I have all this very much to the forefront of my mind and I am sure that Earl Robert will be in common accord with me. I hope that we can work together on this. The family arrangements we are considering will surely facilitate communication between us.'

Milo began to realise the significance of their conversation and how he was expected to play a part in bringing the main supporters of the two protagonists together. But he was becoming chary of whether the King would be so enthusiastic and also whether Maud's party would entrust anything serious to de Mandeville.

Milo threw the ball back. 'How does the King?'

'A most charming man when things do not get on top of him. He has a short fuse though but the Queen is wonderful, very much loved and a great support to the King.'

'And Prince Eustace?'

'Eustace is rather older and, shall I say, more mature than Henry. He progresses well. Do not underestimate him – he wants the throne and the King and Queen will always want their bloodline to succeed.'

'So Robert's idea for Henry to succeed Stephen is not going to be easy to carry – although the country would like it and it is what the old King wished. We hear stories about Eustace which do not augur well.'

'Eustace is a young man and has to sow his wild oats. We expect him to outgrow his recklessness and we must not forget that Henry will soon be of age and could then cause concern and problems. We all know what young men can be like.' Geoffrey switched tack. 'Gregory the Sewer lived here before you, and was not best pleased when the Empress removed him from this house. He does vital work for me in the City. He does there what he did here: organises the water supplies and ensures that the drains function properly. He is most highly respected for the excellent plumbing that he carries out. I saw him today and heard of your visit to the City Fathers. He is on the council and he listened with interest and respect to what you told them.'

So that's how de Mandeville is so well informed, thought Milo. They continued their discussions on the settlement question and both agreed how suited the two offspring seemed to be. Milo then invited Ernulph to join their party at Gloucester Castle for the Christmas festivities so that he could meet Sibilla and the rest of his family and pursue his courtship of Berthe. 'Since the time of the Conqueror, we have always had a hunting expedition on Christmas Eve,' he explained to de Mandeville, 'followed by time-honoured celebrations. The citizens love to see the show and, of course, we look after them. It would give us all much pleasure if Ernulph would join us then and for the holy day on the morrow.'

Thus agreement was achieved and Ernulph expressed his enthusiasm at the prospect of Christmas at Gloucester. Milo sensed that Berthe had some reservations and was slightly surprised at her lack of warmth, but she was a dutiful girl who had realised that the match was in her best interests. Milo hoped that his negotiations would please Sibilla since they had already reached a similar agreement with Humphrey de Bohun over their eldest daughter, Margery, which had been warmly acclaimed by them all. To be fair Milo still had not taken to Geoffrey, who had held his cards close to his chest and was more critical of the Empress and her son than Milo had expected.

Milo returned to Gloucester.

*   *   *

21

The King meanwhile had retreated to St Albans, having recently suffered a surprise attack by Earl Robert who had ambushed him at Wilton. Stephen had been lucky to escape; it would have been mortifying for him to have suffered this indignity again. He was now persuaded to have meetings with his advisers which he had been trying to avoid for some time. His queen and their elder son, Eustace, were present.

'Our main problem, sire, lies in the abuse of the power held by de Mandeville.' The King's brother, Bishop Henry of Winchester, was being blunt. 'He should have been more than satisfied with being created Earl of Essex by you, but then the Empress confers all these shrievalities and confirms his position at the Tower. Now we simply do not know where his loyalties lie.'

Prince Eustace interjected, 'And how dare he detain the Princess Constance at the Tower with no authority whatsoever? It was disgraceful, quite apart from the fact that she was coming here from France for our betrothal. You, as King and my father, should have removed him from being the Constable of the Tower.'

Queen Matilda was not best pleased at her son's impertinent attack on his father in conclave. 'The King dealt with the matter appropriately at the time. The Empress was endeavouring to persuade de Mandeville to join her cause and the affair needed careful handling.'

The King continued to listen and to fidget with embarrassment. The debate continued with considerable reservation regarding the de Mandeville role. It emerged that he was intending to negotiate a marriage between his eldest son and Earl Milo's middle daughter.

Prince Eustace's squire, the young Hugh de Morville, asked permission to speak as he had just returned that very day from London. 'Sire,' he said, 'I have heard tell that Earl Milo is at Westminster this very week and that the two earls are planning to meet. More seriously, sire, the Earl of Essex is intending to discuss your successor, when the dire and tragic event of your demise comes to pass,' Eustace snorted, then glowered. 'That is not all, sire. Earl Milo is negotiating to build a new furnace for producing iron ore. You will realise, sire, that this will hugely improve his military capability.'

It took several seconds for de Morville's revelations to sink in.

He was closely cross-examined. The King's bastard son, Gervase, Abbot of Westminster, who was present, was able to confirm some of de Morville's statements from his own sources, which helped to convince the King's advisers of the truth of his assertions.

'Sire,' said the bishop, 'you will not be safe whilst de Mandeville is at large – he sees himself as the kingmaker and you cannot, with respect, tolerate this. It is a totally unacceptable arrogation of power by him and he must be curtailed – and the sooner the better, sire.'

Both the Queen and Eustace endorsed the bishop's recommendation. The King dithered. 'What shall we do about this new armoury project?'

'That can wait,' said Bishop Henry. 'Anyway, it is only at the planning stage now. The important issue is de Mandeville.'

Eustace was not so sure. 'We must deal with Earl Milo as soon as possible. He is a dangerous man and his scheme must be nipped in the bud – and soon.'

Bishop Henry mentally accepted the point although he found his nephew an extremely tedious and erratic young man, with few of his parent's qualities and more than his fair share of life's defects. The King also gave support to his son's views.

The King looked from adviser to adviser. 'Perhaps we should listen to what de Mandeville has to say.'

So de Mandeville was summoned to St Albans and arrested after an unseemly and bloody fracas. He was then imprisoned until he surrendered all the keys of every one of his castles. There were many in the King's court who had hoped for more Draconian measures. This happened just after Earl Milo had made his return to Gloucester from London.

* * *

Sibilla had never liked the de Mandevilles and she felt that her husband had said far too much. Berthe, whilst agreeing that there was nothing positive against Ernulph and that the betrothal was a brilliant prospect for her, said that she found the young man vapid and of no great seriousness. Yes, she said, he was nice enough but he had very little to say for himself. He was nice looking, but had a tendency to suck his teeth just before he spoke.

Sibilla knew that Berthe had her eyes on another young man

who, whilst of good family, was nowhere near the match that Ernulph offered. Wisely, Sibilla did not apprise Milo of this at this stage. Christmas was some months away and there was plenty of time for the moment.

Or so she thought. Within days, Reginald FitzUrse, the de Mandeville squire, rode hotfoot into Gloucester Castle with the dire news that his master was under arrest and with an obligation to surrender all his strongholds. Ernulph was keeping a low profile, staying for the moment in East Anglia. He assured his prospective parents-in-law that his father was expecting to be released after due negotiations, but more importantly he was hoping that their respective agreements would not be jeopardised by this temporary setback. An assurance was reiterated that the strategic discussions still were vital to both parties. Milo was aware of a veiled threat here but he and Sibilla endorsed their invitation to Ernulph for the Christmas break. Both agreed that by then they would be more aware of developments and that it would be a mistake to break off negotiations too quickly now.

* * *

The Cliffords were invited to join Earl Robert's household at Bristol for the Christmas festivities. They went from Frampton. Walter went on horseback and reluctantly agreed that Jane should ride with him on the pommel. She loved doing this and normally he encouraged her, but the weather was getting colder and if it rained or snowed it would not be good for a five-year-old. But she was a winsome little girl and delighted him with the interest that she took in everything about her. His wife Margaret travelled in a litter with their younger children.

'I need to know about everyone who is going to be there, papa.' Walter loved her phrase 'I need to know', and there was very little that he could refuse her.

'Well,' he answered, 'I can tell you who is going to be there – and you must behave – they are all very great persons and you are very lucky to be asked.' Jane put her hand on his glove and squeezed. 'There is the Earl and his wife, Countess Mabel.'

'Why isn't the Earl the King? I thought that he was King Henry's eldest son.'

Walter Clifford did not beat about the bush and, in any case, Jane was not a girl who was easily fobbed off for long. 'Earl

24

Robert is a bastard, which means that his mother was not married to the King and so he can't be king.'

'The first King William was a bastard wasn't he? Why was he King then?'

'He won a battle against the Saxon King Harold just over seventy years ago. It's a long story but King Harold had promised William the throne and he broke his promise. So you see, you must keep your promises in life. And,' he thought it wise to shift this subject, 'your grandpa, Mama's papa, will be there. He's called Sir Ralph de Toeney.'

'And Prince Henry and his mama too? Why isn't she the queen? And tell me about King Stephen.'

The journey from Frampton to Bristol passed quickly as Jane and her father chattered away.

* * *

The party at Bristol Castle now had gathered for the Christmas season festivities. The evening witnessed the first of many feasts. At the top table was Empress Maud, a most handsome woman of great presence but with a haughty expression. Since the death of her little brother, the old King, her father, had given her every indulgence which had made her wilful and very spoilt. When she was seven years old she had been betrothed to the German Emperor, Henry V, and duly crowned. In 1114, when twelve years old, she was married and lived with her aged husband very happily, albeit with no children, and she was much indulged. Her husband was thirty years older than she was and in 1125 he died and bequeathed his dominions to her. Thus she was an empress in her own right and much loved and respected in the formal German courts. Having lived with a husband so much older than she was and a father who obeyed her every whim she was used to her own way. Then she married Geoffrey, Count of Anjou, who was ten years younger and he was far from being a pawn in her hands.

Jane Clifford was being allowed to watch from a window above the hall, with her little serving wench, Hikenai (called Hickey by everyone) in attendance. Hickey was a little older than Jane and was responsible for her clothes, dressing her and doing all that was required for a little girl of Jane's class and standing. She was the daughter of one of the villeins on the estate at Frampton.

Prince Henry was sitting by his mother. He was a squat thick-

25

set little boy with bow legs, a bullet-shaped head, a mass of close-cropped tawny hair and a freckled, weatherbeaten face. His hands were, even for a lad, coarse and tough, his nails none too clean, and it was obvious that he spent much time out of doors, preferably riding. Compared with the rest of the gorgeously attired company he was untidily and carelessly dressed. It was his eyes that were extraordinary: they were of a soft grey colour. The Prince was always getting up and restlessly walking about and talking to anyone who took his fancy, even those well below the salt, and this seemed to annoy his mother, for she was continually beckoning him or sending a squire to tell him to return. Henry was not always as prompt in obeying as his mother seemed to wish and they were obviously having words.

Jane looked around at the rest of the company. The host, Earl Robert, was not in the seat of honour as befitted his respect for his sister and her rank and position. He had a lively and happy face and was talking animatedly to her grandfather, Ralph de Toeney, a redoubtable broad-beamed warrior from Normandy who had lands in England including some at Stratford in the Ebble Valley, not far from Wilton where King Stephen had been recently ambushed and defeated. It was her grandfather's knowledge of the terrain which had helped Earl Robert to swoop from the Herepath onto the unsuspecting king's army, although de Mandeville had property nearby at Sutton and should have known the lie of the land too. Sir Ralph did not often come over as he found England too cold and damp for him in his advancing years. Jane's mother was devoted to him and her feelings were reciprocated. Jane's parents were thoroughly enjoying themselves. The Earl's lady, Mabel, was a gentle, charming soul who had been most kind and welcoming to the little Jane and had arranged for some delicacies to be sent up to their window over the hall. Jane had noticed Hickey's eyes light up when the trays arrived so they shared the repast which was a real treat to the young village girl who had never seen anything like it before.

A mild fracas suddenly erupted when the Empress pointed to the door behind them and seemingly ordered Henry out of the feast. The Prince ran to his uncle for support but Robert only smiled firmly albeit kindly and reinforced the Empress's instructions. Henry ran from the hall in a transparent rage.

Hickey reminded Jane that her mother had left firm instruc-

26

tions about her daughter's bedtime. Jane prevaricated as little girls have always done, but as Henry had departed from the scene the grown-ups held less interest for her, so she reluctantly followed her servant down the stone corridors towards her bed-chamber. On their way they passed a door on the other side of which they could hear the most appalling screams of rage. The two children paused, then Hickey pulled her mistress to continue on their way. Jane refused and opened the door to look in. The Prince was roaring with temper, rolling on the floor, gnawing the rushes, and his eyes were smouldering. Jane immediately went to Henry. She knelt on the floor beside the Prince, took his shaking hands in hers and held them very firmly and tightly. The young boy looked at her and immediately calmed himself as she put his head on her bosom and cradled him gently. He stopped screaming at once and his fearsome eyes became their soft grey again. They sat on the rushes for some several minutes in silence and communion of spirit, she looking at him and he caressing her in tranquillity.

After some time he asked, 'Who are you, little girl? Where did you come from?'

'I am Jane Clifford, sire, I live at Frampton where you stopped a few weeks ago for a meal with my papa and mama, on your way back here.'

'I remember – your mama is very nice, I liked her. I like you too. And you are the most beautiful rose in the world that I have ever seen. *La plus belle Rose du monde*. For me, and only me, you will be Rosamond. It is to be between us, always.'

'My mama says that I am to go to bed, and that is where I was being taken.'

'I am your prince and I order you to obey me and stay here. And you are to call me Henry.'

Jane smiled and they remained in each other's arms. After a while she said, 'I have obeyed you, but my mama must also be obeyed so I must do my duty by her. May I go now, please,' she caught his eye, 'Henry?'

He grinned and allowed her to go.

The following day Jane was summoned to her father. She went in some considerable trepidation and as she entered her father's room her mother was sitting there too. They were smiling, however.

'Now what have you and the prince been up to?' her mother asked.

Jane blushed and kept very quiet. Her mother did not wait for any answer. 'Prince Henry has specially asked that you attend his lessons with his tutor, Brother Matthew. Your father and I have agreed, but you are to remember that he is much older than you and the Earl of Gloucester, who has a strict curriculum for the prince, says that he must not be distracted in any way. The Earl has consented to your being there on these conditions. If you disobey or disturb Henry, you will not be allowed to stay. Are you happy to go into his lessons and will you be very good?'

Jane threw her arms around her mother and said that she would like nothing better. So she spent the next few days sitting in the classroom, being very good and quiet. Brother Matthew gave her a few little exercises to do and she and Henry were allowed to play during his breaks.

* * *

The party at Gloucester Castle had gathered for the Christmas season festivities. First to arrive was Ernulph de Mandeville and his father's squire, Reginald FitzUrse. The former paid his respects to Milo's wife with effusion. He bowed, took her hand and inclined his lips over the fingers. He sucked his teeth several times during his eulogies over her daughter's beauty, brains and demeanour and rhapsodised over the source of all these attributes. Sibilla knew that he oozed insincerity and had a private smile when she remembered that Berthe's own considerable reservations about that young man. She was glad therefore that she had arranged for him to be carefully followed everywhere. Her Welsh servants were light-footed and very stealthy.

Dear William de Braose arrived and she knew all too well that Berthe had lost her heart to him, but although his father had considerable estates in no less than five counties in the south of England, the family had not been ennobled. But they were solidly and sensibly based and she was an old friend of William's father, Philip, who was now getting on like Milo.

Then arrived the delightful Humphrey de Bohun, whose grandfather was a kinsman of the great King William of Normandy, and whose family had always been friends and supporters of the direct line. He had vast properties in Wiltshire and had recently married their eldest daughter, Margery, and very happy they were.

Next to come was the recently widowered Herbert FitzHerbert who had been, until recently, the Lord Chamberlain to the King but had now switched his allegiance to the Empress. His late wife had been Sybil Corbet, an early mistress of the late King, who had borne him five of his bastards. Her eldest daughter had married King Alexander I of Scotland. When the King had succeeded, he decided that he should make a dynastic marriage and so arranged for Sybil to wed Herbert, which was excellent for her but less satisfactory for her new husband. Sybil was by then nearly past childbearing age and she failed to produce an heir for her lawful wedded husband. Lord FitzHerbert was now looking for a suitably young bride to perpetuate his line. Sibilla considered that there could be no finer a consort for him than her youngest daughter, Lucy, a fine and very pretty girl who nevertheless needed an older man to curb her high spirits. So the season had some pleasurable potential for her, in spite of the odious Ernulph.

Ernulph was meanwhile making a dutiful visit to the splendid Abbey tomb of Robert Curthose. He managed to have a quiet word with one of the attendant monks who escorted him to see the abbot, Gilbert Foliot. Foliot was a kinsman of Milo and a priest of immense intellectual ability and potential. It had become very clear however that he and Milo of Hereford did not see eye to eye and there was a major difference of opinion over the new monastery at the gates of the Abbey, occupied by many refugees from Llanthony Prima in the Welsh central hills. The erstwhile friend of Milo, Bishop Betune of Hereford, had excommunicated him and the affair still rankled and was unresolved. Ernulph and the abbot had private talks about this matter and doubtless the influence of Geoffrey de Mandeville was bruited, despite that person's present problems. One of Sibilla's servants was hovering and reported to his mistress what he saw.

FitzUrse also went into the Abbey precincts and was seen talking to various of the Abbey officials, patently keeping a low profile. A well-dressed stranger on horseback came through the City gates as dusk approached, was seen entering the Abbey and again talking surreptitiously to black cowled monks and to Ernulph, who responded with some surprise. Later this stranger was admitted to Foliot's personal guesthouse.

All these matters were duly reported to Sibilla and she was not at all happy. She had another lengthy talk with Milo about the advisability of continuing their betrothal arrangements with the de Mandeville family.

Milo assured his wife that there were comforting noises from Ernulph regarding his father's incarceration. The negotiations were lengthy and protracted with the King and his court. Geoffrey had apparently assured the King that he would release his castle's keys against a parole for his safety and it was the mechanics of this that was delaying the affair. Geoffrey had also got messages out to Ernulph that the Empress Maud and Earl Robert affairs continued close to his heart. Sibilla wondered how secure these messages were and would have wished for reassurances that the King's party was not aware of de Mandeville's duplicity. Milo suggested playing the long game; there was no necessity for any immediate decisions. Sibilla disagreed.

But Milo for the moment was far more concerned with the organising of the continuation of the tradition established since the time of King William – the Christmas Eve Hunt, which set out from the castle with great panoply and fanfare. The nobles and castle guests together with the Abbey ecclesiastics gathered in the courtyard soon after dawn, were regaled with pies and pasties, wine, mead and ale and then went forth to the Forest of Dean to hunt deer and boar, returning at nightfall to a magnificent feast. The citizens of Gloucester were traditionally fed and watered to their hearts content during that day and on the following day would share in the results of the chase in the forest. Milo had no intention whatsoever of failing to fulfil this custom established by his father's friend and King. He himself had been a page in the twilight years of King William's court.

Sibilla slept badly that night. Her dreams were vivid, she was restless and disturbed by all the reported meetings in so many dark corners, not only in the Abbey but also in the castle and even in Llanthony Secunda. People coming, people going, slipping into the shadows, whispers and cloaks drawn across faces. And who was that mysterious man of quality who had arrived? And who was staying with Foliot – a man usually sparing of hospitality and affability.

30

'I beseech you, Milo, my lord, I beseech you again and again not to go hunting today. There is danger in the forest. There is treachery afoot, I know it, I feel it in my bones. I know that there are many whisperings in corners here and alcoves; this I have told you. Men turn away so that their faces cannot be seen and their voices cannot be heard. There are comings and goings to and from the Abbey. Strangers come to the city who are not recognised and who are let in without authority. I trust not your cousin Abbot Foliot or any of those priests of his – they are sly and jealous, mean people. Go not for the love that you bear me.'

Milo was abrupt and curt. This hunt was an obligation that he had fulfilled ever since the king and his father had passed the duty over to him. He was going to continue the tradition come what may.

'You are not well – let our eldest son Roger fulfil this obligation. It will be understood and accepted as fitting by all.'

'No,' he replied.

'Our great King always had his escort of men-at-arms. He was mindful of his enemies and took care. Why don't you?'

'The great King's sons, Rufus and Henry, hunted from here without any escort. I am not the King and I have all my friends by me. 1 shall take care.'

So he went as he said he would and Sibilla wept as they clattered off for their day's sport. Unlike previous years, no one from the Abbey joined this year's sport. The mysterious stranger of yesterday was seen to leave the City gates soon after and cross the Westgate bridge.

* * *

The entourage passed over Westgate bridge and onto the road by the River Severn leading to the great horseshoe bend and thence towards Newnham. Ernulph de Mandeville was beside his host and, as they rode along, he craved an indulgence.

'My lord, I am so deeply appreciative of this honour of joining your party.' He sucked his teeth. 'May I attend you all day so that we can not only share our sport together, but also pursue our family discussions and my father's ideas, which I have wanted to air with you. It will also fascinate me to see where your foundry scheme is intended to be. I think that you will not wish any others to be present and become aware of what is so exciting and so important for us all. You will know that my father wishes to give you every support and help.'

Milo graciously agreed.

At Westbury a forester told the party that there were many deer grazing in the vale on both sides of the rivulet. He added that it was thickly wooded country and there was an abundance of game, more on the far bank but only a few fine specimens on the near side.

'We shall split,' said Milo. 'Ernulph, you come with me. Mahel, Tracy and FitzUrse also come with us. We shall take the first track out of Westbury towards Blaisdon. We will then turn left along the Flaxley track, head up into the woods there and come down towards the stream just this side of the Flaxley woods. That way my lot will come upon the deer this side of the boggy ground. We won't get much of a chase there but we will be upwind and hope to bag a couple of nice ones for the pot. The rest of you go further down the road, turn right onto the Flaxley track and work back through that hamlet by the old iron works. You will come across the rest of the herd on the far side. You should have good sport and that side of the valley is firmer going, so if they take off you will have a marvellous chase towards the old Roman road further up the vale. With any luck we might get some boar too, there are plenty around.'

They then agreed a rendezvous after the chase. It was just past ten o'clock and the shortest day of the year was only just past, so they needed to start back at about three, perhaps earlier if a mist came down. Mahel was Milo's youngest son. The second party was much larger and consisted of Roger, Milo's eldest son and his other brothers, Walter and Henry, FitzHerbert, de Braose, de Bohun, as well as the large castle contingent and all of their assistants.

They split at the first turning and the larger party continued down the main track. FitzHerbert grunted to de Bohun, 'Trust old Milo to bag the better prey. We get the smaller ones and by the time we get there he will have frightened most of them on our side. Still, we shall get a better run up there. Here's to a good day's sport.'

Roger heard and replied, 'I think my father is not terribly fit now, so he wants an easier day than he used to have. My mother was trying hard to persuade him to give today a miss.'

De Bohun laughed. 'I can't see him doing that until he is in his grave.'

The Milo party cantered up the Blaisdon road and turned left down the boggy cart track leading to the old Roman iron works, where a miserable little hamlet existed. Just short of the hovels the party swung right, making ground up the slope through the thickets and getting well upwind of the rivulet in the vale. Milo felt the chill breeze in his face and knew that they were in a good position.

The Earl turned to the three young men and told them to stay where they were and to keep absolutely quiet. He told them that he and young de Mandeville would work their way as quietly as they could towards the more open ground below them, exploiting the cover, and would try and locate the grazing deer. They then set off down the hill. FitzUrse told the other two waiting squires that it would be a good idea if he moved fifty yards or so to the right so that he could get a different perspective, which could help them all should there be a chase. The other two reminded FitzUrse of their orders but he moved off and went out of their sight.

Meanwhile Milo and Ernulph were moving down the wooded slope and with great cunning and expertise worked their way down the hill. Milo hissed, put his finger to his lips and pointed. Two fine deer were grazing and unaware, as yet, of the two hunters. Ernulph moved twenty or so yards to his left as directed and both of them craftily worked their way nearer to be in range. They had agreed on the signal when both were to loose off their arrows simultaneously.

One deer raised its head and sniffed the air, the other continued unperturbed, then it too put its head up. The riders were now just in range. It was the moment for the combined strike. One arrow whirred through the air fast and true and found its target with unerring accuracy. The two harts were now alerted of their danger and fled towards the safety of the adjoining woods. Milo, Earl of Hereford, toppled gently off his horse, bleeding profusely from his wound and was dead within seconds of hitting the ground. Ernulph turned his horse and galloped towards the waiting squires who had, by now, been rejoined by FitzUrse.

'An appalling accident has happened,' he said. 'I saw a man

on a horse galloping away – he has shot the Earl and escaped. Did any of you see or hear anyone?' The young men all shook their heads. 'You, Mahel, go and comfort your father, I think it's too late, but try.

'You, Tracy, go and find the other party and get help from them. FitzUrse, you and I will return post-haste to Gloucester, warn them and get help from there. We will then come back down the main road to meet you all.'

Mahel asked, 'Shouldn't one of us chase up the valley and see if we can see or catch my father's attacker?'

'No point, he's got too far away by now. Anyway there are only four of us and we've got to get help. Off you two go. Come on FitzUrse.'

With that the party speedily went their several ways.

Mahel went immediately to where his father lay. The arrow had struck Milo in the throat and his blood had gushed everywhere. Mahel was the youngest of the Milo children, being scarcely thirteen years old. The poor lad was promptly sick.

Tracy forded the stream and it took him a little time to find a suitable crossing through the boggy ground. He turned left and rapidly made his way through the hamlet. He could hear the main party still some way off and he was able to make good speed until he met them. There was complete consternation and the circumstances were very similar to the so-called accidental killing, also by an arrow, of William Rufus in the New Forest forty-three years earlier. Roger and de Bohun galloped back with Tracy to the assassination spot whilst some of the others searched for and ultimately found a miserable cart, a poor diseased nag and the owner. All were commandeered amid protests and promises of recompense. The rest of the party made their way to the site and one or two spread out to see if there was any sign of the killer's position but they had no luck. The body of the Earl was bundled unceremoniously into the squalid conveyance and the cortège made slow progress back to the main road, pushing and shoving when the cart stuck in the mud.

A party then went forward to meet the relief contingent from Gloucester Castle, with the hope that a more fitting conveyance would be available with a team of horses to ensure better speed. The rain started to drizzle and spirits already low became lower.

The advance party arrived at the castle to find that there was no trace whatsoever of Ernulph and that the dire news had not been received at all. A hearse of sorts was obtained and horses harnessed and this party journeyed back to meet the Flaxley party. Thus the last journey of the great and loyal Earl Milo ended in a sorry and ill-fitting manner.

Sibilla was utterly distraught and her wailing had to be heard to be believed.

But where was Ernulph?

Ernulph and FitzUrse had originally sped towards Gloucester as they had said they would. But as they neared the city, Ernulph took a side track, saying as the two cantered through the rapidly increasing rain, 'We are going to be blamed for this and there will be an almighty hue and cry after us. Neither of our lives are going to be safe until we reach the King's protection. We must get away as far and as fast as we can.'

FitzUrse wondered if that would be as safe as all that, but he fully realised that the Milo/Robert party would suspect them. The de Mandeville reputation and the mistrust towards him was not encouraging.

They managed to find an empty manor house *en route* where they bribed and threatened the shifty bailiff to provide food and shelter. They took it in turns to sleep and keep watch – a wise precaution as it turned out as the bailiff was continually on the prowl during the night.

At the end of one of FitzUrse's vigils he made a point of noting that his master's quiver contained not the twenty arrows that it should but only nineteen. FitzUrse thought that it would be wise for him to remember this in the future. He was fairly certain that he had recognised de Morville's voice in the Abbey precincts the previous evening, but he was not sure and did not reckon that he should ask his master – just yet anyway.

Ernulph wondered whether he should be concerned at FitzUrse having moved his position just after he and Milo had moved down the hill, and whether the movements by an unidentified rider just afterwards were significant. Later on he noticed that his quiver was one arrow short. He also wondered why de Morville was at Gloucester the previous evening and whether anyone else had noticed him.

2

1143–1148

Earl Milo's body lay in the chapel of Gloucester Castle overnight. A suitable bier with fine and lavish furnishings was obtained and the body appropriately cleaned and dressed. A priest from Llanthony Secunda was summoned to pray and Milo's eldest son, the new Earl Roger, and his four brothers took it in turns during the hours of darkness to stand vigil in the chapel.

Early on Christmas Day Abbot Foliot attended Lady Sibilla to offer his deepest sympathy to her and the family and reminded the widow that he too had lost a dear and supportive kinsman who had encouraged their Bishop to promulgate his own preferment to the Abbey of Gloucester. He asked for an immediate audience with the new Earl to discuss the burial arrangements so as to conform with the Abbey and family wishes in all respects on this tragic occasion. Sibilla insisted on being present but the Abbot was adamant that for this first meeting he wished to speak with Roger alone.

It was with most considerable reluctance that the family agreed and Roger and Foliot met later that morning in a castle anteroom. The Abbot had tried to insist that this meeting should take place in the Abbey but had, with some ill-grace, conceded the venue.

'I shall,' said Foliot 'be pleased to take the service and the full Abbey ceremonial will be available, with choirs, music and muffled peals. I am delighted to tell you that we shall allocate a site for the tomb beside the late and much lamented Duke Robert of Normandy whom we interred in our prime position nine years ago. I am sure that the family will appreciate the honour that we shall accord your father by placing him next to the late King's eldest brother. The embellishments to your father's tomb will, of course, be discussed between us as soon as is practicable and I am sure that the family will wish this to be suitably ornate and richly furnished as entirely befits our most lamented brother.'

Earl Roger was speechless for a moment. Then he said that his father's wish, which was often expressed and well known to everyone, was to be buried in his own monastery and family mausoleum at Llanthony Secunda. There was no question whatsoever of an Abbey burial, although he expressed much appreciation at the honour proposed by Abbot Foliot.

Abbot Foliot then calmly reminded Roger that the late Earl Milo was under excommunication and therefore the family was in no position to dictate terms in these distressing circumstances. He went on to suggest that the Abbey's offer was outstandingly generous and could not be indefinitely maintained: 'All this is due to the high regard that we all have for your great and most honourable father,' he said.

The Abbot and the Earl parted with less than amity.

*   *   *

William de Braose volunteered to ride to Bristol to break the appalling news of the disaster to Earl Robert's house party. At this stage, of course, he knew nothing of the disagreeable reaction of the clergy in Gloucester but he was able to describe the extraordinary confusion following the death of Milo. He told them of the circumstances of Milo and Ernulph being alone, the attendant squires being nearby but out of sight of the scene and, most importantly, the immediate disappearance of young de Mandeville together with his squire, who had said that they were getting assistance from Gloucester. He also repeated the tale that he had heard about the Abbot's mysterious guest.

The Christmas festivities were abandoned at once and Earl Robert instructed Braose to find out all details regarding the funeral arrangements and to report back immediately. Meantime the guests at Bristol were put on warning that they must be in readiness to move to Gloucester at very short notice.

Robert immediately convened a meeting of his advisers to consider if this development might be a prelude to a reopening of hostilities by the King's party, who would immediately realise that here was an opportunity to exploit this immense setback to the Empress' cause. The significance of the vital part that Milo was playing in the armaments development at Flaxley was not lost on Earl Robert nor the fact that his death would delay their plans in this respect very considerably. There was therefore no doubt in Robert's mind that this was an assassination by the King's party, probably through the agency of de Mandeville.

* * *

Ernulph and FitzUrse had left their night's shelter soon after first light on that Christmas morn and made a more than adequate recompense to the surly bailiff. It was a moot point for Ernulph whether he should stage at Oxford, where he suspected that the King and his court were celebrating Christmas, or whether he should push on to the probable safety of his father's lands in East Anglia.

Upon reflection Ernulph was sure that the innate and intrinsic good nature of the King would guarantee his safety and that therefore his news would be welcomed by Stephen. In the long run, if not sooner, it might contribute to his father's rehabilitation and release. He was still perturbed over de Morville's presence and worried whether he would arrive in Oxford before him. He was all too aware that that family was held in low regard and that Hugh de Morville's mother was generally regarded as profligate, licentious and treacherous. It was commonly said that no good could come out of that viper's brood and it boded ill that the King's eldest son had appointed Hugh as his personal squire.

The pair then made their way to Oxford Castle where they made themselves known at the gatehouse, were admitted to the King's presence and duly welcomed with his customary courtesy and asked for their news.

'I cannot but think that you have made your way here to my presence with something of moment since I am aware that you have been pursuing your suit with my Lord Milo's middle daughter at Gloucester. But pray what brings you here post haste ere this day's festivities have hardly begun? I hope nothing untoward.'

'Perhaps,' interjected Eustace, 'the beauteous Berthe has preferred the lovelorn de Braose and you have conceded the match to him.' He paused, then added with a sneer, 'A bird in the hand is always worth two in the bush.'

Ernulph recognised that this jibe was aimed at his father's present discomfiture and made a mental note that this information could only have come from de Morville's recent visit. So he inclined his head to the prince and responded to the King, who appeared displeased at this lack of good manners from his son.

'Sire, I am the bearer of grievous news. The noble Earl Milo was killed in a most dreadful accident whilst hunting yesterday afternoon in the woods at Flaxley.'

The King's astonishment was seemingly genuine as was the Queen's, whilst that of the young prince was controlled and indifferent. Ernulph described the circumstances, paying particular attention to the apparent movements of certainly one unidentified rider in the near vicinity. FitzUrse was relieved that there was no mention of his own lateral adjustment from the other two waiting squires.

'So, sire,' replied Ernulph, following a question from the King, 'I deemed it wiser not to stay on at Gloucester in view of the obvious suspicion that I should immediately fall under since I was so near to Earl Milo, and with the absence of witnesses to support me I was sure that I would be immediately put under arrest as his murderer. My family, as your Highness is all too aware, has always been a supporter of your cause, so thus I have come here both to bring you this sad news and to crave your protection should I be pursued.'

Upon being asked about the visitor to the Abbey precincts, Ernulph said that he had briefly spoken to Hugh de Morville there, but had not seen him since. Eustace explained to his father that he had dispatched his squire to enquire after the present state of the excommunication of Earl Milo and whether the Church needed any help, guidance or influence from the King in this distressing state of affairs.

Ernulph was then encouraged to make his way to one of his father's estates in East Anglia, whilst the evidence of the de Mandeville current loyalties to the King was evaluated.

* * *

William de Braose now returned to Gloucester where he was apprised of the new developments regarding Milo's funerary arrangements.

Earl Roger sent parties out to discover whether any information could be gleaned regarding the fleeing knights. A grange house on the road from Gloucester to Oxford confirmed their

39

suspicions but it was thought unwise to press on further east as they would then begin to enter the territory loyal to the King. The King or one of the parties close to him were still suspected as Milo's assassins. The prompt disappearance of Berthe's betrothed together with his squire, not to mention the presence and immediate departure from Gloucester of de Morville, was especially damning.

But the immediate problem was the funeral arrangements for Milo. A second meeting, which now included Sibilla, was convened with Foliot. Foliot now produced the argument that Llanthony Secunda was technically built on land owned by the Abbey and outside the jurisdiction of those at the castle. He also stressed that he was doing the family an immense favour as Bishop Betune of Hereford would never agree to the funeral of an excommunicate on holy ground, and would certainly not grace the occasion with his presence. On the other hand he, Abbot Foliot, had primacy in his own Abbey and could and would pay due honour to his distinguished kinsman, who had done so much for him, despite his mortal sins against God's Holy Church.

The Abbot and the monks of St Peter's were doubtless remembering the huge increase in pilgrims and their valuable offerings to the tomb of Duke Robert Curthose. There were many who had regarded Duke Robert of Normandy as the rightful king of England and Foliot had been born, bred and trained in Normandy.

Sibilla was Welsh and did not take kindly to all this Norman arrogance. After all it was her family and her connections in the west of England that had kept a fragile peace on their western flank and a secure base for the Empress Maud's party and their aspirations. Braose was again dispatched to Bristol and Earl Robert negotiated for an emergency panel of bishops from Hereford, Worcester and St Davids to meet and resolve the issue. The Earl, ever diplomatic, was careful to remind the ambitious and able Foliot that Betune was now getting on and that that valuable see of Hereford would then require a priest of considerable and outstanding ability. Foliot realised that he would need favourable friends in high places ere long. Thus the panel of bishops, which had craftily included the Welsh St Davids incumbent, respected Earl Milo's wishes; he was duly buried with all pomp and circumstance in his own monastery of Llanthony Secunda, but all his heirs and successors would be interred in the

Abbey at Gloucester – an agreement which was put in writing and signed.

The family were much incensed at the sour note to which the obsequies attaching to the burial of their most distinguished father had degenerated.

* * *

Earl Robert was now all too aware of the potential disasters that could loom. Stephen was no fool and, although militarily weak, would now try for the political and economic high ground. The King did indeed try to make his peace with the Church and promised to regularise many abuses – here it will be recalled the allegation that Morville was negotiating with Foliot. He rewarded many who were uncommitted and some would call this bribery. But Eustace, still in his early teens, continued to show many signs of depravity and Stephen himself often failed to follow through his original good intentions. Robert was all too aware of the intrinsic weaknesses of the King's hand and he was determined to play the long game.

Earl Robert was far more astute and had the rare virtue that he wanted nothing for himself, only the good of the country. The great King William had set the tone and his son, King Henry, had been learned, just and able and brought much peace and prosperity. To this end Robert was convinced that the only solution was for King Henry's grandson, Henry, to be properly educated and trained in every kingly virtue and to this end he redoubled his energies. Prince Henry must emerge to be seen to be the outstanding successor. This required that he be fit in mind and body and able to demonstrate to the nobles, knights, clergy and people that he was worthy to be their king. It says much for Robert's planning and the execution thereof that it all evolved and then turned out so well. But in all these matters luck plays a major role.

The matter that he first addressed was unusual and perhaps unexpected. The Church was not at ease with Milo of Hereford's relations with it and had not with great grace agreed the compromise solution. Milo's family were similarly angry at the insensitive manner of their treatment and the embarrassments to which they had been subjected. Stephen was making overtures which had many facets of repairing damaged relations with the

41

Church authorities. Robert knew that this latter aspect had to stand the test of time but it was the immediate ecclesiastical battle that had to be planned and executed.

The Cistercian movement had been gathering momentum on the Continent and was beginning to make its preliminary impact in England. Its strength lay in an immense capability in agricultural expertise and the concomitant development of under-utilised land coupled with a simple way of life. The richness of the soil in England was ready for exploitation and the food, wool and supplementary produce were badly needed to cater for a growing population who needed a stable environment.

Earl Robert therefore proposed the foundation of a Cistercian monastery on the site of Milo's murder in the Flaxley woods. This would commemorate the death of his greatest friend and supporter, assuage the grief and mitigate the anger of the family, provide a focal point to rally the Henrician party after the disaster of Milo's death, obtain the support of the Church and mollify its antagonism towards Milo's depredations against its interests. And not least, it would take the wind from the sails of Stephen's promises.

There were also two further aspects which need to be remembered. The first concerned the important projected foundries in the Forest of Dean, one of which had already been initiated by Milo at St Briavels a year earlier. The second was the intention at the start for the inclusion of a royal hunting lodge, not only providing facilities for the traditional sporting interests of the Normans but also involving royal imprimatur to the whole concept. Earl Robert never lost sight of these aspects and was determined that Prince Henry should be involved from the start.

Not surprisingly this whole plan caught the imagination of all parties, but much spadework, detailed negotiation and planning still needed to be done.

* * *

It is known that the nobleman from London who was intended to be betrothed to Berthe was present for the Christmas season at Gloucester Castle. This nobleman went on the hunting expedition and disappeared immediately afterwards with one other from the castle party. A nobleman would always be accompanied by his squire who would act as a kind of aide-de-camp. The name of this nobleman is not recorded any-

where that I can find so I have identified a suitably senior and unprin-
cipled Stephen supporter whose loyalty was always suspect and whose
son died unmarried, and without children, soon afterwards. It is known
that there were clandestine meetings and discussions in the Abbey and
castle precincts on the eve of Christmas Eve which have never been
explained. Milo was unpopular with the Church, which was not above
condoning murder at that time.

As Berthe's intended came from London it is probable that he was,
at any rate at one time, a supporter of Stephen. Many noblemen
switched allegiance anyway. It would have been a coup for Milo to have
obtained an erstwhile Stephen supporter for Berthe. Stephen was anx-
ious to recover from his Wilton debacle. Milo was involved in the
Flaxley foundry project. Eustace was a singularly unpleasant and
vicious young man who was determined to succeed his father.

Berthe's intended is therefore identified by me as Ernulph de
Mandeville, Geoffrey's son. The FitzUrse family was much involved with
both King Stephen and the de Mandeville family.

It is clear that Milo's death could not have been accidental, he was
murdered. There are a number of suspects – the squires (all too young
and inexperienced) – the Church (improbable). It has to be Ernulph
who had the opportunity and a motive to re-ingratiate his family back
into the King's favours – in this he may have been suborned by Eustace.
He also disappeared from Flaxley.

* * *

Geoffrey de Mandeville secured his release in 1144 after meeting the King's demands to hand over the keys of all his castles
with singular ill-grace and, when freed, was immediately transported with wrath. He was likened to a vicious and riderless
horse kicking and biting in his rage and went on an extended
rampage of rape and despoliation into the King's territories.

He was obviously still distrusted and was determined to rebuild
his base, power and finances. First he plundered the abbeys of
St Albans and Ramsey. He evicted the monks and seized all their
treasures and costly vestments. He sold as many as he could to
pay his supporters and fortified St Albans Abbey against any
reprisals.

Geoffrey was joined on these depredations by Ernulph and his
brother-in-law William de Say, and was excommunicated almost
immediately afterwards. Stephen however determined to cut

43

Geoffrey's lines of communication in East Anglia and fortified Burwell Castle in Cambridgeshire, not far from Newmarket. Geoffrey, realising his danger, besieged Burwell at once. Unfortunately, whilst reconnoitring this position without a helmet, Geoffrey was shot in the head by an arrow fired by a defender. Soon afterwards, as a result of this wound, he was taken to Mildenhall where he died on 14 September 1144 and his body was transported by the Knights Templar to the old Temple church in London. There the body lay for twenty years in the porch until an absolution for his grievous sins was negotiated by the Templars together with suitable reparations from the family. Only then was Geoffrey buried in the adjacent new Temple church. He seems to have been treated far more leniently in death than he deserved, although perhaps the reparations were sufficiently handsome to assuage his heinous crimes.

Ernulph, meanwhile had fortified and was defending the Abbey church at Ramsey in Huntingdonshire, a Saxon foundation which had once been a hunting lodge for Canute and was the funeral church of that great East Anglian Saint Felix. Ernulph's defence was overcome and he was captured, banished and imprisoned. He too died later that year without marrying and without issue. He knew too much, had done too much and threw his lot in with his father who was playing for high stakes. Hence Stephen and Eustace felt much more comfortable with Ernulph out of harm's way. It is certain that Ernulph did not die from natural causes.

Geoffrey had seen a window of opportunity which he had tried to exploit. From his control of the Tower of London, followed by his elevation to the Earldom of Essex, he thought that he would have the power to make or break the King and his successor. Stephen was a weak king running a much divided kingdom with a dissolute and irresponsible elder son. Stephen's younger son was never rated and must have been deficient either mentally or physically. Maud had lost her chance through outrageous arrogance and her son was still only a boy. Geoffrey de Mandeville could see that, with his wealth, power and control of essential key points, there was every chance of seizing the throne for himself at the opportune moment. He arranged the murder of Milo which was intended to throw the Henrician party into disarray and disrupt their rearmament plans. Unfortunately for Geoffrey,

Stephen arrested him just in time, which removed his power bases and clipped his wings.

Ernulph went ahead with their assassination plan which was then intended to reingratiate the de Mandevilles with Stephen. The King however still distrusted this family but, with his failure to act ruthlessly when it mattered, allowed Geoffrey his freedom. The King then had to divert his military resources to contain the de Mandevilles, thus allowing time for Earl Robert to regroup and rehabilitate their strengths.

Ernulph's younger brother, another Geoffrey, many years later restored the family's fortunes and reputation. We shall also hear more of Reginald FitzUrse in due course.

* * *

Whilst Stephen was committed to subduing the de Mandevilles, the campaigns between him and Earl Robert became much more low key. Nothing much happened in 1144 until Christmas when Robert revived the hunting parties from Gloucester which had been so disastrous twelve months earlier. This time the guests were vetted and some stayed with Earl Roger and some at Newnham Castle. Prince Henry stayed at the latter place so as to be nearer the action and joined in all the festivities with great gusto and zest and won much acclaim from the leading West Country families. To the mortification of Jane Clifford, her family was allocated accommodation at Gloucester and they were thus too far away to be involved as much as she would wish. Jane was however able to follow some of the hunting on her little pony but she was not noticed by the little boy whom she had comforted the previous year.

During the course of the chases Earl Robert arranged for a pilgrimage for everyone to the site of Milo's death and there was complete agreement that a memorial should be erected at the site. There was however a major obstacle in so far that the Forest of Dean was a royal preserve with exclusive rights for hunting only. But the accommodation at Newnham was limited and primitive and, in severe weather, the distance from Gloucester was discouraging for a full day's sport.

Earl Robert was a diplomat and he was determined to overcome all these problems. The Cistercians already had an abbey at Tintern, eighteen miles away and another at Kingswood, thirty-five miles away; their strategy was to achieve a presence throughout England rather than a powerful presence in one county such as Gloucestershire, which was already over-endowed with monastic establishments including Milo's own (Benedictine) foundation. The expansion of the Cistercian Order was closely controlled and centrally agreed at their headquarters at Cîteaux. The criteria for any site was that it should be a remote and solitary place, fit for habitation, fertile with emphasis on fruit and grain potential, supplied with pure water from springs of quality and, above all, a place where the Cistercian ethos of simplicity and austerity could be enjoyed. And as the Earl was to find out, these things could not be rushed.

Earl Roger had married Cecilia, the daughter of Pain FitzJohn, Lord of Ewyas in Herefordshire, and the latter family had donated land in Wales for a Cistercian foundation at Abbeydore which was already being built. The groundwork was already in place for further negotiations.

But Stephen, having nearly repaired his relations with the Church, then made a bad political mistake. Pope Innocent died and the Holy See Legate's office passed to Theobald, Archbishop of Canterbury. The King forbade Theobald to leave the country but his Archbishop refused to obey and travelled to Rheims to attend the council meeting whereupon Stephen banished him from the country. Theobald's riposte was to excommunicate the King and the Pope declared Stephen to be a usurper of the throne – it will be recalled that, at his coronation, his cause had been promulgated by somewhat dubious claims that King Henry had reneged on his promise that Maud should be his successor.

The time could have been opportune to reopen warfare with Stephen but Earl Robert counselled against this – there had been too much strife and both sides were in any event enfeebled. However it did mean that Henry's succession was authorised to come to pass with papal support. One effect of this was that the problem over the legality of building in royal hunting forests was overcome. Maud's gift of the Forest of Dean to Milo was valid and the dispensation of part of this for the Abbey site would be proper. The worship now envisaged in that Abbey of Flaxley could thus be endorsed by the new Pope – this was, of course, a vital prerequisite before anything could proceed. The main platform for the Cistercian objections was now removed.

The next stage in the negotiations and planning could now take place.

The chapter at Cîteaux agreed in 1145 that in consideration of the great support given by Earl Robert and the merits of the Flaxley case an agreement in principle could be recommended and a site survey authorised during the following year. This visit would be combined with a site inspection of progress at Abbeydore.

Earl Robert gave another great Christmas festivity in 1146 at Newnham and Gloucester and increased the invitations to include as many as he could from the leading Welsh landowners. It was important to widen the scope of support from the western potentates for the legitimate successor in the area from which so much help had come over the past few years. Henry was again prominent and every one of those present was most impressed with the way that he was maturing. The Cliffords were also present but there was still no opportunity for Jane and Henry to renew their still very limited acquaintanceship. Jane was by now nearly ten years old and was an extremely intelligent and talented little girl, showing signs of becoming very pretty indeed being fair haired with blue eyes. Henry was nearly fourteen, very stocky with a square face which would be later described as leonine. He was also extremely well educated with a wide range of knowledge and a great appreciation of the arts and poetry. He took an immense interest in everything and everyone and talked to all, irrespective of rank. At this stage he had no interest in girls and that is probably why he still seemed to ignore Jane, but nothing much missed his observant and restless eyes.

In the spring of 1147, the Cistercian inspectorate made their site visit and were enchanted with all that they saw. Here indeed was all that their order would require to conform to their aspirations. The vale was idyllic, the springs abundant, the water pure, the soil rich and the woodland peaceful. Here they could see grain growing, fruit burgeoning, sheep waxing fat, fine wool being clipped and good leather being tanned. The fishponds would be alive with fish to augment the famous river fish from the great Severn just down the road; salmon trout, eels and lampreys abounded. The practicalities of the site were investigated; there had to be good sub-strata, drainage had to be made excellent and there had to be room for all the ancillary buildings attached to the abbey incorporating facilities for a royal hunting lodge. The countryside would become prosperous and trade would boom. It was seen to be a veritable valley flowing with milk and honey. The monks would spend their quota of time in labour and then glorify God and sing his praises in the lovely setting of an abbey, albeit still embryonic. Milo's memory would become venerated and the cause to which he gave his life would prosper. Not least in all this the kings of England would give their patronage and enjoy their traditional sport in this and other neighbouring valleys. The enthusiasm of the inspectors was transparent.

Cistercian monastery buildings were standardised – a visitor to any such would immediately be able to find his way round. The cloister garth was 100 feet square. The church would be on the north side and a few feet higher than the cloister to reduce the flood exposure, and the lie of the land at Flaxley was ideal for this. On the east of the cloister were to be the chapter house, calefactorium, treasury and auditorium. Behind this would be the abbot's lodging, infirmary and offices. To the south would be the buttery, kitchen and refectory whilst to the north would be the abbey. To the west were the royal apartments, which were a negotiated variation on the standard layout and agreed between Earl Robert and Cîteaux. The founder of the Cistercian order was Bernard, later St Bernard, who was still alive, so he would himself have given his approval to this extension of facility. Outside the immediate complex were the farm buildings, granaries, mortuary chapel and accommodation for the king's entourage. The sanctuary was to be on that very spot where Milo fell.

In the autumn of 1147 Cîteaux authorised the building to go ahead, and the following spring detailed planning started. Almost all the abbeys of that time were built with stone quarried, imported and shipped from Caen and the wharves at Broad Oak would have been ideal for this. Tintern, St James at Bristol and Tewkesbury besides many smaller churches were all built from Caen stone. But an astonishing event changed this plan – almost a miracle in the context of the time. A substantial source of honey-coloured stone was found in a quarry a few miles away at Shapridge which had all the same qualities of durability, texture and colour as stone from Caen; 6,000 tons of it were required. Thus Flaxley was unique in being built almost totally from local materials and the impetus in developing craftmanship was considerable. The well that was sunk provided water for all the needs of the Abbey and the attached brewhouse and remained in use until 1961, which included the presence of and use by St Felix School during World War II.

In April 1147 the new Cistercian Abbey of Abbeydore at Ewyas was consecrated under the influence of Earl Robert and on land owned and given by his nephew, Earl Robert of Ewyas. A huge concourse of nobles, clergy and West Country notables and including princes from Wales gathered, hosted by Prince Henry. Milo's widow Sibilla came from her Welsh fastness together with her son Earl Roger and his brothers. The ceremony was performed by Bishop Betune of Hereford.

This successful occasion was repeated twelve months later when the foundation stone at Flaxley was laid by Henry amid immense rejoicing and feasting and the occasion was again blessed by Betune. At both of these events the Cliffords were present and Jane gave her usual close attention to everything, being especially gratified when the young prince approached and greeted her with pleasure and enthusiasm.

'How is my very own Rosamond?' he asked as he held her hands in his own rough horny ones. Jane was astonished that he remembered his endearment which he had first used when she had comforted him five years earlier. Henry went off and was intensely busy greeting all those who had come to see him and he took much trouble in speaking to all and sundry, making a considerable impression by his courtesy and how much he knew about each person and what they did. He had been well and truly briefed, taking evident interest in everything and this was well noted and commented upon by all. At the culmination of the day he went out of his way to bid farewell to the Cliffords and to compliment Lady Margaret on the beauty and deportment of their elder daughter. Her father asked her why she had been called Rosamond by the prince and she blushed prettily and told them the story, to their astonishment.

* * *

Stephen's antics during this period were limited. He was still under immense pressure from his own supporters and the Church continued their interdict upon him. There were abortive negotiations with Earl Robert that came to naught and there was skirmishing and posturing of a relatively unimportant nature.

* * *

Bishop Betune of Hereford died soon after the laying of the Flaxley foundation stone and Earl Robert fulfilled his promise to Abbot Gilbert Foliot: the latter was promoted to and enthroned as the new Bishop of Hereford.

Thomas Becket had spent several short stints away from Archbishop Theobald's household. On the first occasion he was obliged to help his father Gilbert, a merchant in London, who had been reduced to straitened circumstances. Gilbert had been in poor health for some time and died soon afterwards. Thomas was required to make suitable provision for his mother, Rohesia, and his sister. Rohesia was now able to speak more than the two words of English that she knew when she first married Gilbert and could now converse reasonably well in both English and Norman French.

Becket then worked for a short time as a notary with an erstwhile schoolfriend and subsequently as an accountant with a kinsman who had become a sheriff of London. Becket then returned to Theobald and accompanied that primate to Rome but he was denigrated by a French prelate and again left to study canon law at Bologna and Auxerre. By 1148 he had been readmitted to Theobald's household and, in that same year, was involved in the latter's hazardous journey to Rheims. His career was now set for ultimate high office although he was still not priested, having been in minor orders for several years and holding the livings of St Mary-le-Strand and Otford in Kent.

* * *

During these years Sibilla's unmarried daughters were wed. William de Braose was overjoyed to obtain the hand of Berthe after her unfortunate commitment to the obnoxious and tooth-sucking Ernulph de Mandeville. She was well out of that match and the de Braose estates, whilst not nearly as vast as those of Ernulph, were considerable both in the West Country and in Brecknock. Lucy, their youngest, had married the by now widowered, Herbert FitzHerbert, whose lands were mainly in Warwickshire. Her four younger sons however remained unmarried and some were showing signs of living a dissolute life.

50

3

Eleanor and the Second Crusade, 1137–1152

The First Crusade had been remarkably successful, having taken Jerusalem in 1099. This was immediately followed by the establishment of three states: the kingdom of Jerusalem, the principality of Antioch and the county of Tripoli. Unfortunately Antioch was within the claimed authority of the emperor of Constantinople and therein lay a source of conflict within the Christian ranks. Meanwhile in 1133 Prince Henry of England's grandfather, who had by now become King Fulk of Jerusalem, selected Raymond, an uncle of Eleanor of France, to be the bridegroom of the nine-year-old Constance, heiress of the principality of Antioch. A younger brother in the Aquitaine duchy would have had few prospects and Raymond seized this opportunity with relish. In the free and easy, very liberated and artistic court of Poitiers, the departure of Uncle Raymond was a sad event in the life of the young and spirited Eleanor; she missed him more than she cared to admit especially after she was wed to the French King in 1137. Thus Raymond became Prince of Antioch and he will play a vital role in the story that subsequently unfolds.

The court in Paris was stiflingly rigid and intensely priest-ridden and poor Eleanor found little to stimulate her after her liberal upbringing. However she managed to surround herself and fill her household with a few like-minded and enlightened young companions who enjoyed the freer atmosphere to which she had once been accustomed.

It was during this time that Peter Abelard was able to return to Paris after his banishment and his university students pressed him to restart his very avant-garde teachings, to the consternation of the Church authorities. Abelard questioned the many contradictions in the teaching of the Apostles and early fathers and, earlier, this had caused dismay within the Church hierarchy, the more especially as the young were such enthusiasts for his brilliant lectures and the debates that ensued. Among others who came to listen and learn was Thomas Becket and these lively and joyous meetings again attracted the attention of a much wider circle, including Eleanor and the ladies of her household. So it was that many sat at Abelard's feet to listen, learn and dispute, and doubtless some of the women lost a little of their hearts to this still quite extraordinarily handsome, brilliant but, by now, emasculated teacher, who seemed so remote and inevitably unavailable. Eleanor suggested to those with her that it would be particularly enjoyable to persuade Abelard to come privately to their rooms in the palace and she deputed one of her more smitten ladies, Mamille de Roucy, who leapt at this opportunity to initiate a meeting.

Mamille stood, with her knees shaking, beside the great man and shyly broached her request, without saying who had sent her. 'What say you, Tommy?' Peter asked the tall aquiline young deacon beside him who had always joined in all the debates with such brilliance. 'Should I brave these lovely and clever ladies in their own den or shall I be bruised and will the Church canon laws thunder even more loudly?'

Becket, for it was he, answered, 'You, dear Peter, will still be needing as many friends as possible, even at court, and forget not that Ramille's mistress is a kinswoman of your principal inquisitor, Bernard of Cîteaux.'

The two men smiled, for they knew and respected each other greatly, and Abelard replied that he was willing, nay eager, to come and see these ladies in the privacy of their own apartments. So he often came to the palace and continued to propound that the mysteries of faith were subject to private judgement. These visits, being private, drew less attention to the support given by the Queen and her household to his activities.

However, Bernard was furious at the Queen's overt support for this apostate and sinner and told her so in no uncertain terms, for it was he who had led the inquisition into Abelard's original teachings and presided over his subsequent banishment, followed by the dreadful punishment of emasculation meted out to this brilliant, albeit unorthodox teacher. Heloise, the niece of Fulbert of Notre Dame, had long since been banished to a nunnery

52

where she lived in much sorrow and pain. There was still in Paris sadness and indignation at the outcome of this, one of the most poignant of the great passionate stories of all time. Abelard's earlier treatment led to a continuing groundswell of sympathy led by Eleanor for these two thwarted lovers.

In 1142, Abelard became exceedingly ill and Eleanor went to see him on his sickbed. He was desperate to see Heloise again and this the Queen arranged. The erstwhile lovers were overjoyed at this opportunity and it was the first time that Eleanor had witnessed true lasting passion. Abelard's dying wish was they should not be parted in death but joined together for ever in a common tomb. Eleanor gave her promise to see that this would be done, and so it was that Peter died, at peace, in the arms of his very own Heloise.

The spat between Bernard and Eleanor only began to ease after Peter Abelard's death.

*   *   *

On the wider world stage other events began to move dramatically. On Christmas Eve 1144 the overextended Crusader lines were soundly defeated at Edessa and that city was retaken by the reorganised and regrouped Saracens. The Pope proclaimed the Second Crusade to recover a situation which was rapidly becoming fraught with danger.

On Easter Day 1146 Louis VII and Eleanor were immensely moved by an eloquent sermon by Bernard and both resolved to take the cross and embark on the Second Crusade. After her involvement with Abelard, Bernard regarded Eleanor as an evil influence on the King and had trenchantly told her that she would only conceive if she strove for peace. Eleanor had much respect for Bernard, recognising a personality as strong as herself and as this feeling was reluctantly reciprocated it is probable that the latter encouraged the Queen to embark on the crusade with Louis if, for no other reason, to keep her usefully and gainfully employed, not to mention removed from the temptations of Paris. Bernard had become highly critical of the luxury beginning to become so fashionable in the French court under Eleanor's influence. He complained to Rome about the costly and rich dresses of wool, silk and fur adorned with bracelets and pendants, the chaplets of gold accompanied by linen kerchiefs carelessly and provocatively draped over one shoulder. Bernard, the ascetic, asked whether it was right to wear the skins of squirrels or to exploit the labours of worms and was appalled at the way ladies of quality walked with their necks thrust forward, prancing with mincing steps, their faces covered in rouge.

Louis and Eleanor's marriage had not been fruitful. Some sources suggest that a daughter had been born to them in 1146 in response to Bernard's stricture, but Eleanor certainly had not fulfilled the precondition imposed by her cousin. Others suggest that the union was barren at this point. Louis was a monkish king and seemed to have no interest in persuading his queen to bear him any children; he was far more interested and involved in matters spiritual and appears to have been utterly dominated and overawed by the forceful personality of his queen. Eleanor was fifteen years old when she married Louis in 1137 and the marriage brought immense possessions to the French King, which broadened his power base considerably. It was certainly a marriage of convenience, but with the political machinations of the French court it was essential to perpetuate the dynasty and neither party seemed able or willing to do this. By 1146 Eleanor was twenty-four and for those times almost past the zenith of her fecundity, although still in the flower of her youth. She was undoubtedly strikingly handsome, perhaps even a beauty. She had immense ability and a devastating charm. She had been brought up in a talented, artistic, poetical, musical and liberal court and found the French court uncouth, stultifying, arid and overfull of priests. Eleanor had not, at this time, embarked upon any extramarital affairs so her dominance over Louis must have rendered him utterly impotent. Events moved slowly at first in their plans for their crusade to the Holy Land. Louis had to organise his kingdom so that affairs of state could continue on an even keel during his extended absence; this was not always easy in those troublous times and he was also suffering a series of setbacks on the domestic front.

Eleanor conceived the inspiration to lead a troop of armed ladies against the infidels as an Amazonian queen, and devoted her energies to this end. To pursue this project she corralled Sybille, the Countess of Flanders, Florine of Burgundy, Torqueri of Bouillon, Faydide of Toulouse and the lovelorn Mamille de Roucy – all leading ladies in her household – into giving support.

They in their turn persuaded scores of others in France to take the cross in support of their menfolk. The Pope blessed these enterprises at St Denis on 8 June 1147 and all duly set off full of hope and enthusiasm. The leadership was to be under the command of Louis and the German Emperor, Conrad.

Louis was determined to restore his martial reputation, already tarnished by his problems at home. Militarily the Second Crusade started badly and degenerated from disaster into debacle. Emperor Manuel I of Constantinople gave the crusaders a sumptuous reception when they arrived and sent them on their way with every blessing. The two armies landed in Asia Minor and were immediately subjected to harassment by the Byzantine Christians who sniped and skirmished from the start, having been furious at the encroachment of the Antioch principality now under the rule of Uncle Raymond. Louis and Conrad then decided to proceed independently, ostensibly to ease the supply problems *en route*, but actually to reduce the tensions and quarrels building up between their respective forces.

Neither the Roman nor the Byzantine Churches ever realised the position held by the primacy of the Antioch Church and this was vital to the understanding of so many issues. The foundation of the Church in Antioch predated all other Churches in Christendom by a great many years and the primate of Antioch considered that he took precedence over all other leaders in the Christian hierarchies. Raymond, now Prince of Antioch, was becoming more aware of this attitude of his own Archbishop.

However, the Byzantines were also enraged by the behaviour of the Crusaders who raped and pillaged with enthusiastic abandon. As the weather deteriorated and Christmas approached the French supplies were curtailed and their guides mysteriously disappeared. Louis was encouraged by the example of the German army under Conrad to follow in their earlier footsteps and turn inland along the course of the River Meander across the Phrygian mountains. All, at first, went well but as they climbed into the foothills the vanguard came across the rotting bodies of the Germans who had fallen into a trap and suffered a disaster. Louis however decided to press on and instructed the Poitevin vanguard under Eleanor's uncle, Geoff de Rancon, to wait at nightfall on the summit of the bare pass ahead for the main army to catch up. Eleanor and her Amazonian supporters were attached to de Rancon and the vanguard, and when they arrived in the early afternoon at this bleak rendezvous they saw in the nearby valley ahead a much more suitable place to camp and recuperate. The army under Louis was much delayed in their ascent and arrived after dark in appalling weather and had no option but to stay the night with no supplies or shelter available. Then the trap was sprung again and the main French forces were virtually annihilated, although Louis fought with immense bravery and tenacity.

The next day the remnants of the army struggled down into the more agreeable valley below where, at least, there were some supplies available. An immense row erupted in which Eleanor was blamed for encouraging de Rancon to disobey orders. The Queen became highly critical of her husband's lack of interest or attention to the well-being of his troops. She acidly suggested that he should have devoted more time to improving the admittedly poor supplies available instead of wringing his hands whilst sharing their privations, both of which had precipitated this debacle. Louis angrily refuted his wife's intervention and dismissed de Rancon forthwith, instructing him to return to Aquitaine immediately. The Amazon contingent now lost any interest in pursuing the harsh realities of warfare despite the fact that they had not even reached the seat of the crusade in the Holy Land.

The army, now without horses, struggled on foot through further passes, past the ruined site of Termessos, until they arrived bruised and bleeding at the ancient port of Attalya (now known as Antalya). Here the bargaining began to find vessels to take the army on to Antioch. Louis and Eleanor, accompanied by their by now unhorsed cavalry soldiers went on ahead and left the rest behind to follow as best they could.

* * *

Raymond and his Antiochene court greeted the arrival of Louis and his entourage with enthusiasm, panache and much merriment. The only sour note as far as the French King was concerned was the immediate and joyous affection displayed between Raymond and his niece who had not seen each other for fourteen years. These two talked entirely in the Poitevin patois which excluded Louis from any of their conversations. Their gossip and jokes, their laughter and tender smiles, their holding of hands and whispers together enraged him to distraction. Raymond was full of admiration at the beauty and vivacity of Eleanor whom he had last seen as a gawky, spotty child, whilst Louis was still smarting from his wife's contempt at his military inadequacies and their strained relations since then. He resented the transformation in Eleanor's spirits and his suspicious nature took note of every mark of affection which passed between Raymond and Eleanor.

As they entered the gates of the city of Antioch, Raymond led the way. He rose in his saddle as he passed through the arch and reaching up seized a metal ring set in the keystone. His thickset and powerful thighs tightened on the horse which immediately stopped the animal in its tracks. Despite his steed's continual straining to continue on its way, Raymond's arm strength and immense leg power stopped the animal from moving forward.

Eleanor laughed saying, 'I am delighted, dear uncle, to see that age has not withered your strength or impeded your ability to show off your party tricks.' She turned to her glowering husband and suggested that her liege lord might try to do the same.

Louis sneered. 'Perhaps our cousin's horse has been well trained to stop when prompted by this antic.'

Raymond dismounted with a laugh and offered his own steed to the French king for him to try. 'If you think this is a trick, test it for yourself on my nag.'

The surrounding Poitevins all cheered and egged the King on to emulate Raymond. With ill grace Louis, no mean horseman himself, mounted his host's animal, rode through the arch, seized the bronze ring and at the same time ferociously gripped the flanks of the beast. Sadly for him, the horse ambled on and Louis was left precariously and ignominiously hanging. Raymond immediately came to the King's rescue before his weakening grip sent him crashing to the ground.

The King of France was not amused.

Conrad, the German emperor, had fallen ill during their marches through Turkey and had returned to Constantinople for medical treatment, but the remains of his army were also beginning to trickle through. Raymond immediately addressed the military problems of the crusade and identified opportunities for fruitful action. His position was weaker than he cared to admit as the Saracens had encroached very near to his principality and, although divided, were gathering strength and were poised to continue their depredations. Raymond was shrewd enough to realise that any such threat to Antioch would disrupt the crusaders' lines of communication and their supplies as well as placing in jeopardy the strong positions held round Jerusalem. Raymond was also aware that there was little love lost between the main Arab forces at Damascus and those further north at Aleppo. Also, those at Damascus had not been unfriendly towards the crusaders in Jerusalem. The whole political balance needed sensible diplomacy combined with appropriate action when opportune.

Eleanor realised that her monkish husband's generalship relied more upon prayer for inspiration than hard-headed military planning and genius. Her female warriors were already dispirited following their earlier tribulations and she was fully aware that, under her husband's generalship, there was precious little honour, glory or success in the offing. She and Raymond decided to resort to wiles and stratagems rather than misdirected brute force to win the day whilst Louis and his advisers were prevaricating and twiddling their thumbs.

The resident Crusaders in Antioch had acclimatised themselves to the local conditions and customs since they had first arrived nearly fifty years before. Some had even married into local families; a few conformed to the dietary taboos such as eschewing pork; there were even one or two who had become Muslims to the animadversion of the establishment, but they were tolerated. One result of this was that there was a considerable rapport, understanding, even respect, not to mention much social intermingling between both sides. Thus Raymond had met and come to respect three warriors of Kurdish descent who had equivocal relationships with the Saracen leadership under the control of Nur-ed-Din. Two of these dissidents were high up in the Saracen command and were also related: Shirguh and Najm-ed-din-Ayub (known as Ayub, whose son was Shirguh's nephew). The problem, which still pertains to the present day, was that the Kurds had had many promises made to them which were not fulfilled. The third and most disaffected Kurd was Ali-ibn-Wafa, whom Raymond knew best.

Raymond contacted these three Kurds to initiate a meeting in order to explore whether there could be any room for manoeuvre; to corral their supporters with a view of making insurgent forays, thus disrupting the main Saracen forces based in Damascus which were now in the ascendancy following their earlier success at Edessa.

Ali was reluctant to come into the city of Antioch, which posed much danger to him and his party, but he was agreeable to a meeting and would be accompanied by Ayub. They agreed to meet on safer neutral ground in the nearby foothills just outside Antioch on a site with many springs, waterfalls and trees, including lovely cypresses and laurels, and surrounded by ruined temples, palaces and fallen columns. A tented camp in this idyllic place was duly established and each party brought an agreed and equal number of supporters.

Eleanor was intrigued and excited to become involved in such a diplomatic matter with its prospect of better success than seemed probable up to that moment. This crusade had started so badly and affairs were evidently continuing to deteriorate. Raymond was a suave and experienced courtier, who had become all too aware of so many of the jungle paths bedevilling the life of the crusaders who garrisoned the empire left by the First Crusade. The Saracens initially were hopelessly divided but were now much more cohesive, but their inter-tribal divisions were still present and could become serious. Hence Raymond was able to explore one such major rift within the ranks of the Islamic powers.

Raymond told Eleanor that negotiations would be protracted and that they must never rush matters or give an impression of haste. Courtesies would have to be observed and he stressed that in the Middle East, when God made time he made plenty of it. Ayub and Ali were famous warriors, both ruthless and cruel when it suited them. But it was Ayub who mattered in this affair and it was he who had a famous eye for the ladies and whose manners were legendary. Above all he expected the women whom he met to be exquisitely dressed and beautifully turned out. He was witty, charming and devastatingly handsome. He was an intrepid rider, an avid falconer and loved hunting, all of which was common ground for Eleanor.

Eleanor listened with care and made abundantly sure that her apparel was of the finest silks with flowing lines and that her hair was dressed and brushed until it shone, so all was shown off to her finest advantage. She chose her most spirited horse and ensured that it was groomed and caparisoned to perfection. Her uncle, already well aware of his niece's presence and beauty, had never before seen her look so vivacious and alluring. He was entirely happy with all her preparations and attention to detail and confident that their venture was starting propitiously. If she were not related so closely to him, and if he were not already happily married, he would have been much tempted himself. Louis was indeed a fool as well as totally ineffectual where it mattered. Raymond was beginning to sense that problems might loom.

Eleanor and Raymond rode out of the city to their rendezvous and, *en route*, their tactics for the talks were honed between them. As they approached, two splendidly apparelled and unaccompanied figures were seen in the distance galloping towards them at great speed. As they came nearer Raymond recognised them as Ayub and Ali. Raymond turned to his niece and said, 'This is a great compliment to us. It augurs well that they come to greet us without any escort.' He pointed out to his niece which of the riders was Ayub and which was Ali.

The two steeds came to an abrupt halt in front of their own horses in a flurry of dust. Raymond's horse shied in fright whilst Eleanor controlled hers with superb skill, which she saw that Ayub noted with open admiration.

'*Salaam*, my friend, *salaam aleikum*,' said Ayub. 'So this is the lovely lady warrior queen of France who is going to defeat us with her army of noble women and bring glory and honour to the Christian cause. My lady,' he bowed from the saddle as he turned to address Eleanor, 'you have already overwhelmed me and you have me in your power as your prisoner already. Treat me well, I beseech thee.'

His dark hooded and extraordinarily expressive eyes seemed to caress Eleanor with their eloquence and vitality. Eleanor was used to men admiring her, but always from afar, and, with her husband's remoteness and indifference, she had almost lost confidence in what she thought she could offer. There was always a 'look but do not touch' aura about her, but this was dangerously different and she was beginning to get excited.

The four of them cantered back to the camp and Ayub was

insistent that he and Ali would be the immediate hosts in their hospitality tent before any business was even to be broached. They dismounted and entered a richly furnished tent hung with lavish and costly rugs and with rare and sumptuous carpets. They sat on huge and luxurious cushions whilst silver bowls of scented rosewater were brought for them to wash the stains of travel from their hands and feet.

Eleanor had been wondering whether she would be included in this first meeting as she was merely a woman in essentially a male dominated environment. She was astonished to hear how fluently Ayub spoke French and he smilingly told her that while she and her uncle were his honoured guests he would completely conform to the practices of the French and Antiochene courts, adding with a bow and a half smile, 'In every way.'

Ayub removed his burnous and Eleanor was also slightly surprised to see that she was considerably darker than he was. The colour of his hair was the dark side of fair and his eyes were an intense shade of blue, and she wondered why. With her dark hair and suntanned face she could have been mistaken for a Saracen lady, whilst he could easily pass for a Norman. A sumptuous meal was served and eaten with their fingers. Raymond had warned her that it was impolite not to partake of each course. Eleanor had, in any case, a healthy appetite and enjoyed every dish. She asked for a description of each mysterious ingredient and did not flinch when Ayub pressed her to have the main delicacy reserved for the most honoured guest.

'I am but a mere sheikh,' he said. 'Raymond is but a prince, but you are not only a queen but the queen of our hearts. It is your right and privilege to partake first of our *bonne bouche*.'

Eleanor realised that it was a sheep's eye that was being offered and that both the hosts and her uncle were all watching with not altogether controlled amusement. She popped it in her mouth with relish and expressed her evident pleasure and enjoyment with charm and smiling eyes. She had leapt over her first hurdle with style.

After the meal ended Ayub outlined the programme that he had in mind. He was adamant that this was to be a mixture of business and pleasure with riding, hunting and falconry taking place in the cool of the morning and business in the late afternoon after a siesta. The evenings would be devoted to feasting and festivity. He had much to show them of his country and the immediate environs and he would hope, nay expect, that they would spend several days together get to know and respect each other, and understand the common ground that had brought them together as well as the differences that they were trying to bridge. He stressed that an agreement might be impossible to achieve but that he, at any rate, wanted this embassy to be enjoyable and that they should eventually part as friends if not partners. Raymond and Eleanor agreed with no reservations to these suggestions.

By now the sun was past its zenith, so they agreed to meet that evening for a light meal in Raymond's tent and that the discussions should start the following afternoon. Ayub then suggested that they should go for a small ride for some exercise before the sun went down, to which Eleanor readily agreed, but both Ali and Raymond asked to be excused as they wanted to have some essential preliminary discussions between themselves.

Ayub and Eleanor met as agreed and went out into the hills for a gentle ride as the shadows of the day began to elongate and the heat started to diminish.

'As we are to be meeting and talking informally and are going to be joining together in so many activities, how are we to address each other?' asked Ayub. 'Raymond and I have long been on first-name terms. May I have the temerity to call you Eleanor or, as it is sometimes in your language, Alianore? We have a lovely and very similar Arab name, Alia, which I would like to use for you. It means in Arabic, "high and exalted".'

They had arrived at a little stream where they dismounted. An accompanying servant brought a rug and they sat in the shade side by side and then drinks of cool sherbet in richly jewelled silver cups, appeared. Eleanor took off her headscarf and shook her hair free. Their fingers lightly intertwined.

'I am going to tell you a little about my peoples and something about the way in which we have had to fight, endlessly fight, to keep our heritage and our way of life. And what you and your friends may be up against,' said Ayub. 'You would like this?'

Eleanor nodded. Many hundreds of years ago and some miles to the north, Ayub told her, was where the great Greek, Alexander, had defeated the Persians in the battle of Issus. The land around them, Ayub said, was similar to the Issus battlefield. He described how the battle was fought and why the smaller force defeated the larger army of the Persian King Darius. Early in the morning Alexander led his troops into a corrie in the hills with high ground flanking him on both sides. He brought his cavalry through the infantry and marched them all down toward the plain below. The Persians began with their fearsome war cry which was intended to frighten the Greeks, who replied with their own response which echoed resonantly off the hills giving the impression that they were a far larger force than they actually were. Battle was joined but Alexander turned the Persian flank and using the terrain with masterly control of his cavalry routed the Persians who fled in disorder. All this, Ayub said, had been handed down by word of mouth since that time.

'I am telling you all this,' said Ayub, 'for you to understand that battles are won by bold generalship and inspired guile. And I ask you to ask yourself whether your husband and his German friend will be able to emulate Alexander in his confrontation with the famous Darius? I tell you another story. Nearly a hundred years ago our Sultan captured the Byzantine Emperor Michael after the battle of Manzikert and held him to ransom. Michael was given the best rooms and he was treated as an honoured guest. The Sultan asked his prisoner how he would have been treated had the Christians won. The Emperor told him that he would have been thrown into prison and tortured, then hung, drawn and quartered as an infidel. Said the Sultan in reply, "Praise be to Allah, that the victor on this occasion had the Christian virtues of forgiveness and charity."'

They drank deeply and looked into each other's eyes. The pressures between their fingertips perceptively strengthened at the same moment. They both smiled. The evening shadows began to lengthen and a chill descended and they came closer together for warmth.

'Have you ever been to England?' asked Ayub. She shook her head and asked why he wanted to know. 'Alia, you are not going to believe this story,' he replied, 'but when I was a little boy I had a beautiful sister called Rohesia whom I adored. My father had captured a crusader soldier whom he imprisoned and was holding for ransom. Rohesia fell in love with this man, who was called Gilbert, and this passion was reciprocated. So one night she crept down to where he was chained and cut off his

63

shackles to let him escape. Before he fled, they embraced, kissed and promised undying love for each other and that life's paths would one day cross for them again. Gilbert managed to get a ship and return to England. My father was furious with Rohesia, thrashed her and locked her in her room as a punishment. I did what I could for her but I was then only a little lad so I was not as much help to her as I wanted to be. Eventually, she ran away to Acre and stood on the beach until she found a ship going to England. She only knew two words of English – "London" and "Gilbert" – but she got to London at last and landed. She had no idea how big London was or how busy it was or how many Gilberts there were. Eventually, as she wandered the streets, someone pointed her towards a street called Chepe where there dwelt a Gilbert who had been on a crusade, who had been captured and who had escaped. And joy on joy for them, for this was her very own Gilbert, surnamed Becket. She became a Christian and they married and had two children, a boy and a girl. The boy is called Thomas and he is now in your Church and in the household of the English Archbishop called Theobald. I hear that he is doing very well and will go far. So you see that I have a nephew who may be destined to become a distinguished Christian. I am not sure that my Muslim friends would approve!'

Eleanor was enthralled by this tale. She told Ayub that she had indeed met Theobald, who came to France from time to time, and she also remembered Becket who was extraordinarily tall, very dark and aquiline, adding perhaps mischievously, 'Not very like you, who are fair, although you are tall. But what a coincidence though. And you obviously know how Rohesia is doing.'

Ayub told Eleanor how they managed to keep in touch and then added, 'You said that I am fairer than you. I am, and do you know why? My mother was a Circassian lady from the north and she was fair and very beautiful. Rohesia is dark, her mother was an Arab – she is really my half-sister. Same father different mother. We are allowed, as you may know, more than one wife and can, of course, have an harem. My father did in fact marry my mother though.'

They sat as the sun set, watching it sink below the horizon. Both were totally absorbed in the wondrous colours, whilst Ayub entwined a tendril of her hair in his fingers. Then they wended their way back to the camp in silent communion of spirit. As they approached Ayub told Eleanor why this spot was called Daphne, for it was here that Apollo pursued the nymph Daphne. The laurel, into which she turned, continued to flourish and the place was still called the city of pleasures. Later, Mark Antony married Cleopatra there. Eleanor had never felt more at ease with a man before.

That evening the four of them had a light meal in Raymond's recreation tent and made their arrangements for the morrow which would be devoted to some hunting. Raymond was aware that there was an animation and sparkle in his niece's face that he had never seen before. As an experienced man of the world he could read all the signs, but that was going to be a problem for Louis.

The four of them parted at the tent entrance, bade each other goodnight and went their various ways. Eleanor walked slowly towards her tent listening to the splashing waterfall and tumbling streams whilst looking at the stars shimmering and twinkling overhead.

'And what, Alia, do you see in them?' came a soft whisper, and a hand took her arm. 'Are they telling you your future? And will you like what they foretell?'

'And you? Do you too like what you see and want what is foretold?'

And they both went into her tent.

And to Ayub's incredible astonishment he discovered something about Eleanor that he could never have believed. It was utterly incomprehensible to him. But it explained much about the French King.

Eleanor was no longer a virgin after that night. And the course of history started to change direction.

* * *

The Becket story is contained in the Oxford Book of German Verse *in a poem by Conrad Ferdinand Meyer (1825–1898).*

Translation

Day after day, the length of Palestine's shore,
'London?' inquires the Saracen lady, wherever a ship at anchor lay,
'London!' she asked for long in vain, never tiring, never timid,

Until at last the oarsman brought her on board a boat.

Unrestrained she stepped on to the deck of the sailing ship,
seeing only ocean and sky. 'London?' she asked, turning away from
*   her homeland,*
and looking towards the direction of the outstretched sailor's hand
to the setting sun in the glow of the evening.

'Gilbert?' inquires the Saracenic lady amidst the bustle of the great
*   city,*
the crowd laughs and mocks her, until at last it takes pity,
'There are a thousand Gilberts in London' and yet she searches on
*   undaunted.*
'Refresh yourself with food and drink' and yet she feeds only on
*   tears.*

'Gilbert!' 'Gilbert, you know no other word but Gilbert?' 'No?'
'Gilbert!' Listen – that'll be the erstwhile pilgrim Gilbert Becket,
the one who, in slave chains, was burnt brown by the blazing desert
*   sun,*
and whose shackles were secretly cut by the Emir's young daughter.

'Pilgrim Gilbert Becket!' is the cry which rings out up and down the
*   Thames river bank,*
Look, he comes to her, goes the cry from all the people,
She has found her journey's goal and he leads her across his
*   threshold.*
With those two words love triumphs in trust and faith across land
*   and sea.*

(With many thanks to Heather Fisher and Brian Warren)

Meyer got his source from Augustin Thierry (1795–1856), a French
historian who made an important contribution to the revival of his-
torical studies, using anecdotes and legends to give colour and drama
to his writings. The notes in the Oxford Book of German Verse
state: 'According to a legend found by Meyer in Thierry's History of
the Conquest of England, *Thomas à Becket was the son of a Saracen*
lady. She helped the Norman Gilbert Becket to escape from captivity in

Palestine and later followed him to London.' A recent reproduction of a stained-glass window shows Becket with a most swarthy visage.

The Dictionary of National Biography *also refers to this story but is dismissive. Later on, we shall refer to a curious and unexplained anomaly regarding the foundation of a hospital in Acre in 1193 by King Richard Coeur de Lion which reinforces the possible verisimilitude of this Becket tale.*

* * *

On the morrow the first two to be up and about, bright-eyed and bushy-tailed, were Eleanor and Ayub. They were transparently overjoyed with each other, and Raymond noticed the changed and charged atmosphere with some trepidation. Events were moving far too quickly and not altogether as he would have wished.

The morning's hunting was stimulating and Eleanor was very much the match for Ayub's skill and daring. They all rode fast and furiously and jumped the hazards with bravado. The game bag was more than sufficient with deer, hare, roebuck and, to Eleanor's amusement, a splendid and huge wild boar, all of six feet in length, standing three and a half feet high and weighing well over 300 pounds.

'Raymond and I will have to polish this off between us, I suppose,' Eleanor remarked laughing, 'you are forbidden to join us in this feast.'

'Nay, Alia' replied Ayub, 'I hope that you will offer us the eyes as our trophy.' To which Eleanor agreed with a charming gesture of acquiescence.

Raymond noted the endearment from Ayub. After their successful morning's sport, they returned for a light meal together before adjourning for a siesta before their negotiations were to start. Raymond took his time before retiring to his tent and saw Ayub stroll across towards him.

'What has to be, my old friend, has to be. Allah has willed it,' he remarked, and went straight into Eleanor's tent, where they lay at peace in each other's arms.

That evening the talks began. Ayub made it clear that the only hope for any joint action between them lay in an attack, properly conducted, upon Aleppo. Raymond concurred and told them that this had been his strong recommendation to Louis.

This was obvious to both sides and Ayub made his anger transparent over the French king's ineptitude and vacillation.

'I must make it clear that I am not willing to commit my forces to support allies who are going to let me down. I do not back losers, I live here and it is the future of my friends which concerns me. A disaster now will put my cause back for a generation. Ayub has spoken.'

Raymond was not expecting Eleanor to make a contribution and, at the moment, was not too clear in his mind where her sympathies might lie. She had been listening intently to all that was being said. She now spoke.

'We have much common ground. Both sides here know what should be done and both of us realise that an attack on Aleppo is the key to any success. Our friends here are quite right to look at the downside. They have, in my view, more to lose than we have. Our generalship is poor and we all know that. Our subordinate commanders and our troops are good, well-trained and brave. But they do have a tendency to pillage, which needs controlling. All soldiers do this. My uncle knows his strengths but cannot make an attack on his own without good support from my husband. I make a suggestion to see if we can bridge the gaps between us. Aleppo is not too far away. Why don't we go and reconnoitre the ground and the defences whilst we are out here? With the information that we get, perhaps some sense can be knocked into the heads of my king and the emperor.'

Raymond was truly astonished at her grasp of the problems and the clarity with which she addressed them. He could not have put it better himself. So they all agreed and decided to leave early the next day.

As Ayub lay in Eleanor's arms that night, he reminded her that she had omitted one vital aspect in her masterly summary. She nodded.

'I know, *mon cheri*, we are still left with our poor generals, who have no inspiration and little guile. And that is not good news for either of us. But it does give us a few days longer together and that is good news.' He knew that she was as tough as a man when it mattered and a complete woman when that mattered. His hands began to caress her back and she responded.

Later that night, as they lay together, they talked. They agreed that their passion, albeit only in its second day, was quite special. But did it and could it override all problems?

'I am a Christian and a duchess with vast lands in France. I am married to the crusader leader, *mon cheri*!'

'And I am a Muslim, a leader in the Saracen army, a deputy to our commander Nur-ed-Din; but an emir in my people's land. What will both of the protagonists in this conflict say? The crusader queen, unhappy and unfulfilled until now, and the emir, whose proud followers are trampled upon and exploited, the two of us personally entwined and locked together in this rare and lovely relationship. This is such a perfect recipe for reconciliation, but the world will be shocked and rocked and will not comprehend it. They will suspect something base and unworthy. Alia, where do we go from here?'

They fell silent, and finally slept.

Eleanor awoke early and began to recall in those predawn hours that earlier passion that she had witnessed and become so involved in between Abelard and Heloise. An icy breeze began to chill her soul and she shivered. Her marrow froze.

They all set off early for the confines of Aleppo. It was not an easy ride. They climbed into the plain of Self and passed near the fortress of Harim which marked the extent of the crusader territory and influence and which was held by Raymond after being taken and retaken many times since the First Crusade. They now entered Saracen controlled land and then passed the Jebel Sema'an to the north, in the middle of which stood the colossal site of the basilica built to commemorate the ascetic St Simeon who had died 700 years earlier.

The day was getting hotter and the countryside was beginning to shimmer. Occasional travellers were seen and a small caravan group was passed. Earlier in the day Raymond would greet the parties and, once past Harim, Ali would make the appropriate salaams and salutations. Their little group did not unduly attract unwanted attention. Raymond knew the approaches fairly well and this trip refreshed his memory of the terrain. The three men discussed possible tactics and took particular note of the road, which was excellent here and would facilitate any lightning military strike. Ayub reminded them that it had been built by the Romans and used in this way during the Palmyrene campaigns 900 years earlier. Eleanor had never enjoyed such a ride as this with the wildlife and the views. She felt liberated and free as never before.

They stopped some way from the walls of Aleppo and studied the ground and approaches. After their reconnaissance had achieved all that was necessary they turned for home. At a small oasis they paused for some refreshment and to await the decline of the sun. They had decided to stop for the night at Harim Castle which they had passed earlier in the day. This was a small fortress built upon a hill and approached by a steep climb with a bridge over a surrounding moat, with simple but comfortable facilities in the keep. They had made arrangements for servants at Daphne to bring provender from their hunting successes of yesterday, so they were able to enjoy the delights of a relaxed evening feast.

Afterwards Ayub and Eleanor walked the walls of the castle, looking at the star-studded night sky and talking long and late into the night.

'We are the perfect pair for this country,' said Ayub. 'A veritable Apollo and Daphne; a true Mark Antony and Cleopatra. Many years ago, in Roman times, the astonishingly beautiful and able Queen Zenobia of Palmyra, a desert city in my country, challenged the might of Rome when it was at its zenith and very nearly triumphed. She and her husband, Odenathus, perceived weaknesses in the loose Roman controls and by skilful alliances outmanoeuvred the Roman commanders, causing considerable alarm and panic. There was little to stop them rocking the Roman Empire to the roots. Odenathus was sadly murdered but the queen carried on where he left off. She was an astute general and, at the end, only defeated through sheer bad luck combined with treachery. You and I are the Zenobia and Odenathus of today and the world could be at our feet.'

The dream was tempting, but the night was growing old and their time together was now more limited, so they enjoyed what was left to them for the moment.

The next day they indulged in Ayub's other passion of falconry. This sport had been practised since ancient times in Assyria and since then all round the Middle East. Ayub used a long-winged female hawk which he had trained from the nest, but he had brought smaller birds for the others in the party. They went up into the jebels to the south which was fine open country for the sport. Eleanor was most intrigued to see a number of ruined townships dotted about the landscape. The houses were generally substantial and in remarkably good condition but lacked roofs, windows and doors and in each place there were one or two even larger buildings that looked like churches. Ayub told her that they were indeed deserted Christian towns abandoned about 400 years previously, when the olive oil trade collapsed and the Muslims encroached over this land. He added that over all this region there were about 1,000 of these towns and villages, many of which were now occupied by peasant farmers scratching a living. Eleanor observed that these places could so easily be re-inhabited if the roofs, windows and doors were repaired.

'But not the churches,' smiled Ayub, 'unless we converted them to mosques!'

'But,' commented Raymond, 'we crusaders are here for these churches!'

They all laughed and Ayub suggested that they were here for sport and not for re-establishing these deserted towns – yet – and that they should now look for bustard and partridge, hare and rabbits. His control was superb and the others also began to have success.

Eleanor showed a remarkable dexterity and facility so Ayub asked her if she would like to try his hawk. She displayed an understanding and sympathy with the falcon and soon was handling her to the manner born, to the amazement of the others. The day's sport was again splendid and when they had finished they wended their way back to their base camp at Daphne with its backdrop of Mount Silpius. It was to be their last night together.

Eleanor was paying particular attention to her toilette when Uncle Raymond asked permission to enter her tent. She welcomed him with enthusiasm, as she was conscious that she might have behaved rather badly and abused his hospitality and care. As a child in Aquitaine he had been very much the favourite uncle and he had always indulged her in the liberal court of her father. And she was more than aware that she had dug herself into a deep hole and was struggling within herself to find a way to climb out.

Raymond knew that his niece was totally transformed from the wilful and wayward woman who had come out on this expedi-

71

tion. She was now fulfilled, transparently alight and with real problems ahead. He did not beat about the bush.

'You are in love with Ayub, I take it?' Eleanor nodded. 'So what are we going to do about this?' He stressed the 'we'. 'If you are utterly committing yourself, please think it through.'

'I know', she replied, 'I am completely torn. Don't think this is a flash in the pan, it isn't. It honestly isn't. We are both in this.'

'I am sorry but I'm going to be utterly brutal. You know how very fond I am of you, but you are going to cause so much hurt all round. Now, are you aware that Ayub already has several children and that he has at least two wives?' Eleanor started to interrupt but he put his finger up, which he knew might irritate her. 'Of course he can easily divorce. But can you share him with a second or third wife, now or in the future? Can you share him with his harem? What happens if he dies, is killed in battle or is murdered? Even if you were to convert, you will still be a foreigner, an infidel, in a strange land. My dear child, think, think, think and then think again. You won't get any help from our Christian side. You will be cut off from your lands and wealth. I know, I am a younger son, I have no patrimony from Aquitaine, but I am married to an heiress and I am now a prince, something I could not be in France. I have to behave myself here, in a Christian enclave. You will not have this with Ayub. You can only become a drag on him and, when time passes and your beauty fades, he will resent this. I know him. He will be ruthless and once you are lonely and you start to become critical, even shrewish, he will wish for his own kind. The Kurds will not take to you, their leader with an infidel! No. You are heading into disaster. I am so sorry, so very sorry.' She threw herself into his arms and wept.

'I never thought about his present wives, his children, his harem. I wanted him all to myself. He wants me all to himself,' she sobbed.

He comforted her and later on suggested that he could make her excuses for this evening's feast. She shook her head, and said that she would continue dressing. As he left he said, 'Make yourself look as nice as you can.'

If looks could kill, Eleanor's face said it all. She turned herself out stunningly and, that evening, held the party together with consummate skill.

The next morning they agreed to push for the Aleppo thrust suggested by Raymond and endorsed by both Ayub and Ali. It was made abundantly plain that if the crusaders did not follow this plan, Ayub and Ali could not be committed to any action. But they would keep in touch through Ali should events prove to become more propitious later on.

Thus the parley ended and farewells were said with warmth, with heartfelt and underlying feelings of enormous depth. Neither Ayub nor Eleanor had begun to solve their problems but both were entirely confident that their paths would cross again.

*　*　*

Raymond and Eleanor returned to Antioch, initially in silence. As they approached the city they started to talk and Raymond began to realise the full depth of the problem. Eleanor was far more involved than he had appreciated, but she was much more in control of her feelings than he deemed possible. She did tell him that Ayub had now told her about his family and its ramifications. Also that he had received that very morning disturbing news about the health of his eldest son, of whom he was very fond and about whom he entertained high hopes. All this had worried him considerably.

'That,' said Raymond, 'would be his boy Salah-uh-Din. He has great expectations of this lad. I hope that all will be well for them.'

As they approached the city gates Eleanor wavered and put her hand in her uncle's for comfort and held it very tightly. Raymond realised that she was indeed a complete woman when it mattered, but also as tough as a man when it mattered.

'You may always rely upon me for any help and support that you may require. I am sure that you will be needing it,' he told her and they looked at each other with understanding.

But he was disturbed to see one Thierry Galeran, an eunuch and a knight close to Louis, watching them as they entered the castle gates with an expression which boded ill. This gentleman was a mean fellow, always snooping, full of mischievous tattle, who was forever eyeing Eleanor with unfulfillable lechery. He slid away and made himself scarce as soon as he saw the Prince glance angrily at him.

That evening Louis peremptorily summoned Raymond to his

presence with scant notice or courtesy. On his entry to the King's chamber he was not best pleased to see a number of associates from the royal entourage including not only Galeran but also a sly monk William from Tyre. He was also startled to be greeted somewhat effusively by Patriarch Fulcher of Jerusalem who seemed to have just arrived. Louis started by cross-examining Raymond over his absence, the length of this and any reasons that he might care to give for taking the Queen – his Queen – with him.

Then he added with a sharpness of expression, 'I understand that you were not accompanied by *your* wife. Was that wise and was she privy to your exploit? And does she know what you might have been doing?'

'Sire,' replied Raymond, 'I was on a mission of extreme confidentiality and of vital importance to the crusade, for which you and the emperor are entrusted by His Holiness to pursue to the best advantage of the Christian cause. I do not wish to discuss my negotiations other than with you alone. I can only assure you that they are in our best interests.'

'I remind you that I am in command and that I am to be fully involved in all negotiations. I will in fact undertake all these affairs in person and I shall decide who shall advise me. You are to be relieved of any duties in the pursuit of our crusade. And you are seeing much too much of Her Highness and you are far too closely involved in her affairs. I forbid you to see her at all from this moment on.'

'May I ask if my niece, Eleanor, has given her version of our trip?'

'I have spoken,' the King replied, 'and that is all that is necessary for me to say. You may go.'

'Your Highness is reminded that you are a guest in my principality. That I am under no duty of obedience to you. The kingdom of France has no jurisdiction here whatsoever. I shall always treat you in accordance with your rank and I shall be obliged if you would reciprocate and extend to me the customary courtesies of my rank.' 'In this country,' Raymond added, 'our tradition is that the guest is sacred. And, may I remind Your Highness that my niece is very dear to me and that her welfare is close to my heart.'

The King flushed and was about to explode with rage when

74

Galeran leant forward and whispered in his ear. Louis turned again to Raymond. 'You also have to explain how it was that you brazenly rode into this castle today holding the hand of the Queen, my wife, in an unnecessarily amorous manner for all the world to see and exchanging intimate looks with her, totally insulting to my dignity.'

'I have to tell Your Highness that I do not permit in my court the affairs of any lady to be bandied about in such a manner in public. It is a slur upon her good name. I demand that you withdraw this slanderous remark and apologise.' Raymond turned and picked up a poker from the fireplace. Louis started in fear and looked around for help. A guard at the door moved towards them. Raymond flexed his muscles, bent the poker in half and threw it on the floor at the King's feet. 'Match that,' he said contemptuously. Louis was shaking uncontrollably. Raymond picked up the bent poker and straightened it before throwing it back into the fireplace.

Patriarch Fulcher, by now highly embarrassed, intervened to calm the charged atmosphere and suggested that it would be better for this discussion to be resumed later on, when all parties had given some thought to the concerns of mutual interest. Raymond bowed to each and left the room.

Things did not improve. Louis then discovered not only about the trip to Aleppo, but also that Eleanor was in that party.

'How dare you expose my wife to danger in enemy territory?' he demanded.

Raymond was not inclined to reveal who their escort was, as he was conscious of security and the French were notoriously indiscreet. There were spies everywhere. Raymond privately advised Louis that Patriarch Aimery of Antioch was incandescent with fury that Fulcher had come to Antioch without so much as a by your leave. Raymond reminded the King that Aimery took the seniority of his primacy very seriously, as did all those in the Antiochene Church and that he, Raymond, was doing his best to defuse a dangerous situation.

*   *   *

The first church that was ever established was in Antioch. See Acts 11.26: '[Peter] found himself in Antioch ... they assembled themselves with the church ... and [they] were called Christians in Antioch'. To this day the diminutive congregation still in Antioch claims supremacy and primacy in the Christian Church.

* * *

Patriarch Fulcher reminded the King that Conrad was already in Jerusalem although the German forces were now mainly in Acre. He went on to say, with some reluctance, that the Germans could be redeployed on the Antioch front if really necessary. He then stressed that the primary reason for his visit was to urge Louis and his army to make all speed to Jerusalem where the main attack should be mounted. Louis dug his toes in when Raymond continued to press for an attack through the gap in the Saracen defences at Aleppo. Under no circumstances would he go any- where until he had made his pilgrimage to Jerusalem.

Eleanor weighed in, showing her shrewdness in her assessment of the military situation. Unfortunately Louis' interpretation of her intervention was not based upon strategic common sense or upon the vigorous implementation of the crusader objectives, but upon his firm belief that her interest in Antioch was completely biased because of her seemingly incestuous relationship with her uncle which was, obviously, reciprocated by the latter.

Louis announced that his army would depart immediately for Jerusalem. Eleanor told him that she would not be coming with him but would stay in Antioch, not realising that this merely con- firmed her husband's suspicions. She was at once put under room arrest by the King and told that she would do as she was told. This was the first time in their married life that Louis had stood up to her and to say that Eleanar was angry was to put it mildly. She had never taken kindly to this sort of treatment and was used to getting her own way. On the following day Louis was seen to sport a black eye – history does not relate how he got it. Those who are kind may suggest that he stumbled against the bedpost.

Meanwhile Raymond told Louis that he would not bring any of his troops to the southern front of the campaign and, sadly, would not be able to join and support any attack under consid- eration from Jerusalem. In fact Raymond washed his hands of the crusade from that moment. He also had potential problems looming in Antioch from the Christian Byzantines, who did not always regard the crusaders as being on the same side. There were also difficulties with the Turks from the north and the Saracens from Aleppo.

Raymond's wife, Constance, who was by now a young mother and the Princess of Antioch in her own right, was able to visit the confined Eleanor in her quarters. The two young ladies chatted and confided in each other. Constance was entirely convinced of her husband's fidelity, as she knew that he had always been a man pure in conduct. She knew of the expeditions to Daphne and Aleppo and of who was on them. Before Eleanor was dragged off to Jerusalem by Louis Constance noticed that she was beginning to suffer from a sickness in the morning. At this stage Constance kept her own counsel.

* * *

In the spring of 1148 King Fulk's widow, Queen Melisande, and their son Baldwin III of Jerusalem greeted the French and German leaders with immense enthusiasm. It is worth reminding ourselves at this point not only that the late King Fulk had been Count of Anjou and was therefore the grandfather of Prince Henry of England, but also that Queen Melisande was the half sister of Eleanor.

The nobility and prelates now assembled in Jerusalem had never before been equalled. The feasting and celebrations were lavish, and were destined to be the prelude to an outstandingly successful campaign to restore the considerable gains of the First Crusade which had been so disastrously squandered since then. In June 1148 Melisande and Baldwin gathered all together in a great assembly at Acre to plan the campaign in detail. Perhaps it was significant that Eleanor was not invited to be present at Acre. She had other matters exercising her mind at that time and also a healthy contempt for the plans likely to be promulgated at that meeting. The details of the deliberations have not survived but it is clear than there were some who dissented from the final decision.

The plan agreed upon was an attack on Damascus. The factors leading up to this decision were complex. It was a mixture of greed, a desire to control the fertile plains, the kudos of controlling a city as holy as Damascus, revenge for recent defeats, and an empire-building enthusiasm to widen the territories under the sovereignty of the King in Jerusalem, thus providing further huge rewards for the crusader followers. But the flaw in this approach was that the Damascene leaders had hitherto been supportive to and tolerant of the crusaders. The main enemy was in Aleppo under Nur-ed-Din and there was little love lost between these two Muslim cities and their leaders. The nobility of Jerusalem knew this and did not see fit to advise the incoming crusaders, presumably for reasons of self-interest and potential aggrandisement. Raymond was only too aware of these problems and Eleanor, who was no fool in these matters, had done what she could to knock sense into Louis, to no avail. Thus the plan of campaign was utterly foolish and would inevitably drive the two Muslim factions into collaboration.

The largest Christian army ever to take the field in Palestine set forth in July and reached Damascus by the end of that month. The extraordinary plan very nearly succeeded, largely because Unur, the Damascene leader, could not believe that the crusaders could be so foolish as to do what they were trying to do. Surprise is always a vital constituent in warfare but it must be allied, as Ayub had told Eleanor, with flair, dash and, if possible, genius. Unur summoned help from the Aleppine command who responded rapidly. At one point the crusaders were within a whisker of success, but they delayed twenty-four hours too long. The very next day a savage counter-attack rocked them in their covered positions in the orchards. Louis and Conrad ordered their army to move to open country thus removing the cover afforded by the trees. Unfortunately the new positions chosen for this disastrous redeployment were totally bereft of any water and were hopelessly exposed to sallies from the strongest section of the Damascus walls.

The crusader leadership fell apart in recriminations. Much time was wasted in arguments about who was to become the Christian Prince of Damascus whilst the main objective of trying to capture the city was completely ignored. Further reinforcements from Aleppo were due imminently, which could lead to a catastrophe of the gravest proportions. The crusader army retreated in ignominy, harried and sniped at throughout their humiliating withdrawal. The Muslim morale surged upwards and the Christian cause lurched downwards.

A furious Conrad departed for home as soon as he could. Louis was in a cleft stick so he shillied and shallied. Eleanor was now hardly speaking to him and it was becoming transparently obvious that a divorce was likely to be the only solution. But the really cogent reason for a divorce was concealed from him. The Patriarch of Jerusalem was much concerned and in discussions with the archbishops and bishops in Palestine was negotiating for a damage limitation exercise and working towards a solution involving a reconciliation. For the leading Christian crusader leader to be involved in such a messy business was hardly the best example for the world to see.

Eleanor had no intention of pursuing her original master plan of leading her ladies into battle, now that she realised the stupidity of the master plan and the incompetence of the leadership. Thus she stayed in Jerusalem where she managed to conceal her condition with skill. She was fortunate in so far as she had managed to keep her figure and, by dressing with artifice, no suspicions were aroused. In any case she and Louis had never cohabited. Towards the end of the year, following a warm invitation from Constance, she announced her intention to spend Christmas in Antioch with her uncle and, to Louis' surprise, Constance came to fetch his wife. He was even more surprised to see the cordiality between the two women. In any event Louis wished to spend Christmas in Jerusalem, combining this with a visit to Bethlehem. He stayed on to spend Easter there.

Eleanor's confinement in Antioch came sooner than they expected and she gave birth to a fine boy, fair-haired like his father, who thrived from the start. Raymond and Constance were most supportive of this development and they had many talks regarding the future of the child. There was absolutely no question of Eleanor keeping him with her. Obviously he could be brought up with their own children in Antioch. Raymond had kept in touch with Ayub via Ali and, soon after in the New Year, Ayub proposed a discreet visit to them, ostensibly to take on responsibility for bringing up his new son. Eleanor was transported with joy at this prospect of meeting Ayub again and even toyed with the idea of eloping, despite all Raymond's sensible advice earlier on. Raymond, at this stage, was unaware of his niece's real intentions and arranged for them to travel to Tyre where they were all intending to rendezvous. As far as Raymond was concerned this was all that was intended to happen. But Ayub was similarly tempted by the prospect of persuading the

French Queen, the richest and most noble lady in Christendom, to flee with him. He set sail from Ascalon and duly landed at Tyre.

The reunion was ecstatic and the happy couple stayed together on Ayub's vessel. Ayub's son had meantime died. Ayub's solution was that he would substitute one child for the other and would bring Eleanor's son up in his own household.

But Raymond's worries re-emerged when one of Eleanor's handmaidens told him that Eleanor's luggage contained all her jewellery as well as two cases crammed with gold and silver. He was urged to do something very soon as it was indicated to him that the besotted couple were intending to elope without any further delay.

'Sire,' said the maiden, 'there's trouble brewing and my lady's vessel is in the harbour and is about to go to Ascalon. Hurry, sire, in God's name.'

At this stage Raymond was unaware that Louis had already travelled to Antioch to rejoin his recalcitrant wife. Finding disturbing and most unwelcome news there, Louis now returned post haste to Tyre and dispatched a messenger to Raymond telling him that he, Louis, was now on his way. Raymond, who was about to dispatch an urgent message to Jerusalem summoning the King to come quickly, now sent his message to Antioch. Louis, already *en route*, reacted promptly and raced towards Tyre as fast as he could.

Raymond meantime now went on board to try and contain the situation. Ayub and Eleanor were torn between their love for each other and the devastating consequences of their intended actions. They both realised that their own peoples, on each side, would be outraged and that the crusade would end up becoming a personal and vicious vendetta.

After much tearing of the heartstrings they agreed to part, each to their own people, carrying in their bosoms that precious memory and relationship which never again would be created elsewhere.

'I shall call him by the same name as my first son, Salah-eh-Din, and his family name will be Jusuf. Think of him, Alia my dear, as S'alia-eh-Din. He will become a great leader of men, a real Palmyrene descendant of the great Zenobia and Odenathus and a true fruit of our loins. He will go down in history as a successor to Alexander and the world will know him as Saladin the Great.'

Their last night together had special meanings for both. And again Eleanor especially remembered that unique love between Abelard and Heloise in which she had the privilege of playing but a small part.

'Go back to Europe and produce another son in the same mould from your own kind. Choose a man worthy of you – a man of honour, of mettle and of inspiration – let him be the father of your Christian children. The special one that you will bear will become a soldier of honour and chivalry of strong heart, of greatness and success. He too will go down in the annals of our race and one day he and our Saladin will meet and know their mothers to be one and the same person.'

A nurse was produced and the little boy was borne away by Ayub to Ascalon and afterwards to the desert fastnesses to be brought up. When he was old enough he would join his father and be initiated into manhood.

And so Eleanor and Ayub parted for ever.

*   *   *

Louis clattered onto the quayside just in time to see Eleanor stepping off the gangplank, her hair loose and rippling in the evening breeze. He watched the plank drawn up, then the ship slipped its moorings and started to sail away with a figure standing on the prow and waving until he was out of sight. Louis cantered down to where his wife stood and seized her arm with anger in his heart. Eleanor shook herself free with eyes dry but tears in her heart, and she watched until the speck dipped out of sight over the horizon. She turned to Louis.

'Why did you want to do this?' he demanded. 'Why, why, why?'

She replied, still refusing to show her tears to him, 'On account of your having no manhood. You are not worth a rotten apple, in God's name. You are a puny, useless man of no account. You'll never get any satisfaction in holding on to me.'

Louis took advice from his barons who told him to let Eleanor go, she was a she-devil and no good would come to him if she stayed with him. And they added that she had never borne him a child.

*   *   *

Baden Watkins in his Flaxley book first mentions this story but he gives no sources. I have not, however, found Baden to be inaccurate in his major assertions. One source close to Baden does not think that he made anything up.

Louis, supported by the Church, made considerable play with the incestuous relationship between Eleanor and Raymond, but this was carefully ignored in the grounds for the subsequent divorce in 1152. Raymond was, in any case, dead by then so it may not have mattered other than the unseemly scandal which would have attached to the French monarchy and the Christian cause. Eleanor had every reason to make herself scarce in Palestine at that critical time. Louis had every reason not to abandon her there.

Runciman's Arabic sources (The History of the Crusades) *refer to Saladin's history being written after his death and being based on hearsay. Most sources give Saladin's date of birth as being ten years earlier, thus discounting any possibility of Eleanor being his mother, which would have been as embarrassing to the Saracens as to the crusaders.*

Military leaders on both sides emerged very young and Saladin was becoming well known in the late 1170s. Saladin and King Richard of England were astonishingly alike in size, colouring, military ability and chivalry and had an immense rapport.

There are many further unexplained factors regarding this relationship which will emerge later in this book and which will reinforce this extraordinary story.

William, later Archbishop of Tyre, had no regard for Eleanor and is one source for the Tyre story. Gervase of Canterbury mentions 'matters best left unspoken'. In 1260 a minstrel from Reims gave a full account of this episode.

The Arabic authorities are complex to interpret and later books are based on the earlier source. It is not unreasonable to promulgate that the earlier birth date was a convenient red herring for both sides or that a substitution was effected, as I have suggested.

Runciman also states that Raymond had many excellent qualities suitable for his position as Prince of Antioch, but in particular was noted for his purity of conduct as well as his gallantry. Runciman quotes a contemporary source for this judgement.

A most significant point is made in the legend when the barons point out to Louis that Eleanor 'had never borne him a child'. What is the point of bringing this into a legend if the whole matter is false? But if it is true, then the whole complex story begins to make sense. It explains the Antioch problem, the Aleppo reconnaissance, the return to Antioch by Eleanor, the child, the Tyre story, the Pope's efforts (mentioned in a moment) and the birth of Mary later on in 1149.

The Dictionary of National Biography *does however note Eleanor's affair with 'Saladin' but is dismissive because of Saladin's age at that time. It is therefore much more probable that the affair was with Saladin's father. The* Dictionary *gives its source. How did this story arise? The* Dictionary *also, incidentally, says that Eleanor 'joined' her husband in Italy and did not leave Palestine at the same time.*

*   *   *

In the early summer of 1149, Louis and Eleanor left the Holy Land and sailed from Acre, albeit in separate ships. Their voyage was beset by dangers and problems after a reasonably safe start in the eastern Mediterranean. Louis encountered a Sicilian vessel which he boarded in order to obtain news. He was astonished to learn that the Sicilian King Roger was in conflict with Manuel of Byzantium, both these parties being allies of a sort of the French King. A Byzantine vessel then bore down on them, capturing Eleanor's ship as well as the baggage craft. The Sicilian ships gave chase and managed to rescue the Queen and some of the impedimenta. Storms then blew up and the royal parties were separated, Louis landing at Brindisi, where Roger entertained him, whilst Eleanor landed at Palermo.

It was here that Eleanor gave a most extraordinary promise of gratifying the French with an heir. It was, after all, two months since her last torrid meeting with Ayub at Tyre and obviously she and Louis had not cohabited on their voyage.

After a few further vicissitudes Louis and Eleanor were rejoined and Roger entertained them in Potenza, where he proposed yet another crusade. The royal couple then departed for Tivoli where they were received by Pope Eugenius III. Eugenius had been fully briefed of the royal couple's problems by the patriarchate in Jerusalem and put his mind to effecting a reconciliation between them, as he believed this to be the only solution for all concerned. He seemed to achieve the impossible. He fêted them, he flattered them, he spoke to them together and then he had private sessions with each in turn. Finally he put them in a luxurious apartment with a fabulous bed richly embellished and, in effect, told them to get on with it.

Louis was duly obligated by his obedience to his Father in God and minded to do his best, encouraged by aphrodisiacs surreptitiously passed to him by the Pope's confessor. These pills and potions had been discovered in the Middle East during the crusades and the religious leaders there hoped that, with the blessing of the Holy Father, they would do the trick.

Eleanor was willing to go along with all this as she was beginning to realise that she had had such a loving and recent reunion with Ayub that she was again *enceinte*. Luckily she was able to encourage Louis to imbibe more freely than was his wont, so that he was so legless as to be utterly incapable of knowing whether he had any success or not. But Eleanor knew.

The Pope was delighted. His papal advisers were less sanguine – as one said, 'One lone swallow does not make a summer'. Louis was over the moon and Eleanor was relieved.

The French royal pair returned to their kingdom of France.

* * *

En route Eleanor was saddened to learn of the death in battle of her uncle Raymond. As Raymond had foreseen earlier, the Muslim forces from Aleppo began raids on Antioch combined with diversions emanating from the Turks at Konya. Raymond re-approached Ali-ibn-Wafa for support from the Kurdish faction which achieved some respite, but this upset Shirkuh, the Kurd, who did not come to Daphne and who had a family connection with Ayub.

Against Ali's advice, Raymond committed himself to a foray which led to an entrapped position. Unfortunately Raymond's brave attempt to escape was blighted – the lie of the land was unsuitable and the wind rose and blew sand in the faces of the counter-attacking Christians. The force was annihilated with both Ali and Raymond perishing, Eleanor's uncle at the hand of Shirkuh himself. Life was indeed brutal.

Eleanor remembered an original suggestion that her son should be brought up in the Antiochene court with Constance's young family. Now that princess was a widow and surrounded by danger, Eleanor was thankful that she had entrusted Saladin to Ayub's safe keeping.

* * *

In due course, Eleanor was delivered of a daughter, Mary, to

84

whom she was always devoted. Louis considered that he had achieved fatherhood at long last albeit, not yet, a son. Eleanor recalled two sayings: 'Man proposes but God disposes' and, from the Jewish faith, 'The mother is always a matter of fact, the father is always a matter of speculation'.

After Mary's, birth, Louis, encouraged by his apparent new-found ability and his confidence engendered by the Pope's help, forced himself upon his queen so that she could produce for him the son and heir that he so badly needed. Eleanor was outraged by this intrusion. It was no less than marital rape.

However, in 1151 a second daughter, Alice, was born. This event certainly did not cement their marriage and their relationship became utterly intolerable to both parties. Divorce negotiations now began in earnest.

Louis accused Eleanor of incestuous relationships with her uncle, who being now dead could not refute these calumnies. Other allegations of adultery were also made. A commission of archbishops convened to consider the matter and, wisely, did not pursue these unfair and totally unwarranted accusations which would have caused immense damage to almost every involved party. They found that there was every reason to dissolve the marriage, now of fifteen years duration, on the grounds of consanguinity, as Louis and Eleanor were second cousins once removed. Both the Pope and Bernard of Clairvaux were in agreement. On 21 March 1152 the decree was made absolute.

It is worth noting here that when Eleanor and Prince Henry of England were married later, they too were second cousins once removed.

4

1148-1152

In the latter part of 1148 both Prince Henry and Maud, his
mother, returned to Anjou with the intention that she and her
husband should begin to pass control of their possessions in
France across to their son in fulfilment of the next stage in his
preparation for the greater responsibilities that he would ultimately inherit. Count Geoffrey had fallen ill at this time and
some concern was expressed that Henry should be at hand,
should events take a turn for the worse.

But it was in England that a potentially serious disaster arose.
Earl Robert of Gloucester, who had seemed to be in reasonably
robust health, collapsed and died at the end of that year. He had
been assiduous in the fulfilment of all his duties and obligations
and had led a blameless and selfless life, and this had taken its
toll on his constitution. He had taken a firm line throughout to
reduce the debilitating effect on all classes of a divided country
and always insisted upon taking the long view. Earl Robert was
buried with full obsequies and ceremonies in St James' monastery
at Bristol. However it says much for his wisdom that the country
was not immediately plunged into further opportunistic strife at
this critical moment and that Henry's upbringing for his ultimate
responsibilities was to bear fruit.

Later in that year, Henry undertook a somewhat disorganised
expedition back to England to vindicate his claim to the throne.
Surprisingly soon after he landed, he ran out of money to pay
for his small force and had to appeal to his uncle, King Stephen,
to bail him out. Stephen, ever the most unpredictable of persons,
generously and willingly gave him the required sum, albeit that
his nephew was intending to tangle militarily with him.

Henry then hurried north to meet with his Uncle David, the

Scottish King. They undertook some desultory skirmishing to harry the English King's position in the north, which seems rather ungenerous of Henry after his uncle's earlier support, but it must be remembered that some sabre rattling was necessary to remind Stephen not to be too pugnacious. In May of that year, King David knighted Henry in the Scottish order of Chivalry in front of a large concourse of notables in Carlisle in recognition of his meritorious exploits. Again Henry's bearing, demeanour and character made an excellent impression upon those present. Henry returned to Anjou but travelled frequently between France and England to foster his connections, now that he was bereft of his uncle's influence.

King Stephen meanwhile had been declared a usurper in 1147 by the Pope and was endlessly involved in strife with the Church in order to maintain his position. The character of Eustace, Stephen's son, had continued to deteriorate and he was now called 'Eustace the Dissolute'. At about this time, in 1149, the Pope had become so exasperated that he threatened Stephen with excommunication, but Archbishop Theobald, aided by Becket, interceded to good effect. But Stephen still continued to chance his arm with the ecclesiastic hierarchy by refusing permission for two important dignitaries from Rome and Paris to visit England. In the following year Stephen laid siege to Worcester, and after a successful assault sacked the city, set fire to it and gained vast plunder.

During his visits to and from the Continent, Henry came to know and appreciate the considerable abilities of Thomas Becket, and the two men began to develop a friendship which was to become vital to them both over the next few years. Becket was of obscure origin but was beginning to display his remarkable administrative qualities. His wit and intelligence appealed to Henry who was on the lookout for men of talent to become part of his team when he succeeded to the throne. The two men shared many interests, especially Henry's sporting passions of hunting and falconry.

* * *

Meanwhile the construction of Flaxley Abbey and all the ancillary buildings was proceeding apace. It was now necessary to appoint the first Abbot and his chapter; detailed planning was required for the grand opening and a date for this had to be agreed. Cistercian establishments had to pay particular attention to the improvement of the agricultural economy, and this had to be implemented so that all could become aware of the benefits that would accrue to the public. The iron-working forge to the east of the Abbey was being built to reinforce the metal requirements for the defence of the realm. The royal hunting lodge facilities had to be ready for occupation by Henry immediately after the opening ceremony. The days following the opening were meant to be devoted to hunting and sporting enjoyment by the attendant throng.

It was intended to be the most lavish affair in the West Country and to reassert the power and stability of the Henrician party. It was to be a solemn reminder of the death of Earl Milo, in whose memory the Abbey had been built, as well a poignant tribute to that great man, the lately lamented Earl Robert, Milo's friend and mentor who had initiated all this and had nurtured and trained the prince in whom so many were putting their trust and hope.

Becket, with his flair for showmanship, was put in charge of all these arrangements. As soon as Becket was given this assignment Henry announced that he wished both of them to go and make a site visit to see how the building was progressing. Henry told Becket that he had a very special place in his heart for Flaxley and reminded the latter that he and the late Earl Robert had made a trip there when the idea had first been mooted. Now that his uncle had died, Henry needed to make sure that all was proceeding as Robert would have wished. When Henry and Becket were in Bristol they set off early one morning, reaching Flaxley before noon. Henry walked up the roofed but, as yet, unembellished nave to the site of the high altar where he knelt and prayed awhile. When he arose he inspected the round pillars of the nave, though still in the Norman style, carved in a mixture of chevron zig-zag patterns in accordance with modern taste, the arches being similarly varied, many in the dog-toothed style. All of these embellishments were in accordance with the imprimatur and interest taken in this establishment by royalty. Henry then walked up to the triforium and looked down into the body of the building and admired the proportions and sense of space and solidity. Before going round the rest of the site Becket drew his attention to the west front with its mouldings and a

88

magnificent tympanum carved in the vigorous and vibrant style associated with the Herefordshire school.

Then they turned to inspect the western range intended to be the royal hunting lodge extension and Henry was immensely pleased with the facilities. They both looked at all the other buildings, discussing the outline of the arrangements for all the many guests who would have to be accommodated in tents in the nearby meadows. The monks had already made considerable improvements to the draining of the land in the valley, sinking a well and changing the course of the streams. Finally, and some would say most importantly, Henry visited the kitchens and brewery and invited all the workmen to join with him in jugs of freshly brewed ale. He drank to the success of work and paid tribute to their skill and enthusiasm.

Before leaving Flaxley Henry paid a visit to the iron-working forge which was now in operation, demanding to be shown all the processes and insisting on undertaking all facets of their work himself so that he could properly understand them. The foreman, one Robert from the ward of Flaxley, was immensely pleased when the Prince ordered a sword to be made for him for use in the jousting that would follow the Abbey dedication later that year, and he promised to cast this from the iron smelted by Henry himself. Robert and his workmen were delighted in the interest being displayed and in being able to talk to their future king so informally, and they toasted Henry with ale from the Abbey.

Henry's energy and enthusiasm were infectious but the daylight was now passing. Becket, ever mindful of the Prince's passion for riding and his ability to cover an immense distance in a day, and not wishing himself to ride through the gloaming back to Bristol, suggested staying the night at Newnham Castle and shoehorning in two further visits. Henry had earlier mentioned his wish to have some facility to watch comings and goings on the River Severn and to monitor activity across the ferry route and in Broad Oak harbour. Becket had used some of his time at Flaxley that day to make discreet enquiries and discovered that there was a hermit called William who lived in a cell just above and overlooking the harbour. The Severn at that time was far wider than it is today and the famous river bend came to within but a few hundred yards of William's cell. William was fiercely independent and not easily approachable, and was in no way impressed by a royal visit or by a counter-jumper like Becket. But after some cajolery he agreed to talk to them. Henry explained what it was that he wanted and Becket also stressed that when the Abbey was open it would be necessary for someone to look out for intruders and poachers. Henry said that he might also be wanting a facility for urgent and discreet messages to carried. An offer was made for a suitable reward to William which he contemptuously rejected. William reminded the Prince that the nearby hamlet of Westbury needed a church building, instead of the present wattle and daub hut, and that a vicar of wisdom and ability should also be found. This Henry promised to undertake and instructed Becket to see that it was implemented at once.

Before going on to Newnham, Becket suggested that he and the Prince should return to the Abbey site in order to see it in the evening light when the rays of the setting sun would illumine the new freshly-cut red sandstone to its best advantage. They galloped back to the vale of Castiard and paused at that magical moment in the twilight of a summer's evening to look at the stunning sylvan scene in front of them. They were both overcome at the magic of the occasion.

Before they entered the Castle at Newnham, Becket suggested that Henry should visit the famous recluse and anchoress who, like William the hermit, had withdrawn from the world and gave herself to meditation, prayer and fasting in a cave on the bluff near the castle overlooking the river. She had a reputation for wisdom and much good advice. She also had a facility for looking into the future. She never revealed her name although it was suspected that she came from a good family from nearby, and when Earl Milo was alive she was often visited by him. Some indeed thought that she might be related to him. Becket went in to her cell first and they prayed together for some time. She warned him of his tendency towards arrogance and intolerance and foretold great things for his future.

'You will be venerated for all time,' she told him, 'but in so doing you will cause great grief and distress to those nearest to you.'

Becket came out somewhat less ebullient than when he had entered. Henry smiled. 'It takes a lot to make you so glum! Has she taken you down a peg, eh, Tom?' Then he went in himself.

He could hardly see anything to begin with and then he noticed a woman prostrated in front of a tiny altar. She beckoned him to kneel beside her, which he did. Thus they remained for several minutes until she took his hand in hers and raised him up.

She looked at him and then said, 'I see much happiness here in Castiard for you but much unhappiness elsewhere. You will be successful but will breed disloyalty. Your seed will be revered for many generations but will often be reviled. Remember God always, but you will often forget him. There will be one who will always be your friend but many whom you thought of as friends will fail you.'

* * *

All new abbeys were colonised from another monastery and each had to be self-supporting. A young man of immense probity was to be appointed as the first abbot – Brother Nicholas – and he would be installed immediately after the dedication. Meanwhile he was seconded to the site from his mother abbey of Bordesley in Worcestershire to initiate all the administrative and agricultural planning. Nicholas needed a deputy prior who was also selected. In view of the vast display for the opening all the Abbey's administrative assistants had to be in place long before the dedication. This involved not only the farming experts but also the staff attached to the guest house, refectory, cellar, bakehouse, brewery, kitchen, stores and all the outhouses attaching to such an establishment under royal patronage. All these arrangements were to be under the control of an almoner, a hostelier, a cellarer, a kitchener, a fraterer, a brewer, a baker and a treasurer, all of whom had to be working harmoniously on the day. No failure was to be tolerated in any aspect. Becket made certain that all preliminary planning was meticulously enacted.

The Cistercian order did require endowments for any new abbey and these had already been long since regularised by deeds transferring lands and much surrounding properties to the foundation. Earl Roger of Hereford had effected all this long before the plans were finalised but it could be potentially awkward since the original grants of all these lands, woods, fields and streams surrounding the Abbey had been gifted from Princess Maud to Earl Milo during the time of the insurrection. The deeds could therefore be invalidated since the lands were part of a royal forest. Earl Robert had not altogether been happy with these anomalies and had wished for matters to be regularised, but he was now dead, Stephen was still king and Eustace was an ever-present menace. The efficient and effective Becket took matters into his own hands. In 1151 Henry issued an undated authority as Duke of Normandy and Earl of Anjou confirming that Earl Roger's transfers were all valid. To the litigious of the day, this authority could still be open to dispute since the King had not been a party to this confirmation. These instruments would have to be ratified again when Henry succeeded to the throne.

* * *

In the summer of 1151 Prince Henry accompanied by his father, Geoffrey of Anjou, travelled to Paris to receive from Louis the investiture of his Duchy of Normandy as well as the reversion of Geoffrey's hereditary dominions of Anjou. They were accompanied by Thomas Becket. During this visit Eleanor took the opportunity of mentioning to Becket her meeting with Ayub and told him that she had learnt of the relationship between Becket's mother, Rohesia, and Ayub. She did not, however, disclose her own closeness with Becket's Uncle Ayub. From this moment a cordial friendship and mutual respect began to develop between them. They kept in constant touch and were able to exchange news from Palestine. Eleanor was also much intrigued by the young Prince Henry about whom she had heard so much in the French court. She and Becket had some useful and very preliminary thoughts and discussions which they both held close to their chests. The problems between Louis and his queen were well flagged. Becket arranged a private meeting between Geoffrey, Henry and Eleanor so that they could get to know each other better.

Unfortunately Geoffrey misinterpreted the thrust of this and Henry, being so much younger, quickly got bored with the civilities and took himself off as soon as he could. He felt that he was *de trop* and left his father and Eleanor to pursue their acquaintanceship. Eleanor thought that this might be the opportunity to broach, very tentatively, a closer connection between their respective ducal houses. Geoffrey tried to take advantage of what he thought was on offer, having heard that Eleanor was a full-blooded woman. Eleanor quickly realised which way the wind was blowing. The last thing that she now wanted was to compromise her delicate position with Louis and the impending divorce negotiations. She was certainly not going to start an affair with the man whom she was considering as her prospective father-in-law.

Geoffrey was a handsome and most experienced man, who seldom misread the tea-leaves. He had begun to think that here was a heaven-sent opportunity that would never be likely to occur again. He stripped for action, but Eleanor was more than his match and quickly put him in his place. They agreed to forget and forgive and she left his room.

Unfortunately Henry was walking down the corridor and saw Eleanor emerge from his father's room, perhaps more dishevelled than she realised. The Prince was intrigued and thought that there was still life in the old dog. He bade Eleanor a good night, pleasant dreams and a sweet repose and they passed like ships in the night. Eleanor however was fully aware not only that Henry had huge prospects and a surprisingly good intellect, but also that he was a man in every sense of the word, albeit somewhat uncouth and very much younger than she was. She and Becket pencilled this match into their notebooks.

Geoffrey and Henry returned to Chinon and, after a warm day and a hectic ride, Geoffrey stripped off and decided to have an evening swim in the river. Henry was intrigued to see that his father sported a vivid birthmark on his chest, a disfigurement that he had never seen before. Sadly Geoffrey caught a violent chill and died very soon afterwards, on 7 September 1151. Henry arranged for his father's burial at Le Mans with almost indecent haste and returned to England at once, where he had a long-standing commitment that would shape his destiny. Henry was now Count of Anjou and his dominions, not to mention his prospects, had made a further quantum leap forward.

* * *

The day set for the dedication of Flaxley Abbey was 30 September 1151. The ceremony was to be performed by Earl Milo's kinsman, Gilbert Foliot, who had now become the Bishop of Hereford. The robed clergy included the abbots of Abbey Dore, Tintern, Kingswood, Bordesley, St Peter's of Gloucester and St James in Bristol, the priors of Llanthony Prima and Secunda, both of which had been founded by Milo and his father, as well as fifty priests and clergy from far and near. The concourse of nobles included Earl Milo's son Roger, Earl of Hereford, his four brothers, his mother, the Lady Sibilla, now in a convent, and Lord Walter Clifford, Milo's nephew, accompanied by his charming and handsome wife, Margaret. Milo's comely daughters were there with their husbands: Bertha and William de Braose, Margery and Humphrey de Bohun and Lucy with Herbert FitzHerbert. The late Earl Robert of Gloucester's son, William, was of course present with his mother, the Countess Mabel. Earl Robert of Ewyas, an old friend of so many in Wessex, attended for it was on his land at Abbey Dore that the sister abbey had been built and so recently dedicated. Among the numerous secondary figures invited were William de Tracy, whose family had close connections with Milo and who had squired the Earl on that fateful Christmas Eve over eight years previously. Tracy had continued in the Earl of Hereford's household and was a loyal and much valued servant of that family. He was astonished to see Reginald FitzUrse who had been squire on that same day, to the young Ernulph de Mandeville. He gave a cautious welcome and remembered the immense suspicion attaching to the de Mandeville family after that dreadful episode. However he had quite liked Reginald as they had both been young men thrown together to look after their respective masters, and, as young men in similar circumstances always do, they had caroused together and exchanged banter. FitzUrse told him that after the deaths of the de Mandeville father and son, he had returned to his family estates at Williton in Somerset. His family's sympathies had veered towards the Wessex factions led by Earl Robert of Gloucester and he was now well received at Bristol. But what intrigued them both was to see Hugh de Morville arrive very soon afterwards. He greeted them both effusively.

'It is a long time, no see. How is the world treating you two?' De Morville had always been a smoothie, but he was not without some qualities and had always had the ability to survive. Both Tracy and FitzUrse wondered how on earth he had the temerity to appear on this occasion and in such circumstances. De Morville read their thoughts with remarkable accuracy.

'Our great and noble King and his inestimable son, Prince Eustace, would not wish this auspicious occasion to take place without their very best wishes and support. The King has therefore deputed me to represent him, under, of course, protection of honour from his cousin, Prince Henry FitzEmpress. Besides,' he added, 'our Prince Henry has most valid aspirations to be the King's successor and His Highness, not to mention me, his humble ambassador, wish to show their approval to anything so dear and close to his heart and to make this apparent to all.'

Both Tracy and FitzUrse agreed that de Morville was keeping his options open, should Henry succeed.

*　*　*

Becket was understandably nervous as to whether the guest of honour could be present. He had been present in Paris when Henry and his father had rendered homage to Louis for his Norman and Angevin possessions, and had become aware of Geoffrey's sudden death immediately afterwards and the obsequies that would have to ensue. But Prince Henry was not intending to let him or anyone else down, especially as he was fulfilling a tribute to the memory of his late uncle, Robert of Gloucester, whose vision had set all this in motion. Henry arrived, as only he could, in a flurry with his entourage panting behind him.

On the eve of the opening the roads and tracks were thronged with the populace and pilgrims converging onto the pristine Abbey, sparkling in the autumnal sunshine and so attractively located in the sylvan setting of this verdant valley. The meadows were vibrant with tents, both for the nobles and their attendants as well as for the common folk. Above all, hundreds of children had been encouraged to come from far and near, many of whom came barefooted and in rags; they too were to have the time of their lives and see sights and ceremonies never before experienced. Becket was well aware that this was to be a time of joy and merriment for all; splendid arrangements were made for feeding everyone and a plentiful supply of ox and venison was to be available. The new Abbey brewery had made special efforts to produce ample ale for the festivities, and Becket did not forget to ensure a goodly supply of wine. Neither did he neglect the vital aspect of the sport which the Abbey was to support for its royal patron and his family and friends.

On the eve of the dedication, Becket reminded the Prince that the sword that he had ordered from Robert in the smithy was ready and Henry went down immediately to fetch and test the weapon. The quality was superb, the cutting edge finely wrought and the balance ideal. Henry swished it around his head and ordered a jug of wine for all those who had honed it to such perfection, and his health was duly drunk.

Henry then inspected his royal lodgings, now complete and ready to welcome all those gathering for the festivities due to start on the morrow. The magnificent refectory was in pristine condition and the kitchens ready and spotless. The royal parlour upstairs awaited use by those especially invited and the royal retirement rooms were now ready for use by their prince and his immediate retinue. Becket had intended that Henry should host a small private function that evening, but Henry had travelled from afar and was tired. So the two of then had a light repast, going over the details of the following days' heavy programme.

That evening, Tracy and FitzUrse, quite independently of each other, were taking a stroll about a hundred paces to the north-east of the east end of the new Abbey, having walked around the cloister garth to the south. Here the ground was on a slight incline with many bushes and shrubs. The hill behind was still thickly wooded. The north side of the Abbey complex had still not been cleared at all – the main clearances had all been down the valley to the west of the buildings. The two men suddenly saw each other and were both mutually embarrassed, for they were both on the same errand. They were standing together on the very spot where Tracy and Mahel, Milo's youngest son, had stood on that fateful Christmas Eve, nearly eight years ago. Even now that end of the Abbey was screened from their view. Without a word between them, FitzUrse walked about fifty paces to his right and stood still. They could see the east end of the Abbey, the site of the high altar, where Milo fell with the arrow in his throat.

'De Mandeville was out of my sight at that moment, about where the transept window now appears above the bushes,' said FitzUrse.

'Then you could see the Earl Milo from here?' Tracy said.

FitzUrse recognised the danger in which he might have landed himself. 'Be fair,' he replied, 'it would have been an impossible shot, with the branches in front of us and between here and there.'

Eight years' growth and the nearby building operations would have made much difference and, wondered Tracy, was this exactly where Reginald had said that he stood? They heard a commotion in some bushes, rather further down the slope and very near to the north porch of the Abbey which had not yet been completed or opened. To their intense surprise de Morville stood up, buttoning his shirt, and greeted them cheerfully. A wench also rose up, glanced at them and then scurried off into the gloaming gathering her kirtle about as she ran off. Tracy thought that he recognised the girl but he was not sure.

'Ravishing is a sport, gentlemen,' said de Morville, 'and sport is a vital part of the festivities scheduled for this occasion.' He gave them a lecherous wink and departed.

'This,' Tracy murmured as the retreating back disappeared, 'could have been an excellent spot for that alleged horseman to have stood to shoot at Milo, and in those days his escape route up the valley in the lee of the Flaxley woods would have been ideal.'

FitzUrse was grateful for this observation from Tracy and their friendship began to blossom with more cordiality from that point on.

*　*　*

The morning of 30 September dawned. The early autumnal sun broke through and the valley mists were soon cleared by a light breeze. The vale of Castiard was ablaze with the colourful flags and bunting, the meadows abuzz with noise and good cheer. Woodsmoke arose lazily from the barbecues cooking ox, pork and venison. A crowd of 6,000 persons had gathered, a number never before seen there and never to be seen again.

Henry rose early and slipped out to mingle with the crowd. He was soon recognised and greeted and, being hungry, ate with gusto the viands on offer. He shook hands and welcomed all and sundry and the crowds loved his affability and informality. One group asked him to join them in quaffing some ale and to toast the success of the new Abbey. Henry was an abstemious man and was aware of the long day ahead. He declined with a guffaw, saying, 'You know that I shall soon be in the Abbey with three hours of listening to the bishop and his sermon. He would not be best pleased if I were to be caught short and had to rush to the necessarium whilst his sermon was in midstream and my bladder wanted to be in midstream at the same time.'

97

The group around him roared with laughter, toasted him and then cheered their prince.

Early that day the common folk had been admitted to the Abbey. First came the representatives of the chase – the huntsmen, the bowmen, the fletchers and the falconers. Then came the smiths and the stablemen who looked after the horses. Finally, and this was at the insistence of the Prince, all those who had contributed to the building of this glory to God were accommodated – the masons, the builders, the tilers, the carpenters, the quarrymen, the carters and many others as well as all the villagers who lived in Flaxley. All these stood in the nave, allowing ample space down the centre for the great and the good to enter later. The weak, the lame, the old and the halt went to the wall where they could sit on the stone benches.

Henry slipped away from the folk outside and went into the Abbey and talked to those privileged to stand in the nave. He welcomed them and hoped that they too would enjoy the ceremony and the festivities afterwards.

Although the Abbey was not yet consecrated, a temporary altar had been blessed and erected in front of the high altar the previous evening. At midnight, as the day of 30 September began, the twelve resident monks and their Abbot-to-be celebrated their first matins; at six o'clock as dawn began to break, lauds was celebrated, immediately followed by prime, a service of seven penitential psalms and the litany of saints. The temporary altar was then removed and the monks retired to their ablutions and the breaking of their fast. They donned for the first time their pristine white Cistercian robes and hoods and by seven-thirty were gathered in the choir. By now they were augmented by singing monks from the two Llanthonies and other nearby sister monasteries.

At about this time the standing congregation was being admitted to the nave and, although the precentors could not see him, Prince Henry had by now slipped in to greet those in the nave before going up to his private apartments to enrobe. Then, as the outside processions were beginning to form up at the assembly points, the monks began a very, very soft chanting, which slowly increased in volume.

The service was due to begin at eight o'clock and was scheduled to last three hours. The main processions were then formed up. First the honoured and noble guests in their gorgeous robes and accompanied by their ladies processed and, prior to entering by the west door, were greeted by a fanfare of trumpets outside the Abbey. Their banners, standards and shields had first been handed to their servants. Then there followed the six squires in green among whom were the three who had been witnesses to the death of Earl Milo. The VIPs were the only people to be allowed to sit in the crossing. It is said that nigh on a thousand were crammed in on that day, so they could hear and join in the celebration of the dedication, although some may have overflowed into the cloister.

There then followed the clergy procession in reverse order of seniority. First came the lay brethren, then ten local priests and fifty other clergy from parishes in the vicinity. Then the visiting priors and abbots, followed by Bishop Foliot. Next came the tall, dark, aquiline Thomas Becket, most richly apparelled and with his hawk eyes watching everything. Finally came Prince Henry, who was mounted on a grey charger draped with silver and gold trappings and accoutred in a glorious red robe, holding his helmet under his right arm. At his side, in a bejewelled scabbard, was sheathed his Flaxley sword.

At the west door, Henry dismounted to a fresh fanfare and the chanting from the east end of the Abbey reached a glorious crescendo of noise and joyous singing. Then, in a sudden silence, the Bishop came forward and greeted his Prince and escorted him up the nave to his seat alongside the high altar between Becket and Earl Roger of Hereford.

The three-hour marathon service started. Initially there were the bidding prayers, followed by the Venite and Te Deum both in plainsong. The Abbot Elect, Nicholas, then prayed for and extolled the virtues of the Cistercian order. This was immediately followed by his reading of Prince Henry's recent Charter to the Monks of Flaxley which granted the Abbey many demesnes, lands, ironworks, fisheries, easements, tithes and woods from many places near and far.

Then came the prayers for the souls of Earl Milo and the Prince and their respective ancestors. Bishop Foliot now mounted the pulpit and commenced his threnody for his kinsman in whose memory this Abbey had been founded. Foliot was not noted for brevity and he was opportunist enough to make the most of this occasion – for he had a captive audience including, he was beginning to realise, his future King. He was also pragmatic enough to realise that Henry's boon friend, Becket, was destined for high office and future preferments depended upon nurturing such contacts. But the Bishop had not experienced the Prince's boredom threshold, which was about to be breached.

Henry began to fidget and looked around first at those sitting in the crossing. The light was not good albeit that it was a clear early autumn day outside. The Norman windows were set high up and were still in the narrow heavy style, and it was difficult to see properly. He recognised many of Earl Milo's family. He was not impressed with Milo's sons and brooded that he could expect future problems with the present earl. The daughters, however, were a handsome bunch and had all married well. He distrusted Milo's widow, Sibilla, for she was intensely and proudly Welsh and the Welsh were always being encouraged to rebel. Only Milo had been able to keep those troublesome tribes in order and his son, now Earl Roger, was half-Welsh. Henry wondered where Roger's real loyalties now lay.

He could just see, in the front row in the crossing on the same side as he was sitting, a family consisting of father, mother and two girls. The attention of one of the girls also began to wander, and as she glanced towards the high altar she caught and held his eye. She looked stunningly pretty. Could it be? Yes, surely it was. Henry nudged Roger and asked in a loud whisper who they were.

Roger was embarrassed as Foliot looked down at the interruption and replied, 'That is Lord Clifford, my father's nephew – my cousin. And his family.'

Henry now knew exactly who they were and, my goodness, the girl had grown up to be an absolute corker. But he was irritated by Roger's evasive reply, so he pursued his question. His grey eyes began to smoulder – a dangerous sign. 'And the girl between them, who is she?' His voice was, by now, more than a whisper and Foliot again paused in mid-sentence, not tolerant of being distracted even by his Prince and future King.

Roger wriggled. 'That is Lord Walter's elder daughter Jane, sire.'

'Rosamond you are and as you will be known. *Rosamunda pulchrissima* – the most beautiful rose in all the world.' And at

100

that moment and in that place, Henry relaxed as he was always destined to do when in her company, and his fate was sealed.

The Bishop finished his sermon and moved to the high altar to intone the prayer of dedication of the Abbey to The Blessed Virgin Marie de Dene before moving, in procession, to seal with holy oil the already incised crosses of dedication. Next Foliot installed Nicholas as the first Abbot, who swore obedience to the Bishop, 'saving our order'. Cistercian abbots were primarily answerable to their order and they were obliged to make an annual visit to Cîteaux. Local bishops took second place in the line of command to Cîteaux.

The service ended soon afterwards.

* * *

The afternoon was devoted to jousting in the meadows to the west of the Abbey. Henry participated enthusiastically and successfully to the joy of the assembled throng. He was an accomplished and tough performer, an astute and able horseman who unseated many of his opponents. The standard of the jousting was extremely high and the putative successor to the discredited King Stephen, the descendant of the legendary Alfred the Great and Edmund Ironside and the great-grandson of the Conqueror gained stature as well as thrilling the crowds. And there was one young lady who was more thrilled than all the rest put together.

Rosamond's little maid, Hikenai, sat behind her and cheered on the Prince and someone else whom she seemed to admire. William Tracy, Reginald FitzUrse and Hugh de Morville also took part in the proceedings and, somewhat to the surprise of the first two, de Morville was more proficient than they expected. In one bout Tracy suffered an unexpected comeuppance at the hands of de Morville.

As these two left the lists, Tracy spotted the excited Hikenai dancing up and down with pleasure and recognised the girl as the wench who had been playing in the hay on the previous evening with de Morville. He knew the Clifford family, who lived at Frampton and were frequent visitors and friends of the Earls of Gloucester and Hereford. Tracy feared the worst for the girl and doubted if de Morville would give a toss.

William Tracy was much flattered however as he approached the enrobing tent just as Prince Henry came out. Henry accosted him warmly, seized his hand and said, 'I have just realised who you are and must apologise for not having spoken to you earlier. My grandfather, the late King Henry, sired through your grandmother your uncle William de Tracy. Your uncle William, my uncle Robert of Gloucester and my mother were all half brothers and sisters.'

William Tracy inclined his head as he replied, 'You are quite right, sire, although I have never presumed to remind you as we have no actual direct blood bond between us. My father's brother, or half brother, William, died fifteen years ago now, when I was about ten years old.'

'And your grandmother, King Henry's concubine, is she still alive? My grandfather took a great interest in his, what shall I say, wifelets as well as his children by them.'

'Earl Robert, sire, was instructed by King Henry to look after our family and confirmed an estate at Toddington, in this county, for my grandmother and was always very kind to them. She sadly died some years ago. Uncle William had only one daughter, Grace, who now has the Toddington property. My cousin Grace's husband has taken the name of de Tracy to perpetuate the honour of your grandfather's connection with us. My side of the family have taken on the Devon property at Bovey, sire. The Earl Robert also was kind enough to take an interest in me and arranged for me to join the household of the late Earl Milo.'

Prince Henry clasped Tracy's hand again. 'You must not be so reticent in future. If I seem to forget at any time, I instruct you to remind me. My grandfather always trusted those families with whom he found common ground and I shall take a great interest in your career. I shall need you in my entourage ere long. God be with you, William, and send greetings to our mutual cousin, Grace, at Toddington.'

FitzUrse and de Morville noticed the cordiality between Tracy and the Prince and, in due course, discovered the reason.

The great day drew to a happy close and as the evening dews began to fall the merriment, feasting and drinking came to an end for all the revellers.

Henry gave an inaugural feast in his refectory to all those who had been guests of honour. The Prince was an abstemious man, never eating or drinking to excess, but he was a most generous host and always encouraged his guests to enjoy themselves. He never liked to sit still and made a point of moving about the hall, talking, chatting and bantering with all and sundry whatever their rank or status. He was not fond of protocol and made his guests change their places to mix them up at his whim.

He sat, at one point, by the Clifford family. He had forgotten that Lord Walter's mother had been Milo's sister and that Milo had been involved in the construction of the Clifford castle on the Welsh borders. He reminded Lady Margaret of the time some years ago when his uncle Robert, Milo and he had arrived at Frampton and how well she had looked after him and cosseted him after a hectic few days in the saddle. And he complimented her on how beautiful Rosamond had become, to the demure embarrassment of the girl. Lady Margaret invited the Prince to come and stay with them at Frampton.

'I shall be delighted to accept your most kind invitation, Lady Clifford. Tomorrow I am engaged to go hunting here, but on the day after a few of us will come across the river and spend some time with you and your family. I am told that the riding on your side is perhaps better than ours here. We are somewhat too wooded for the chase although the game is better. Frampton is more open and the hunting will be most enjoyable. I am sure that we shall see plenty to chase.' Henry noticed, with some amusement, that Lady Clifford was taken aback at the prospect of such a distinguished guest and his entourage appearing at such short and unexpected notice. 'You will need to send a message across to your steward. Speak to Becket, who will tell you our party – it will not be large. And we have arrangements for sending messages across through the good offices of the hermit, William, near Broad Oak.' Henry wanted to test the systems that he had set up with Becket earlier in the year.

He turned to Rosamond, took her hand, and led her to the seat of honour by him at the top table, having earlier persuaded the brooding Sibilla to move somewhere more congenial to her. Henry had found Milo's widow made him uneasy and there was no doubt that this banqueting hall, but seventy paces from the spot where her husband had fallen made her most unhappy.

Rosamond was now fourteen years old, a mature fourteen, with an abundance of curly fair hair and the most lovely violet-coloured eyes. She had excellent features and an extraordinarily calm temperament coupled with a lively disposition. Henry had always relaxed in her company and she had defused many of his tantrums to which he was often prone. Part of the secret of her success lay in her ability to treat and respect him as a human being and as an equal. She had been commanded all those years ago to call him 'Henry' and this she had always done, thus sealing the intimacy of their original friendship. Henry's upbringing had conditioned him to being a future king with vast domains and huge responsibilities. Those around him were always subservient, wanting favours and prone to disloyalty. Rosamond was to give him a stability that he had always lacked and an intense loyalty that few gave to their kings in those troubled times. That evening he took her to his personal apartment, next to the royal reception room on the first floor above the refectory. Here their affair began, and it was to last for twenty-five years with complete accord and trust between them. Unusually, too, there was absolute discretion among those close to them for many years to come.

The following day, Henry rose early and went hunting in the vale with great success. On the following day the party went down to Frampton, although the royal companions were few in number. The voyage across the Severn estuary was easy and there was an old track by the landing stage on the southern bank which took them to Frampton. The few days there were not all spent in hunting and the young couple spent much time together. Rosamond's parents were concerned at these developments. The position for a royal mistress was equivocal and might lead to Rosamond's ultimate happiness. They were also aware that the potential rewards for their family could be considerable. For the time being, they were prepared to accept the situation.

Rosamond knew that Henry was restless and would be always on the move in the discharge of his responsibilities. And so, after a very few days, he was off again to France where he had much to do to consolidate in his father's domains.

Becket was uneasily aware that these developments would not be in Henry's best long term interests.

* * *

On the 21 March 1152 a Church council at Beaugency under the presidency of Archbishop Samson of Reims dissolved the marriage between Louis and Eleanor on the sole grounds of consanguinity. Eleanor was now a most marketable and eligible commodity. Events began to move quickly. Within days she was nearly entrapped at Blois by King Stephen's brother, Count Theobald, only escaping his clutches by a hasty night voyage. She reached Tours where Prince Henry's younger brother, Geoffrey, seized an opportunity to try and upstage his elder brother and very nearly succeeded. After all, Henry had so far scooped the pool by his inheritance of both Normandy and Anjou and was poised to get England. Aquitaine would have been a splendid consolation prize. Again Eleanor evaded the younger scion of Anjou, but only just. She made it to Poitiers, now fully aware of the machinations from both the Blois and Angevin camps. A quick solution had to be found, as other European princes started to polish their glasses. Luckily Becket, ever mindful of their agreed grand design, was waiting for her and he immediately set off to locate Henry.

Henry was not too enamoured of the prospect. For one thing, Eleanor had a pretty poor reputation. Secondly she was eleven years older than he was, and at the age of eighteen he did not want to be dominated by a woman who had always been difficult and wilful. And he certainly did not want to inherit his father's erstwhile mistress or the woman who had so contemptuously rejected his young brother. Finally, he was genuinely and deeply in love with Rosamond.

Becket was persuasive and very tactful, giving Henry a loose rein. Henry set off at speed for Clifford Castle. He always had messengers telling him where his friends were at any time but generally gave some scant notice of his arrival. On this occasion he arrived before his emissary and unexpectedly burst in on the family. He arrived, as always, in a muck sweat, appearing at the gatehouse and demanding entrance to the consternation of the guard. Clifford Castle was on a ridge immediately above and controlling a vital crossing of the River Wye on the English/Welsh border. The castle was a huge structure and provided an essential defence against the marauding Welsh and the appearance of the Prince with but a few heavily armed companions in such circumstances was highly suspicious. Lord Clifford lived in considerable style and his household controlled what was virtually a petty kingdom. Henry chafed at the bit at the lack of recognition and virtual contempt with which he was being treated at the draughty guardroom. A series of officials of increasing importance appeared until finally Lord Clifford's master of the household deigned to come. Luckily he was persuaded of the identity of this guest and, with suitable apologies took the angry Prince, now with his eyes blazing, to the keep at the top of the mighty motte. Lord Clifford, being apprised, nervously hurried down, with Rosamond scurrying after him. She warmly and affectionately greeted their unexpected visitor and, as always, defused a potentially disastrous explosion from Henry who thankfully embraced her.

Henry had not realised the style and luxury in which his border barons lived. The floor of the keep hall was tiled and strewn with green rushes and a carpet of crimson velvet lay in the centre, upon which comfortable cushions lay scattered and the family were reclining surrounded by their immediate retainers. Henry asked to see Walter and Margaret at once and privately in their solar. Once there, he did not beat about the bush and demanded the hand of Rosamond.

The Cliffords were both dumbfounded and delighted and could not gainsay the Prince his request. Lady Margaret did say, with great gentleness and tact, that although Rosamond was a most dutiful daughter and would always do as her parents wished, she did think that the girl should be consulted. The Prince's command would, of course, be her own wish. Rosamond then came in and was apprised of Henry's suit. She became very pale and began trembling. Henry took her hand to reassure her. She asked her father and mother if she could be alone with Henry. Walter and Margaret then left them together and were perturbed for they knew that Henry was never happy when crossed.

Rosamond took her lover in her arms and calmed him. She told him that she loved him to distraction and would always do so and would always be his. Then she told him that his destiny and future lay in a powerful and dynastic marriage. His bride to be would bring immense power and possessions to augment his inheritance. 'And,' she added, 'King Stephen and that odious Eustace must not diminish you.' She added that his position in the world should not be constrained with a union with an obscure albeit honourable landowner's daughter, and that the kings and princes with whom he already mixed would expect and demand a marriage of quality. She could not and would not marry him but she would always be ready and available for him.

106

Theirs would be a marriage in heaven but never on earth and she would give him the comfort and rest that he would need. His children would inherit a vast empire, created by him, but their children would support and give loyalty to his children.

They talked for hours but she was adamant and he finally came round to her way of thinking. She reminded him of the success of the King Henry's illegitimate children and they both agreed that he would not be spreading his favours as his grandfather had done. That night they conceived the eldest of their children, and it was truly a love child. To this day the tower built by Earl Milo at Clifford's Castle is known as Rosamond's Tower.

Becket was mightily relieved.

At Whitsun on the 18 May 1152 Henry FitzEmpress and Eleanor of Aquitaine were married in the cathedral of Poitiers. Thus Henry and Eleanor were to control lands from the Cheviots to the Pyrenees and were to become the most powerful force in Europe. What Ayub forecast for Eleanor was starting to come to pass.

During the early months of the couple's marriage they toured Aquitaine where Henry was admired and respected, if not dearly loved. His tactics were always to see and be seen. But it was Eleanor's home patch and she was always loved, accepted and popular. At least the Aquitaineans saw a lot more of Henry than ever they had of Louis in earlier days.

Meanwhile back in Frampton, Rosamond's maid disclosed that she was well advanced in a pregnancy but, at this stage, did not reveal that Hugh de Morville was the father. The Cliffords were not best pleased, but at about the same time were embarrassed to learn that Rosamond was also in the early stages of a pregnancy. In the midsummer of 1152 Hickey was delivered of a boy, who was called Roger.

Early in 1153, Henry returned to England leaving Eleanor in Angers. He arrived at Frampton in time for the birth of his first child, a boy, who was christened Geoffrey Plantagenet. Rosamond had an extremely difficult labour and, at one stage, they all feared for her life, but she survived and her strength gradually returned. But she was unable to breast-feed Geoffrey so Hickey became the child's wet nurse.

As the two boys were so close in age and as Hickey had developed a natural bonding with Geoffrey, Henry and the Cliffords agreed that the children would be brought up together as playmates, although in due course Geoffrey would be schooled into his acknowledged status as a royal bastard. It was also agreed that it would be politic not to deny the story that Hickey could have been Geoffrey's mother. After all Rosamond was an eligible heiress and, in the fullness of time, a suitable husband could emerge for her. Neither Henry nor Rosamond were altogether happy about this but Henry's recent dynastic marriage could not be prejudiced at this early stage, especially as Eleanor was already pregnant. There was also a complication emerging with both the King and his son Eustace beginning to be difficult again. However, both Walter and Margaret were better pleased.

* * *

The main controversy over the Henry/Rosamond affair arises over the dates. Most sources allege that Henry met Rosamond very much later than 1151 and point to 1170 as being much more probable. But Baden Watkins is adamant that they met at the Flaxley Abbey dedication and, if he is right, then the timings can all fall easily into place.

The House of Clifford *by Lord Clifford suggests that Walter Clifford could have married in about 1133 and that Rosamond may have been born as early as 1135. Walter Clifford was a nephew of Earl Milo and a leading and distinguished Marcher lord. The family would have had to be leading guests at the 1151 Flaxley ceremony. An old road led directly from the landing stage opposite Broad Oak to the Frampton property and so access to and from Flaxley would have been easy. It is inconceivable that such a beautiful and eligible girl as Rosamond would not have been married in the early 1150s, if she had been free so to do.*

It is also inconceivable that Henry would have fallen as late as 1170 for an elderly spinster of thirty-five or so who had been for so long on the shelf. The marriages of Rosamond's sisters are well documented and there is no suggestion or evidence that Rosamond had been a nun before she met Henry.

Geoffrey Plantagenet was the much loved and eldest son of Henry and had a most distinguished, albeit controversial, career. He was evidently close to two of Henry's sons, Richard and John, both of whom succeeded to the English throne later. The Dictionary of National Biography *discounts the legend that Geoffrey could possibly be Rosamond's son because of the dates. But the dates could be probable. In 1173 Geoffrey became the Bishop of Lincoln so he must have been* born in the early 1150s. The *Dictionary* says that Geoffrey could have been born as early as 1151. He could not have been born much later than 1153, a date also accepted by the Dictionary.

I have taken a later date for Rosamond's birth (1138) and suggested that January 1153 could have been the time of Geoffrey's birth. But if we take the earlier Clifford suggestion that Rosamond was born in 1135 it becomes possible that Geoffrey was conceived in 1151 and born in 1152.

The Hikenai story says that she was a woman of the most degraded character, who by trickery persuaded Henry to acknowledge Geoffrey as his son. Although royalty had always been known to consort with and generate bastards from such a class, it is most unlikely that Geoffrey would have achieved such distinction or been so readily accepted by his half brothers had his mother been of such 'degraded character'. At a later stage Geoffrey was to be regarded as a contender for the throne – hardly likely for a son of 'a degraded woman'.

My suggestion of what happened is extremely plausible and fits the facts now known. Rosamond was the right age and met Henry before he was married. She was kept in the background for years and the story emerged much later. There was a Hikenai who had a son, Roger, who appears later on causing problems. Perhaps he felt that his mother had not been sufficiently well rewarded for the modest role that she had been asked to play. Henry's marriage was vital to his cause and he had to keep Rosamond under wraps, certainly until he was long established on the throne. Hence Hikenai became the wet nurse to Geoffrey at Frampton and agreed to act as Geoffrey's substitute mother during the early critical years of Henry's reign. As this story develops we shall see the interplay between the legitimate and illegitimate sons of Henry.

One of the most extraordinary vignettes arising out of the research for this book is the discovery that one of Henry I's bastards was William de Tracy, who was probably born about 1100. William died soon after his father's death in 1135 and left a Grace, who was the matriarch of the Tracys of Toddington in Gloucestershire. Grace's husband took the Tracy name and their descendants were the Viscounts Tracy, created in 1642, the title dying out in 1797. William Tracy, who was one of the murderers of Becket, was from Toddington and Bovey in Devon. He could well have been a son of the bastard and hence Grace's brother, but I have taken him to be a cousin.

109

5

1153–1154

Henry had business to attend to with Stephen, but before he could deal with him his attention was diverted. Louis attacked in Normandy at the same time as Henry's brother, Geoffrey, raised a rebellion in Anjou. Stephen could wait, so Henry hurried back and crushed these two uncoordinated attacks. The speed of Henry's reaction and his brilliant handling of the insurgencies gave him a breathing space before returning to England.

Stephen's position was weakened by his continuing quarrel with the Church, but he was determined to endorse his son's succession, despite opposition from the clergy. The previous year Stephen had tried to have Eustace crowned but the archbishop, supported by the Pope, absolutely forbade this and reminded Stephen that he had obtained the throne unlawfully and by trickery. The King's position was becoming more tenuous, but he was not prepared to submit without fighting for his throne.

Steven and Henry first met in battle in January at Malmesbury Castle when the weather was propitious for Henry. The river was normally merely a stream but incessant rain had made it unfordable and this was followed by a ferocious blizzard which blinded the King's forces as the two armies faced each other. The dripping royalists retreated in complete misery back to London leaving Henry in possession of the castle. The morale in the King's forces now plummeted and this was immediately noticed and exploited by the Prince's faction, whose own morale received a corresponding boost. It has to be admitted, however, that with the arrogance of youth Henry chose to ignore the fact that his side was enjoying the relative comfort and safety of Malmesbury Castle whereas his opponents were wet, miserable and still struggling through snow, sleet and rain without any benefit of shelter. God, said Henry's friends, was on his side and it was made abundantly plain to the other army that God was certainly not on their side.

Henry's strategy was to secure his position in the Midlands and during the ensuing months he quickly seized Evesham, Gloucester and Coventry. In June both Warwick and Leicester surrendered and he then besieged Tutbury on the borders of Staffordshire and Derbyshire. In a major coup, he was now able to win over the Earl of Derby to his cause. He now swung south and plundered Bedford and embarked upon a siege at Stamford.

Meanwhile Stephen, who had been intending to regroup, was faced with a serious domestic problem. His dearly loved wife Matilda, who had been such a support to him, went into a decline and died in the early part of the summer. She was buried at Faversham Abbey, a building that they had both built and endowed. This marked the beginning of the end for the King, as he was bereft of the support and partnership which had carried him through all these troubled times. Together they had faced the problems of their unsatisfactory son, Eustace, and they had always hoped that he would mature in the same way that his cousin Henry had done.

Henry now turned his attention to the King's main power base of Wallingford Castle. He decided to build a ditch round the salient of Crowmarsh which boxed that castle and its line of retreat into the Wallingford stronghold. Stephen, supported by Eustace, and Henry were now ready for the showdown and the two armies again lined up for battle with each other. The leading barons on both sides were most reluctant to force a conclusion which could very probably exacerbate problems in the future. They persuaded Stephen and Henry to meet alone on each side of a nearby stream, and they were encouraged to negotiate a truce combined with a solemn undertaking that Stephen would continue as king during his lifetime and that Henry would then succeed, thus terminating the endless series of conflicts. This agreement would be binding in honour until a subsequent treaty could be signed and sealed. It says a very great deal that Stephen was meticulous in observing the terms and spirit of this solemn verbal undertaking, although it could also be said that his supporters may have insisted that he do so. It was almost certainly not lost on them that the prospect of the succession by Eustace was quite horrendous.

Henry however returned to Stamford to complete the subjugation of that stronghold and this appears to have been the last serious military operation of his campaign.

* * *

Eustace was incandescent with rage at this development and went upon a deplorable rampage with a party of his boon companions into East Anglia. He despoiled a number of abbeys and seized all the treasures that he could. The King by now realised that matters were more than likely to get out of hand so he instructed Hugh de Morville to attend the Prince. Although de Morville was known to be flawed, both the King and Eustace listened to him and Stephen was most anxious that the knight would counsel some sense into his son. Eustace now approached the richest prize of all, the famous Abbey of St Edmundsbury, always respected and revered by the royal house of England. He and his armed retainers clattered up to the Norman gateway of the abbey and demanded admittance whilst summoning the saintly and much respected Abbot Ording to attend upon them and to give them all due hospitality immediately.

Ording was engaged at the midday service of sext in the abbey and was not as quick in arriving as the Prince had expected. The signs were not propitious for a happy visit but it was a fine summer's day so Eustace demanded of the fraterer immediate and copious refreshment for his followers who lolled about in an insolent and noisy manner. De Morville was instructed to summon the abbot from his devotions and not to keep the Prince a moment longer, but fortunately the service ended and the abbot emerged from the vast west front of the abbey and hastened towards Eustace.

'Welcome, sire, to our humble and most loyal abbey. Our facilities are, as always, at your full disposal and I shall arrange for Your Highness to have available our royal suite.'

Eustace immediately demanded exclusive use of the Abbot's lodging and instructed the unfortunate Ording to find alternative accommodation for himself at once, adding 'I am not interested in occupying quarters that have lain empty, cold and unaired. And your fat and lazy monks can all also move out and make room for my retainers. I shall expect a feast this evening in your refectory and you, Abbot Ording, can personally wait

112

upon me. Your officials will also serve my companions. Sir Hugh, here, will be advised of what you intend to serve and we are all very thirsty and hungry. Nothing is to be stinted. Go to it. I shall now retire to your quarters. Show me the way.'

The abbot hurried towards his lodgings. As one of the premier clergy in the Church, his quarters were most luxurious and well furnished and he was used to living in fine style as befitted his rank and status. Abbots of St Edmundsbury were treated as princes of the Church and the kings of England had always given them immense respect and deference. But what was embarrassing to Ording at that very moment was that, like many of the senior clergy at the time, he was not celibate. He was always most discreet and when he was expecting visitors he made appropriate arrangements for his family to remove themselves and to keep out of sight. But he was unable to do this on this occasion. Eustace followed hard on his heels and surprised two ladies in the abbot's private rooms.

'What's this?' Eustace demanded. 'Who are these women – hardly nuns from the convent.' Eustace knew perfectly well who they were, but was not going to lose any opportunity to embarrass the abbot. Many of the ordinary clergy were married in those days but when some of them were promoted they kept these relationships discreet. Others often kept their mistresses flagrantly. Roger, the great Bishop of Salisbury, lived openly with Matilda of Ramsbury and their nephew, Bishop Nigel of Ely, was a married man. The Church tried vainly to impose discipline but the kings found these irregularities a most profitable source of income by means of the imposition of fines. Eustace had not known about Ording's peccadillos but he made a mental note to exploit the situation at an appropriate moment. For the time being he had his eyes on other more valuable and seemingly pleasurable activities.

The abbot stammered, 'Sire, my sister and my niece, who have sought my hospitality.'

Eustace sniggered and his piggy eyes noted with lechery that the younger girl was extremely nubile, so he began to anticipate some splendid bed sport with her. Her mother was also sufficiently handsome to make play with.

'Your, er, sister and her most lovely daughter will remain here in attendance on me and will look after all my wants and desires,' he declared. 'Now go and summon your chapter immediately as I wish to meet with them and, shall I say, discuss my requirements. But before they assemble, I shall want you to take me on a tour of inspection of the abbey, the treasury and those two handsome and no doubt richly endowed town churches of St James and St Mary's on either side of your gateway.'

The unfortunate abbot was sent scurrying to summon his chapter for an imminent meeting. On his return he accompanied Eustace on a rapid tour of the huge abbey and its treasures. The Prince kept his goblet in his hand and insisted that it be kept filled. De Morville was beginning to become extremely worried as it was a warm day and Eustace had not eaten for some hours. The Prince was not noted for holding his liquor well and the signs were looking ominous.

Eustace swaggered into the chapter house in front of the abbot where the assembled clergy were waiting. Ording opened the proceedings by welcoming the Prince and suggesting, as was their custom, an appropriate bidding prayer coupled with a prayer for the king and his family. Eustace interrupted.

'Get on with it! The only prayers that you will be needing are those relating to your future. Now, firstly, I am taking over the abbot's lodging and my retainers will take over all your accommodation. Tonight we shall have an appropriate royal feast in your refectory and you will all be serving us. The fraterer will liaise with de Morville over all those details, but I must make it clear that I am most partial to your local eels, so make certain that an ample supply is obtained. During tomorrow, in the name of the king, I shall require and request you to load up in the carts all your gold, silver, vestments and holy objects of every description and sort. I want nothing omitted and all this will be supervised by my staff. If they find anything unsatisfactory or if anything is omitted, then the culprit will be immediately strung up. This will be an example to anyone else who might not do my commands as I would expect. I have spoken, now go to it. You have much to do.' He paused. 'I am thirsty and my goblet is empty,' and he threw the golden cup viciously at an elderly canon, hitting him on the head and drawing blood. His next remark was outrageous: 'The blood of Christ, I see.'

Abbot Ording paled and, without exception, those in the chapter house went ominously quiet and the anger at this sacrilegious

114

comment could be felt. Eustace then stormed out leaving Ording and his priests in dismay. De Morville stayed behind and discussed the arrangements that were now necessary both for that evening and for the following day. There was not much time, so a sense of urgency was inculcated. It was transparently obvious that the despoliation of the largest abbey in the kingdom would take rather more than the day that the Prince seemed to indicate. The question of the safety of the treasures was paramount and it was agreed that the carts could be kept, for the time being, in the nave with suitable guards.

Even de Morville was shattered by all that was now happening and he realised that the repercussions of all that Eustace was intending to do would be quite horrendous. The King's supporters had already made it clear that there was no question of Eustace succeeding his father and the build-up of the huge treasure chest from this rampage through East Anglia would prolong the strife in the kingdom for many moons to come. Meanwhile the knight had work to do to try and contain the situation as best he could. He returned to the abbot's lodgings to find the Prince in a rage as he could not find the two ladies, who had sensibly retreated out of harm's way – at any rate for the time being. De Morville took his time going over the details of the evening's arrangements and convinced the irate Prince that the two women had withdrawn to attend to their toilet in honour of their Prince. By this time Eustace was too drunk to realise the truth and took a nap. De Morville stayed with him and managed to slip a message to Ording that he would do his best.

Eustace had partially recovered by the time of the feast and staggered to the refectory, still clutching a goblet, most of which he contrived to spill *en route*. The evening was an appalling display of greed and drunkenness. Eustace stuffed the famous elvers for which the abbey fishponds were famous and never stopped swigging cup after cup of wine. His appetite for the most lavish and excellent food was prodigious. Eustace did not seem to be able to stop eating or drinking. At one point he made the poor unfortunate Ording fetch his mitre into which the Prince vomited with gusto and then placed it on the head of the abbot and forced the assembled company to laugh, cheer and clap their hands at the discomfiture of the poor prelate. Many in the Prince's entourage who had hitherto behaved quite reprehensibly and had followed their leader's example were now beginning to realise that matters had gone far too far and were rapidly sobering up. There were many present who were not only embarrassed but becoming angry. De Morville judged it to be more prudent to remain sober albeit that the Prince was encouraging him to drink glass for glass. He feigned drunkenness and spilt as much as he could down his front and poured a considerable amount onto the floor.

When de Morville judged that the Prince was utterly incapable and unlikely to sober up, he suggested that the time was opportune to taste the pleasures of the flesh in the abbot's bedroom. Eustace was by now incoherent and legless and de Morville instructed two of his own men to take the Prince by his legs and arms and carry him to Ording's chamber. He told the abbot to ensure that the unfortunate ladies made themselves scarce and took full responsibility for this. There were many sullen and louring men in the close as they made their ignominious way to their lodgings.

The Prince was unceremoniously dumped on the couch and de Morville dismissed everyone. The knight had never seen any man so utterly incapable and he stayed long enough to realise that there was no hope or help for this disgusting man. He retired to his own adjoining apartment until the morning.

Ording awoke de Morville early, in the most dreadful state, shaking with fright and terror. Eustace had died in the night, apparently from his gross over-indulgence in food and wine. It would seem that the Prince had choked on his own vomit, although he had rolled off his couch and struck his head on a metal fender beside the bed, which may have been the finishing touch to his life.

De Morville instructed Ording to say an immediate prayer over the dead prince and to shrive his soul. The two of them knelt in apparent sorrow beside the body. De Morville found no difficulty in persuading the abbot of the cause of death and the sadness of the suddenness of the Prince's passing whilst alone. He immediately countermanded all the instructions about the loading up of the abbey's valuables. He sent a messenger to the King and told him that his son's body would be suitably and ceremoniously brought to London at once for Stephen's orders regarding burial. The very hot weather at that time made it sensible for the body

116

to be sent as soon as possible to London. Ording arranged for the abbey to observe full mourning and masses were to be sung hourly until the burial. There was little enthusiasm from the monks for the obsequies for the soul of Eustace but much relief and thanks for deliverance from him. The abbey was inclined to regard his death as a judgement of God.

De Morville was, of course, aware that he would be under some suspicion, but there were many who bore Eustace a grudge and many who were terrified of the future. The atmosphere in the abbey grounds during the previous day was transparent to all and there was little doubt that there were many, both lay and clerical, who had murder in their hearts. The abbot supported de Morville and had been much relieved at the saving of the honour of his wife and daughter, quite apart from the rescue from despoliation of the abbey and its immensely valuable treasures. Before Hugh's departure the two women expressed their gratitude and he gave them as much comfort as he deemed appropriate for he, too, had noticed that they were a most comely pair. He was quite sure that he would be welcomed back, but for the time being he needed all the support he could get from Ording. After all, de Morville had been suspected of being present at Earl Milo's murder, when many were glad to see that nobleman out of the way. On that occasion it could be said that it was happenstance, now it was coincidence. De Morville was becoming very aware that one day his luck might run out.

There were some who said that Eustace was strangled after his excesses. There were some who said that he had died from gross overeating and there were others who suggested that he died from a drunken frenzy. But all agreed that Eustace died suddenly in August 1153 whilst on a rampage of vicious raids on East Anglian abbey properties, ending at the Abbey of St Edmundsbury.

De Morville led a most chastened and subdued crowd of Eustace's supporters back to London with the funeral bier. He made it perfectly plain to them that the King would not be best pleased at their behaviour during the past few weeks, but that if they were sufficiently contrite and remorseful he would intercede as best he could.

De Morville was so highly respected by Stephen that it was never suggested that he might have been involved in a much more sinister way. He was instructed to convey the bad news to Prince Henry and this he was to do.

Stephen was devastated by this further domestic blow so soon after the death of his dearly loved wife. Eustace was buried in the abbey, founded and endowed by his parents, at Faversham in Kent beside his mother and a tomb was prepared for his father to join them at the appropriate moment

* * *

Henry had spent as much time as possible with Rosamond, staying at either Flaxley or Frampton. He hunted as often as he could and relaxed as he was always able to do with Rosamond. He doted on the infant Geoffrey and this was a completely different side to the frenetic prince of old. Rosamond was fascinated to see it. They made plans for the manor house at Frampton which was surrounded by water, thus giving the place considerable protection in a part of the country which was so low-lying. He and Rosamond proposed to construct an artificial island in the middle of the twenty-two-acre lake on one side of the property and then to build a summer-house on the island. To this day that site, now a semi-waterlogged meadow, is still called Rosamond's Bower.

Here it was that a messenger came in late August with the news that Eleanor had given birth in Aquitaine to their first son whom they were to name William, after the Conqueror – Henry's great-grandfather. A few days afterwards Hugh de Morville clattered up to the Clifford house with his dire news of the demise of the King's son. Henry greeted the news with obvious sadness for Stephen, but much relief at the easing of the succession agreement which had still to be formally ratified.

He recognised Hugh and greeted him with some affability. However it soon became apparent that Rosamond's serving maid, Hikenai, was covered in confusion. She had never revealed who had been the father of her child, Roger. It did not take long to establish that Hugh was the father and the Clifford family put pressure on the knight to make some suitable provision for the maid and her child. Henry suggested that as the King was now under some obligation to de Morville he should be persuaded to grant a suitably modest piece of land to the girl with reversion to the child. The Prince promised to endorse any such

118

request and would, in the fullness of time, confirm any such gift. Hugh did not know, at this stage, that the Cliffords and Henry had obfuscated the relationship between the Prince, Rosamond and the child Geoffrey for political reasons. So this arrangement seemed to give satisfaction all round and in due course Stephen granted some land. Eventually Rosamond became the administrator of this on Hikenai's behalf.

* * *

The Cliffords also had property in Woodstock near Oxford. This had been in the territory most loyal to Stephen, but with the likelihood of Henry's succession looming it seemed sensible that Rosamond should think about making herself available there to fit in with Henry's movements. Henry always had a number of assistants in his entourage who were dispatched to warn his next point of call of his imminent arrival and he had begun to take note of the courier from Stephen as an eventual recruit to his entourage.

It was now considered opportune to ratify the Wallingford agreement. Although the obvious danger of Eustace had passed, Stephen had another son, William, who had never played any part in the military or political manoeuvrings. However it was deemed sensible to, in effect, buy him off. One of Stephen's main supporters was William de Warrenne, Earl of Surrey, who was a leading commander in the king's army. In 1147, Warrenne joined Louis VII in the crusade, from which he never returned. There is no record of how he met his demise, but we know that that crusade was a fiasco. Stephen's son was betrothed to Warrenne's daughter which provided him with a rich inheritance. It was also agreed that Stephen's personal wealth, which was also considerable, would revert without let or hindrance to William.

* * *

Stephen, Henry and their advisers all gathered at Winchester in November to draft and ratify the previous agreements. The Treaty of Winchester was signed by fourteen bishops and eleven earls and many others and this, at last, signalled the end of all the turmoil.

In the early part of 1154 Henry expressed displeasure that no efforts were being made to dismantle a number of castles which had been built during the earlier troubled times, and therein lay the seed of a subsequent problem. But Henry was not able to address this in any depth as trouble flared up across the Channel and he had to hurry back to contain the insurrection.

At some stage during this year Eleanor spent a few weeks with her formidable mother-in-law, Maud, at the latter's court at Rouen. She was taught some of the complexities of the Norman and Angevin politics and perhaps a little of the tactics in dealing with a much younger husband. She found that Maud was a vigorous, albeit devious and tough woman, who had survived remarkably well. Henry was still likely to listen to her. Neither woman became close but they respected each other.

The relationship between Henry and Eleanor is both confusing and puzzling. Eleanor was vibrant, experienced and full of fun, but intense. Henry was years younger, much more immature and far less intellectual, but with an intensely questing mind – he would talk to anyone and was astonishingly well informed. He would examine everything and demand to be told how it was made and fashioned. Eleanor had dominated and intimidated poor Louis who had been reduced to mouselike status. Eleanor, as we have seen, had had a tempestuous affair with Ayub whilst on crusade, resulting in certainly one son and more than probably in a daughter. She had been genuinely and passionately in love with Ayub and was thankful to be rid of the French king. She found that she was an immediate pawn in the political machinations in eastern Europe after her divorce so she moved with masterly brutality to marry Henry within weeks. There were immense advantages in merging the two largest independent land masses into one unit. The marriage arrangements negotiated by Becket were purely and simply a business plan of outstanding simplicity and brilliance, but it was a business plan, nothing else. Eleanor could clearly see that she could very likely dominate the young prince, thus achieving a dominion over the largest country in Europe and a power base second to none. She was also intensely sexual and she saw every reason why their joint venture should not only be a marriage of estates but also of bodies. Many commentators consider that she was as much in love with Henry as Henry was alleged to have been with her. But love did not come into her make-up. She had been in love once, now she was committed to being a career woman. She would produce children to ensure her succession and she already knew that she could produce boys, one from Ayub and one from Henry both conceived very quickly.

Eleanor could accept that men would always have mistresses. Her father had strewn bastards all over the place. Henry I of England had had thirty-five known mistresses and had twenty surviving illegitimate children. It is always difficult to find out how many bastards survived as many died young and often the girls went into convents. Henry could have as many mistresses as he liked providing he remembered what the master plan was.

Of course Henry's reactions came into the equation. He was immediately wary of Eleanor's determination to dominate him. He was quite certain that his father had had an affair with the woman who was then the wife of Louis and was clearly setting her sights on him. He knew of her reputation from the crusades and was entirely convinced that whatever she did there she did not emerge unsullied. And anyway he was in love with and loyal to Rosamond, by whom he already had a much-loved son. He was also an outstanding leader and most practical in the arts of ruling his huge kingdom to be. He knew the terms of the agreement between them and would abide by all of it.

During the early part of 1154 Louis remarried. He too needed to ensure his succession and he found a very much more compliant wife.

During that same year, Eleanor took into her court at Poitiers an itinerant troubadour, one Bernard, who had just been expelled from the Count of Ventadour's domain. Bernard had made an amorous approach to the Countess of Ventadour, whose husband took exception. This young man, who was of humble birth, had considerable ability and was ardent, handsome and the same age as Eleanor. His ability to flatter caused many of the ladies of the court to lose their hearts to him and he was prone to pay court to the wife of the great lord. His poetry was full of expressions of endearment such as 'noble and sweet', 'gracious, lovely and the embodiment of charm' and 'my Comfort'. He extolled Eleanor's beauty and waxed lyrical over her eyes, 'so full of fire and eloquence'. He was thrilled that his lady-love could read and interpret all his secret messages to her. Eleanor encouraged music and the arts in her liberal circle, and Bernard's lyrics betray feelings which are more than those of a mere court minstrel – they show genuine and seemingly reciprocated longings. Eleanor began to encourage her entourage to indulge in serious, albeit secret, flirtations. These affairs stimulated intimate ardour and then reverted to an aloofness, thus inflaming the poor troubadours to further protestations of love.

Henry soon realised what was happening and cut off this lyrical affair between Eleanor and Bernard by summoning the ardent young man to England and instructing him to turn his songs towards more martial themes. Thus Bernard's ardour was cooled and by the time he returned to Poitiers, Eleanor had gone to England.

Whether Eleanor and Bernard had had more than a mere dalliance or a full blown affair, we do not know, but Henry was thus early in his marriage aware that his wife was not averse to looking elsewhere than their conjugal couch. It was about this time that Eleanor built the small church of St Pierre in Mons near Belin in Aquitaine, very close to her birthplace in a nearby chateau of the dukes of Aquitaine. In this churchyard it has been said that many of her numerous bastards are buried, but it is probable that these burials would have taken place some years later.

What we must do is be realistic about how many of the children born in this court were legitimate and as far as Henry and Eleanor were concerned how many of their own offspring were sired by Henry. But we must be aware also that Eleanor became pregnant again in May 1154.

* * *

In the autumn of 1154, King Stephen suffered a chill and died as a consequence at Dover on 25 October. By this time the King had become tired, disillusioned and dispirited. His lovely wife and simply appalling son had both expired the previous year and he had conceded all that he had fought for so bitterly during his reign. He was essentially, and surprisingly, a kindly man but he was indecisive and trusted so many who were utterly unworthy. He was politically naïve and lost the confidence of all sections of the nation and, in particular, the Church. His end was especially sad. He was due to be buried in his great abbey at Faversham where his tomb had already been made ready and was to be beside his wife and son. On the way back from Dover the coffin was stolen, the lead stripped and his body tipped unceremoniously into a nearby stream.

The winds were inopportune, so Henry and Eleanor were not able to cross immediately to lay claim to the throne of England. Their two immediate predecessors had made full speed to London and seized the throne before other contenders had appeared, but this succession had been argued about for so long that the country was prepared to wait a few weeks longer. But the weather continued inclement so Henry decided to delay no longer and they sailed from Barfleur to Southampton, braving the storms and tempests that were continuing to lash the coast and being unable to land for nearly two days. They arrived finally on 7 December and went straight to Winchester where they surprised many barons still loyal to Stephen's cause and who were not expecting their new king to appear quite so suddenly. Stephen's brother, Bishop Henry of Winchester, gave the new king unequivocal support which swayed many who may have wavered. No hand was raised against Henry and the new king continued to gather his forces quickly and efficiently as they made their way to Westminster.

On Sunday 19 December Henry and Eleanor were crowned with great splendour and pomp by Archbishop Theobald of Canterbury in the abbey where successive Norman monarchs had been proclaimed. Theobald had assembled a great concourse of bishops and nobles and there was a genuine and heartwarming acclamation from all the assembled throng. The abbey had become dingy and run down, but despite the tawdry fittings the buildings retained their majesty and grandeur and the abbey authorities had done what they could to brighten things up for the occasion. After all, Gervase the abbot, and the late king's bastard son, still hoped to keep his lucrative post under the new regime. As always on these occasions Henry, now but twenty-one, cut a fine commanding figure. His robust youth, his fearless eye and his bustling gait coupled with his reputation gave a confidence for the future which augured well. The speed of his arrival in England despite the appalling time and tide proclaimed that here was a man who would get things done and end the indecisiveness and injustices of the past reign.

During the ceremony a small incident occurred. Amongst the nobles were the Cliffords and Rosamond, sitting in seats of distinction. Henry had insisted that Geoffrey, now a child of nearly two, should be present to see his father crowned and to have a good view of all that was happening. Hikenai was looking after the child and sitting beside Rosamond. As the crown was placed on Henry's head, Geoffrey ran forward crying 'Papa, papa, can I have a hat too!' The King turned and gathered up the child, kissed him and returned him to Rosamond who comforted the boy. Eleanor noticed the incident and that the child was acknowledged by Henry. She did not resent this but she asked who the mother might be and the King gave the diplomatic answer that Hikenai was responsible for the upbringing of Geoffrey. This incident appeared to maintain the story that Rosamond was not the mother and 'that a low-born woman persuaded the king of his bastard at his coronation'.

At the magnificent ceremony, Eleanor had noticed that Becket's mother, Rohesia, was in the congregation, so she took the opportunity of speaking to her again afterwards and learnt news of Ayub and their son Saladin who was now a lad of four and growing apace. This bond between Rohesia and Eleanor was much valued between the two ladies and there is little doubt that Becket was fully aware of their common interests.

After the feasting and general jubilation, Henry and Eleanor decided that the Palace of Westminster was in such a despoiled and dilapidated state that they would occupy the palace across the river at Battersea until such time as Westminster could be refurbished in a fitting manner. Stephen had allowed everything to deteriorate hugely during the last years of his reign and since his death his followers had ransacked everything of value that they could lay their hands on.

Battersea was a damp and dismal place looking across the river to London. It had neither the bustle of Paris kindled by the noisy students nor the warmth and sparkle of Poitiers enlivened by the minstrels.

6

1155–1161

In the modern idiom, King Henry hit the deck running. He immediately issued a charter declaring his methods of government and the restitution of all liberties of Church and State as promulgated by his illustrious grandfather. Next he ejected the mercenaries, mainly from Flanders, employed by Stephen who had abused their position. He gave them short notice to leave the country, made dire threats in the event of non-compliance and all were surprised at how quickly these detested soldiers melted away across the Channel. Now he turned his attention to the numerous castles, built over the past two decades, which dominated the countryside. His agreement with Stephen was that these should, with only limited exceptions, be demolished or rendered useless. Of course, there was immense opposition from many of the powerful nobles at this erosion of their strongholds, but Henry was adamant and tackled those who dragged their feet with both alacrity and ferocity. He then addressed the problems of justice and administration. He appointed his intimate friend Thomas Becket as his chancellor, who handled all the administration of the realm. This was an inspired move.

The systems of justice, finance and general administration were overhauled and every part of the dominions from the Cheviots to the Pyrenees were subject to scrutiny. Judges were dispatched on a regular circuit and Henry went on endless tours making sure that all that he had set in motion was working to his satisfaction. He also treated those followers who had supported Stephen with generosity and used their talents to good advantage. He was a good picker of men and encouraged bright, young, up-and-coming men of education from all walks of life. This was indeed the new England and it caught the imagination of the nation.

The main opposition to the castle problem came from William of Aumale in Yorkshire, Hugh of Mortimer and Roger, the son of his old friend Milo, Earl of Hereford. Hugh had been espoused to Stephen's cause and had vigorously opposed Henry's succession and persuaded Roger to refuse the King's orders. This last episode caused the most pain and bitterness. Roger was not the man that his father had been and his mother, Sibilla, had powerful friends and relations in the turbulent principality of Wales. Roger tried to argue that his castle of Gloucester was essential for the control of the west, but Henry was adamant and did not trust Roger who had many weak characteristics. Fortunately, Gilbert Foliot, Bishop of Hereford and a kinsman of Roger, intervened and persuaded the latter to concede. Not long afterwards Roger went into a monastery and, as a monk, died in 1158. He had no sons but two of his brothers succeeded to the title, but they too had no male heirs and that earldom then became extinct. By mid 1155, the demolition of the major castles had been achieved.

In February 1155, Eleanor was delivered of a second son at Battersea and this child was baptised Henry, after his father, by the Bishop of London. The English people were fascinated at their first sight of the fabulous Eleanor about whom they had heard so much. She was indeed a dark-haired beauty of immense vitality and authority with an astonishing vibrance. But she was no chicken – by this time she was thirty-three years old and middle-aged for those days, but she carried her age well and like women of all ages she had recourse to artifice. But the cold, damp, misty rain, the sleet and the snow depressed her and the surrounding boggy land on the south bank of the river was uninviting. Eleanor was cut off from the throbbing mercantile life of the City of London and she longed for her beloved Aquitaine and the sunshine.

In the autumn Henry was minded to subjugate Ireland, but was dissuaded from so doing by his mother. He was in any case diverted by problems in Anjou and Maine stirred up by his brother, Geoffrey, who should have long since relinquished his claim to them. After a brisk campaign, Henry deemed it more prudent to buy Geoffrey off. Eleanor had remained in England and was deputed to act as regent. Henry also deemed it tactical to renew his homage to the French king, Louis, for his possessions across the Channel.

One of the early projects to which Becket turned his attention was the repair and restoration of the palace of Westminster to be a fitting residence for the new king and his wife. His experience in the building and establishment of Flaxley Abbey a few years earlier was invaluable and he was able to call on many of the leading artisans who had been so involved there and who were already a well coordinated and effective team. Eleanor was also astonished to discover that Becket's flair and taste which he had brought to the refurbishment project could not be faulted by her. She had been expecting to have to make her own views clear to him, but she found that this was largely unnecessary. He was always meticulous in involving her and asking for her support. Eleanor was delighted, since this rebuilding would bring the court more into the centre of affairs and she was already aware than the new chancellor was taking more of the detailed administrative work on his shoulders which diminished her influence as regent. Eleanor was overjoyed therefore when Becket with his customary energy threw himself into the new palace arrangements which would restore her own proximity and influence at the seat of government.

Eleanor was fascinated by Becket as they had so much in common. Becket's mother, Rohesia, was Ayub's sister and there was a vital, albeit intermittent, exchange of information from the Middle East routed through Becket's household, now with the added dimension of Saladin's progress. They were both vibrant personalities with immense energy, ability and intelligence. Physically they were both dark and almost swarthy, Becket being exceptionally tall at six feet six inches, and she being about a foot shorter, tall for a woman in those times. They made a strikingly handsome pair. Also, Becket was so much nearer her in age, being but four years older, whereas Henry was eleven years younger and, in so many ways, too immature for this experienced woman of the world. Eleanor tried to interest the ascetic Becket into having an affair, but Becket was not that way inclined so she came to the reluctant conclusion that he lacked any interest in sexual matters.

But Becket had been tempted more than she perhaps realised and she completely underestimated the turmoil that she was causing in his breast. Becket was all too aware that he owed everything to the King, but he was intensely ambitious as well as very able, and to respond to Eleanor's overtures would blight his career irrevocably. Besides this, Becket was genuinely friendly with Henry, feelings which were strongly reciprocated. He curbed his desires and sense prevailed. After the reign of William Rufus, when homosexuality was rampant at the court, attitudes had changed. Nevertheless, Becket found that it was diplomatic to create the impression with Eleanor that he was sublimated in other directions. Thus it was that their relationship always remained comfortable, cordial and intimate and no breath of scandal has ever emerged, but it would not have been for want of effort on the part of the Queen.

Eleanor found London exceptionally dull after the fun, sunshine, warmth and sophistication of Aquitaine. Even Paris had swarmed with irresponsible and stimulating students to offset the intense and stultifying Capetian court. Battersea was on the wrong bank of the Thames and London was essentially a city of traders and rich merchants. The ever-present smells of rotting fish, meat and decaying vegetables combined with the raucous cries of wharfingers were in sharp contrast to the delights of Poitou.

Henry was not a man who enjoyed his creature comforts. His household was the epitome of Spartan turmoil. The King would appear suddenly and without warning in a flurry of chaos and confusion. Meals were hurriedly prepared and of limited quality and variety. The household was essentially abstemious. His was a life in a permanent campsite and there was never any requirement for elegance or tidiness. His departures were equally precipitate when, at an unpremeditated word, the whole of his household of some 200 souls would disappear to far-flung regions in a frenzy of commotion and disorganisation.

Becket's household was a startling contrast. It resembled a huge civil service of some fifty highly trained and industrious clerks, with a leavening of young nobles and talented and ambitious men who were being schooled for future success. His hospitality was prodigious and his tableware magnificent. He entertained all those who were desirous of paying court to the Plantagenet king. Becket's food and wine were of the finest quality and exceptionally well prepared and served but, despite this, he insisted upon sobriety and discouraged any form of gluttony. Eleanor enjoyed her own contribution to these gatherings and performed her statesman's role with immense experience and *élan*.

Sadly the cold and damp at Battersea affected the health of the royal pair's eldest son, William, and he died in the spring of 1156. However, the birth of a daughter, Matilda, born in the newly-occupied Palace of Westminster at Whitsun was a joy to them both. This event was hoped to be a happy augury for the future.

The move to the refurbished Palace of Westminster also meant that Eleanor was closer to the fine houses of the nobles and prelates whose dwellings clustered on the north bank of the Thames. This also meant that she was nearer to what passed for the English equivalent of the elegance and artistic activity to which she was accustomed. But she was all too aware that these standards were but a poor shadow of those in her native Aquitaine.

During the first year of Henry's reign he was primarily involved with stabilising the mess left by Stephen in England. He attached immense importance to seeing and being seen and left his young aides in positions of authority throughout the land to dispense justice and restore order. His main provincial assizes were based at Winchester, Wallingford, Oxford, Nottingham, Lincoln and Marlborough. He did not however ignore his original power base in the West Country round Bristol and the Welsh border counties. He had already tackled the intransigence of his larger landowners and nobles who were intensely reluctant to reduce the strength of their castles. Henry had an extraordinary perception and instinct of knowing where incipient trouble was brewing and this stood him in excellent stead. He would suddenly appear when he was least expected and cause consternation. He was capable of covering up to 170 miles in a day and, with determination and decisiveness, solve the problems and head off any trouble. Those who have this facility have more than a touch of genius. Henry's approach also had the effect of keeping all his subordinates on their toes as they never knew when he might gallop in through the gloaming without any notice and cross-examine them on their shortcomings and failures. These tactics were invaluable in consolidating his kingdom.

Becket had an intensely orderly mind although he was no scholar. He had a clear idea of justice and was encouraged to be free with his advice. Henry needed his chancellor's wisdom and sense to curb what might have been youthful excesses. Becket joined the King on many of his journeys throughout the kingdom. They shared many pleasures and sports together and Becket introduced the King to the game of chess at which they both became equally proficient. Chess was a game originating in Persia and from there it had spread to the Arab countries of the Middle East. Becket had been introduced to the game by his mother. Henry and Becket shared their meals together and both had a passion for hunting, hawking and the chase.

So it was that Henry took whenever opportunity arose to repair to one of the hunting lodges built by his predecessors. In particular he much enjoyed Clarendon Palace which was an idyllic retreat on an escarpment close to Sarum, as well as Woodstock, close to Oxford. In both of these domestic and unfortified properties he expanded and improved the facilities thus making them into excellent and relaxing retreats. He also was able to bring Rosamond and little Geoffrey to share in these delights. It was not always easy for him to go as far as Flaxley or Frampton and he found it very much more convenient for them to come to these other places. He would dispatch one of his aides ahead to summon and escort Rosamond to meet him when it was convenient and he began to use two discreet young men in his entourage whom he could trust for this purpose – Reginald FitzUrse and William Tracy, the latter being a half cousin through one of his grandfather's liaisons. He did not use, or for that matter trust, the third of that infamous group involved in the murder of Milo, Hugh de Morville, although this man always made a point of being pleasant to Rosamond, especially when her handmaiden was present. It was not lost on Eleanor that the other child being brought up in that household was of a totally different class and calibre to Geoffrey. Roger was treated as the latter's playmate but otherwise very much below the salt.

The Clifford family made it abundantly plain to both to Hikenai and de Morville that there was to be no more playing about in the hay for them. Hikenai had been well rewarded for her part in this modest deception and her place in the Clifford family circle was assured providing she behaved. She was also all too aware that de Morville was not so reliable.

Both FitzUrse and Tracy enjoyed their escorting duties and the former in particular became decidedly smitten by the King's paramour. Reginald looked with unfulfilled longing at Rosamond, who herself basked in this unrequited adoration from her young swain. But she was most careful not to give him any encouragement although she became aware that he was most attentive in helping her whilst mounting and dismounting. FitzUrse's hand pressures were perhaps too longingly and closely held for his feelings to be altogether disinterested.

The King maintained his discretion about Rosamond and in these early days of his reign was not anxious to disturb the advantages of his marriage of convenience with Eleanor. He had made it clear that Rosamond was primarily responsible for raising and training young Geoffrey to the standards required in the first, albeit base-born, son of the King. He was also more than aware of his Queen's propensity for encouraging any young and personable young man in her court. The moral attitudes were in any event robust and tolerant. His own father had undoubtedly had his fun with Eleanor and his brother Geoffrey had done his best to make his mark with her. Eleanor's father and grandfather were both quite notorious, the latter even founding a convent for prostitutes at Niort for his pleasures. Henry had wisely obfuscated over the question of Geoffrey's mother but he was not unaware that anyone with an ounce of instinct would soon realise that it was not Hikenai where his interests lay but rather with Rosamond. He decided therefore that the proximity of Woodstock to Oxford could give rise to problems which could be avoided by some intelligent planning. There was an ideal site nearby, close to Woodstock, in a vale with a stream running through it, called Everswell. Here he decided to build what was in effect a comfortable and convenient country cottage. Here Rosamond and her household could stay when it might be unwise for her to be up at the main house of Woodstock. Henry and Rosamond took immense pleasure and joy in drawing up the plans and Becket's experience and advice were quite invaluable.

Meanwhile, Henry left Eleanor as effective regent in London and she enjoyed this authority, albeit that Becket was the main tower of strength at the centre. Henry however had problems emerging over the Channel in those possessions that he had inherited from his father, some of which were inflamed by his overlord, the French king. Thus in the following year, 1156, he again had to turn his attention to Anjou and Maine and undertook a series of successful campaigns elsewhere to maintain some degree of tranquillity.

Eleanor was anxious to provide a stable base for the royal Easter and Christmas courts and she took these family and entourage gatherings seriously. During the following year, 1156, she was anxious to return and see her French domains from which she had been parted for far too long. She took her children across in the autumn, travelling through Aquitaine, and, with Henry, they spent Christmas at Bordeaux.

It was difficult but Henry managed to spend as much time as he could with Rosamond. She employed a monk from Flaxley, one Haymo, to tutor Geoffrey and his Clifford cousins as well as the de Bohun children who lived on the estate next to Frampton. Milo's daughter Margery had married Humphrey de Bohun. During the spring and autumn this whole group would migrate across the ferry to Flaxley where all the families enjoyed idyllic holidays. Whenever possible, Henry would join them and take part in all their activities. The adults spent much of their days hunting and Henry kept a close watching brief on the nearby iron foundries which were now so important for his military arsenals and which had contributed to his earlier military successes. Thus the foresight of Milo, his uncle's close friend and colleague, was immensely appreciated by the young king.

There was one aspect of the Henry and Rosamond relationship which could pose a potential problem. Geoffrey's birth had been exceedingly difficult and Rosamond had recovered very slowly. She was also finding it very difficult to conceive again and she was prone to miscarriages. They both wanted more children but so far they had not been so blessed. They agreed that the schooling arrangements set up by Rosamond were ideal and the happy relaxed atmosphere for the holidays was marvellous. Henry was anxious that his legitimate children should join in when they were old enough, and to this end he would send Henry and any future princes to take part in these activities. He also was extremely keen that all his children be encouraged in the 'step' relationship with each other and should become friends from childhood. This could only be of benefit to the country. Here he was following the practice of his grandfather, the first King Henry, which had been so outstandingly successful in the relationships between his step-uncle Earl Robert and his mother. Henry also always paid tribute to the manner in which his uncle had brought him up and schooled him in the role that he was now playing. Other bastards of King Henry's had made extremely valuable dynastic marriages which had cemented relationships in many places, such as in the Scottish kingdom.

Thus it was that Henry conceived the idea that all his children should holiday as often as they could in the delightful surroundings of Flaxley under the benign and happy tutelage of Rosamond, whilst at the same time she would continue the schooling and upbringing of their own children and the various cousins at nearby Frampton.

Another of their building projects was planned at Frampton. The Clifford family house, the old twelfth-century one by the church and now no more, was inadequate for entertaining the King and his mistress and their household. Henry was more than happy with intimate surroundings whilst he was away from the affairs of state but from time to time he needed his advisers to be near him in case they had to consult with him. Henry never worried about the standards of accommodation for his entourage but they did need to be addressed.

Rosamond's younger brother, Richard, was destined to live at Frampton where he lived quietly and happily. Their parents were mainly involved at Clifford Castle on the Welsh borders. Henry and Rosamond planned a spacious family living room by the solar on the first floor at Frampton where they were able to maintain their privacy and intimacy. This overlooked the river running by the property and gave them the quietness and tranquillity that they both needed, especially Henry after his frenetic activity and travelling. Rosamond had always realised that the peace and quiet that she was able to offer to her king and lover was of inestimable value to his well-being and stability, the more especially as the Plantagenet and the Aquitaine bloodlines were quarrelsome and ever prone to turmoil and commotion. So it was that this room also came to be called Rosamond's Bower. When this branch of the Clifford family moved 200 years later to their present farmhouse they reconstructed a first-floor room which continues to this day to be called Rosamond's Bower in memory of their ancestor.

The approach to the Frampton house was protected by an intensely soggy patch of ground. This was partially drained by Henry and a small island was built in the centre, the approach to which was by a secret path of firm stones. Here they built the

133

summer-house where they were able to have picnics and where the children could play.

In early 1157, Eleanor and her children returned to London. Henry however stayed in France until Easter having travelled from France to Broad Oak, where he was able to spend a few days at Frampton and Flaxley before rejoining the Queen in London. After this he continued his incredible schedule of bustling about the country to immense effect, but with a brief interlude and campaign to deal with an insurrection in Wales.

On 8 September in that year Eleanor gave birth at Oxford to Richard, the future Coeur de Lion, who was to be her favourite son and who, from an early age, was destined to be the successor of her domains of Poitou and Aquitaine. Henry spent some of his days hunting at Woodstock and keeping an eye on the building of Rosamond's residence at Everswell, which was being constructed on a hillock above the stream tumbling down into the valley below. After the success of the secret mini-causeway to the island of Rosamond's Green, Becket had the inspiration of suggesting making a maze in front of the new house. Becket's mother, Rohesia, was a Saracen and she well remembered the use of water gardens, fountains and secret entrances to the Arab houses where she had been brought up in Palestine, and the lie of the land here was ideal. Both Rosamond and Henry were enchanted with the idea which would add to their sense of security and privacy.

The three of them met at Everswell to discuss this project. A spring of pure, fresh water came tumbling out of the hillside and formed a small stream which joined the river lower down the valley. Becket's idea was to form a walled courtyard garden with a series of interconnecting ponds from which fountains played. Two small intimate niches could be placed with room for two seats from which a good view of the water could be obtained, and further along the upper wall there would be seating for a larger party. The area of this courtyard was some twenty-five paces square. The overflow water would be channelled out at the lower end and the stream would run down the hill to join the River Glyme below. Becket suggested that a few fruit trees, such as apricot and gages, would give shade and a pleasant leafy aspect, and provide a source of sustenance in summer. The ponds, he suggested, could even be used in hot weather for

134

bathing and cooling down with the playing of the fountains over those in the water. Up above and behind the courtyard a fine gatehouse would be built leading up to the house.

Henry and Eleanor decided to spend Christmas at Lincoln. This city had been a power base for King Stephen, from which he had fought bravely and effectively towards the end of his reign. They deemed it politic therefore to put on a considerable show of hospitality and celebration, culminating in a recrowning of both of them as an endorsement of the value they put upon this part of the country and the interest they would continue to take in it. Several of the leading families were confirmed in their lands and holdings. This was a most successful public relations exercise, much appreciated by those in the north of the kingdom. Henry brought Rosamond and her household to participate in these ceremonies, primarily, or so the King said, to add a dimension to Geoffrey's upbringing. Geoffrey, now seven years old, had become excessively bored and fractious during the service and was not controlled or rebuked sufficiently. The boy had undoubtedly inherited his father's Plantagenet temper. And Eleanor was beginning to have her suspicions confirmed.

King Louis' amiable wife, Constance, produced yet another daughter for the Capet line in the early part of 1158. Louis was heard to mutter that he was condemned to a 'frightening superfluity of daughters'. This infant princess was named Marguerite and ere long was to become a further pawn in the dynastic succession.

At Easter in 1158, Henry and Eleanor thought that it would be an excellent plan to repeat their success at Worcester. This city had been pulverised by Stephen in the conflicts of the previous reign and much reconstruction, support and interest were now needed to restore morale and the mercantile infrastructure. This idea was brilliant in conception and seemed to be a prelude to a further pattern of regional participation in royal ceremonials. The local dignitaries were immensely flattered by the magnificent pageantry and there was much enjoyment and pleasure from all the populace who participated in the hospitality. But something went seriously wrong between the royal couple and this concept was never again repeated.

Eleanor made it abundantly plain to the King that on no account was she going to tolerate the presence of Rosamond with the little bastard, who had behaved so badly at Lincoln. Henry flew into his own tantrum and took not the slightest notice. The Clifford family appeared in force having travelled from their own stronghold on the Welsh border. But it was not this alone that forced an issue already fraught. As it happened, Rosamond's much loved mother was present; she was able to control her grandchild and Geoffrey was a credit to all.

Theobald of Canterbury, assisted by John de Paghan, Bishop of Worcester, with Becket in attendance, duly crowned the royal couple and they were enthusiastically acclaimed by the congregation, but in the midst of all this Henry and Eleanor embarked upon a furious argument. Eleanor accused Henry of lack of faith and deliberate flaunting of his bastard. Henry's grey eyes began to glow with rage. With one accord they both removed their crowns and placed them back on the high altar.

'Never again will I go through this charade with you. Never again will I wear this crown. You may do what you will.' The Queen was incoherent with fury and Henry fell to the ground gnawing the rushes in rage as was his wont.

And never again did the royal couple wear their crowns. Fortunately, perhaps, the congregation did not realise that there were such angry scenes and thought that the replacing of the paraphernalia on the altar was all part of an esoteric ceremony. Lady Margaret Clifford counselled her daughter to keep well in the background although she was probably the only person present who could defuse Henry's rage.

Afterwards Becket took the royal couple aside and reminded them both that their destiny had already been established. They had an established succession, their kingdoms were the most powerful and widespread in Europe. The French king had no heir as yet and a spat of this nature at the present time was not to anyone's advantage. Both of them had had affairs before and only Becket knew of the potentially catastrophic dangers of the Ayub affair. Henry's close, cordial and real friendship with his chancellor allowed Becket to say what had to be said. This, coupled with his intimacy with Eleanor, restored a semblance of order to an affair which could so easily have got out of hand.

It was Becket who was made aware by Eleanor that there was an additional complication to this episode. The Queen was herself pregnant. Becket handled this matter with his usual diplomacy and tact and re-emphasised to both that a further male scion to the Angevin dynasty would strengthen their succession, owing to their ability to produce heirs of the 'better sex'.

*   *   *

Soon after the Worcester ceremony Henry met Louis in Normandy and negotiated a most advantageous bargain. He arranged for the tiny infant princess Marguerite to be engaged to his elder son Henry and, more importantly, her dower was to be the enormously strategic territory of the Vexin and its castles, which controlled the approaches to his power-base of Rouen. Henry's father, Geoffrey the Fair, had bartered these back to Louis just before his death.

Becket was much involved in a number of tidying-up operations. Firstly a new coinage, long overdue, needed to be issued in England. Next he turned his attention to the brewing industry which was maddeningly inconsistent, uncoordinated and incompetent. The quality of the beer produced in England was far too variable and well below the standards achieved in Normandy. He established certain criteria which had to be met and a system of licensing to guarantee some consistency. Then he realised that the charter to Flaxley Abbey had been issued whilst Stephen had been on the throne and that this now lacked royal approval. Becket took the opportunity to regularise this matter by issuing a second charter in the early summer.

Henry spent some time relaxing, hunting in the Vale of Castiard and around the Frampton area, and brought his entourage with him. He was at this time using four knights as his advance party: Reginald FitzUrse, William Tracy, Hugh de Morville and Richard le Breton, usually called Brito by the others. Richard was a small, dark and fearless man from Brittany who was incredibly brave and an intrepid rider. When the King decided where he wished to go one of them would organise the changes of horses required for the journey and generally these would be provided by the abbeys and monasteries *en route*. Another knight would alert the place where the King would spend the night so that food and accommodation could be prepared. When the King gave his instructions, he required an instant and immediate response, and these four had honed their reactions to a fine art. When they were told to go, they went.

Thus Henry sent Reginald FitzUrse ahead to warn both Rosamond and Geoffrey to come immediately from Frampton to Flaxley. William Tracy was despatched straight to Flaxley to warn the Abbot to prepare for their arrival. FitzUrse was always delighted to escort the lovely Rosamond and spend a day admiring her beauty without the distractions of Henry and court life. He arrived at Frampton and found Rosamond and her son and many of her family present. Geoffrey was overjoyed at the thought of a few days with his father and the excuse of a holiday from the schooling that he and his cousins were having with their tutor Haymo. Rosamond's face lit up and sadly Reginald realised that it was not because of his presence but due to the prospect of spending some time with the King. She busied herself with her toilet and gave instructions for the party to set off post-haste across the river ferry from Arlingham to Broad Oak. Reginald could only admire the heightened beauty of the girl to whom his king had given his heart, and her eager anticipation at the imminent meeting was totally apparent to him. He felt a deep pang of sorrow that her eyes and thoughts were not for him in any way.

Rosamond wished to meet the King's party on the road and urged FitzUrse to make all possible speed. However, she also wished to make an important call before she met Henry. After landing on the north bank, she made her way to the cell of the anchoress. The mystic was paid a penny a day to observe and report to the Abbey on the shipping on the River Severn just below her cell. Rosamond was not altogether surprised to find that the woman was expecting her. She was beckoned into the tiny cell and knelt in prayer whilst waiting for a sign of welcome. After some minutes the woman spoke.

'My child, you are unhappy and have come for help. I am not certain that I can or ought to help. You have sinned and you must reap as ye sow. But the merciful Lord will listen and it will be in His hands.'

'I have tried to do my best to give comfort to my...' she paused to find the right word.

'Paramour.' The anchoress was blunt but not unkindly.

Rosamond nodded and a tear stole down her cheek. 'The King has his destiny to fulfil and his realm has been torn apart. The Queen leads her own life and he desperately needs the solace that I give him.'

'And he wants another child from you. His grandfather did not set him too good an example.'

'But many of his offspring have given much support, greater often than the legitimate children do. The late Earl Robert was an inspiration to us all. Yes, he does want another child by me and the good Lord has not found it in his heart to give us one.'

'Geoffrey will be the son from his present brood who will always stand by him and he will be an everlasting joy to the King. Pray, my child, pray and promise that nigh unto the time that the good Lord wishes to call you to His bosom that both you and Geoffrey will render unto Him that which is required of you both. Your role in the bringing up of all the King's children will be remembered for all time. Pray now my child whilst I withdraw for the moment to ask for God's guidance.'

After a while a small phial was given to Rosamond to drink after her next meal. 'This is an ancient remedy to help women to conceive. It contains love-in–a–mist, rosemary, false unicorn root and pounded oats mixed with some other herbs from my garden. And the King should partake of oysters on St James' day. Sweet cousin Jane, fare thee well.'

And they kissed and parted.

Knowing the speed at which Henry travelled, Reginald hoped that they would not have missed him, but they were in luck. The King was ahead of his party and they saw him some way off. Rosamond waved frantically and set off at a gallop towards them and flung herself off her steed to greet him. Henry was astonished at seeing her and realised that she had come especially to greet him. He jumped off his horse and they flung themselves into each other's arms with ecstasy. Little Geoffrey was overjoyed, and the King hugged him with warmth and affection.

The party now made their way down the Vale of Castiard towards the Abbey where Tracy accompanied by Abbot Nicholas came out to meet them and to confirm that all arrangements had been made for their arrival. Tracy had suggested that the main party, not so far behind, would have refreshment in the refectory after their arrival and enquired whether the King would wish to dine privately that evening in his own apartments upstairs.

'No Sir William, we shall all be together this evening. We are on holiday and we shall start as we mean to go on – my staff are all on holiday, except for those who may have duties to perform, eh Tom?' He winked at Becket.

'And tomorrow, sire?'

'The chase, bright and early, for all and before the dew disperses. We shall have fine sport, a good appetite and much for the table, I trow. You, Tom, can spare a little of your valuable time to join us perchance. Meantime, until the rest come, we shall refresh ourselves and have a drink on the grass outside our apartments – perhaps the beer produced here will be up to the quality that you are insisting upon in our kingdom.'

'Sire,' responded Becket, 'the brewing here at Flaxley was started under my auspices and was the prototype for my new legislation.'

'Already we know how excellent this ale is!' responded the King affably.

So the party went off to wash and brush up. Henry and Rosamond came out after refreshing themselves and drinking horns and a leathern jug of beer was set in front of them. It was soon after the longest day and the fine day was just beginning to lose its heat. The evening had that calmness and serenity that only English summers can produce. The happy pair toasted each other and watched Geoffrey and Hikenai's little boy, Roger, go off to play in the adjoining bushes. They relaxed and laughed and began to plan the week ahead. After a little while screams and roars emanated from the two children. Roger came running out in floods of tears pursued by the irate Geoffrey in a towering rage, brandishing a stick with which he was intending to chastise the other. Rosamond took the other boy into her arms whilst he sobbed his heart out. Geoffrey fell to the ground foaming at the mouth and gnashing his teeth. Roger was told to run off and find his mother whilst Rosamond then comforted their son.

'You have this extraordinary ability to quieten both of us when we are upset. How do you manage to do this?' Henry said.

'Like father like son,' murmured Rosamond, 'and you can say that, in my time, I have had plenty of practice!' She took the King's horny hand in hers and pressed it with tenderness. Their eyes met over their son's head, now lying quietened in his mother's arms.

'What was all the fuss about?' Henry asked.

'Roger told me that my mama is Hikenai and not you, mama,

140

so I thwacked him for his impudence. I called him a right bastard which we all know he is,' replied Geoffrey.

'What did Roger say?'

'He called me a right bastard too so I thwacked him again.'

Henry roared with laughter. 'You asked for that, my son. Your mama is here and a lovely lady she is and we all love you. But remember, Roger is here to serve you and to play with you. He is a friend too. Keep your friends in life, you will always need them.'

The rest of the entourage arrived in a clatter soon after and the party gathered as soon as practicable for a most welcome and liberal meal. Henry wandered up and down the hall, speaking and chatting to the company and ensuring that they were being looked after and comfortable in their quarters. Rosamond and he then repaired to the upstairs room and then to their chamber. Their immediate staff had never seen the couple so happy and relaxed.

The following day dawned and there was no sign of them. They were taking the opportunity of a long lie in. When they arose there was a king who did not seem to have a care in the world and Rosamond had an inner depth of serenity and allure never before seen by the party. It seemed as if they could not bear to be apart or to stop holding each other's hands. There was no question of going into the forest that day.

Becket had plenty to occupy his mind meantime as the new Abbey charter needed many revisions, amendments and extensions as well as the confirmation of many of the original provisions. The grazing area was hugely extended, fishing rights in the Severn were now included and the forestry rights much widened. The food at the King's refectory at his Flaxley hunting lodge was now to become a gourmet's delight.

'Not much time for chess or the chase,' remarked the chief justiciar, Richard de Luci to Becket as he watched the chancellor putting the final touches to his documents.

'I am thankful for this small respite to catch up with all this administration,' smiled Becket in reply. 'Long may the happy couple keep on enjoying themselves thus. We do not get this sort of thing with the Queen in residence.'

So the next few days passed in tranquillity although sport was not neglected. Henry and Geoffrey went down to the iron works and the King gave assurances that an even more ample supply of charcoal under the new arrangements would be forthcoming to maintain the furnaces. Henry gave Geoffrey a children's sword cast from the forge for him to play with – 'But not to beat Roger with,' he said sternly.

'Can I have another sword to give to Roger, papa, please? And I won't let him beat me with it either.'

Henry discussed with Rosamond the arrangements for Geoffrey's further schooling. His son by Eleanor, young Henry, had been allocated to Becket for upbringing but the King was mindful of the necessity for all his brood of children to be on intimate and relaxed terms with each other from an early age. It was therefore arranged for young Henry to spend his summer holidays with Rosamond and Geoffrey at Flaxley and Frampton.

'Do you see him as a soldier?' Henry asked Rosamond.

'Darling,' she replied laughingly, 'he is only six! Give him a chance. He loves playing with his tiny swords, but he is very intelligent and bright. See how he matures in a few years time.'

The new charter was witnessed by Richard de Hummet, the constable of St Briavels, William de Crevecour, Philip de Columbarris and William de Augerill and presented at the nearby Newnham Castle to the Abbot and chapter. The royal party then went on to Frampton for some more days of relaxation. Everyone continued to remark how Rosamond was such an incredibly beneficial and calming influence on Henry and a vivacious hostess to all those present.

The time came for Henry to move back into affairs of state which had been somewhat neglected during this happy interlude. The King looked younger, more vibrant and revitalised. And Rosamond had become more and more radiant as the days had passed. The King had spent many more days lying abed in the morning than was his wont.

*   *   *

After this holiday, Becket started to organise his magnificent progress to the French King's court in Paris and took much advice from Eleanor as to how he could make the best impression. Henry's agreement with Louis regarding the betrothal of young Henry and the infant Marguerite needed considerable diplomacy and tact to allay the French distrust of the aggressive Angevins

142

and the suspicion that Henry had gained far more than he was giving away.

The journey to Paris took nine days. The procession was led by eight wagons containing the chancellor's personal effects, followed by his mobile chapel surmounted by a sumptuous gilded cross. Then came carts containing his bedchamber furnishings which preceded his kitchen paraphernalia. Then followed the commissariat with wine, food and drink and many barrels of the new English beer for the journey. Afterwards came huge wains covered in skins, containing vestments, carpets and bedcoverings for the chancellor's tents. Then twelve horses carrying the table plate and furnishings for his meals; on the back of each horse was seated a long-tailed ape. Armed guards with fierce and terrible dogs protected the procession. Grooms and hawkers brought hounds and high-bred gyrfalcons from the King's falconries. Marching foot soldiers in ranks of five rendered their local songs, many of which were in incomprehensible dialect and undoubtedly of a robust and bawdy nature, luckily not understood by the onlookers. Finally came, two by two, the squires, clerks of the household, servants and accompanying knights, culminating in the magnificently caparisoned charger of the chancellor himself.

The bystanders were truly overwhelmed and astonished. 'If this,' they said, 'is the King's servant, how does the King himself live? Our very own King travels but as a poor man compared with this. And his one-time wife, Eleanor of Poitou was right to forsake the Capet court for this more sumptuous and gracious style of living.'

Louis was overawed by this display of wealth and ostentation. He closed the markets, fearing that these Englishmen would take everything and leave nothing for his own people. But Becket was magnanimous and generous to all, be they citizens or impecunious students, and he was more than delighted that all enjoyed the new English beer – a new export market was likely to emerge for this. Not so very long ago Thomas had been one of those rumbustious and scruffy students when he sat at the feet of the Abbé Bernard and Master Abelard. Now he sat with kings and dispensed largesse to all and sundry. He was not so grand that he had forgotten his humble origins. His mission achieved an outstanding success and was a triumph for his negotiating ability.

Not least was the prospect that, in the fullness of time, the vast wealth and territories of the Plantagenet King and Queen would be merged with the powerful lands of the Capets. It was truly an alluring prospect for both sides.

In September Henry travelled quietly, modestly and with restraint to Paris to finalise the arrangements with Louis. He visited all the shrines, he distributed plentiful largesse to the poor, the sick and the needy and paid especial attention to the lepers. He dined frugally at the rambling palace of the Capets and gave complete reassurance to the Frankish court of his sense and trustworthiness. Queen Constance delivered Marguerite to Henry to be raised in accordance with custom in her new domain. Louis and Henry travelled with the little princess to Mantes, where Robert of Newburgh, a man of great probity and piety, would bring her up appropriately. Louis had made two immensely sensible provisions – firstly that his erstwhile wife Eleanor should have no hand in the child's upbringing, and secondly that the territories of the Vexin should not be surrendered until the day of the marriage. Henry had agreed to both with no reservations but had noted in his own mind the weakness of the French king's position with regard to the second stipulation.

On 23 September Eleanor was delivered of yet another son, named Geoffrey. Eleanor was acting as regent in England whilst Henry was in Paris so it is almost certain that this child was born in London or Oxford.

In the autumn Louis became unwell and decided to make a pilgrimage to the shrine of the archangel Michael at Mont St Michel. Henry's eyes glinted when he heard this for, in this transitory life, some of his machinations could mature sooner rather than later. Louis wished to make a progress through Normandy and, as he was entitled, demanded to be escorted by his vassal in France, King Henry of England. *En route* he visited Marguerite in order to see how she had settled. Henry had recovered his territories of Brittany following the death of his younger brother and had imposed a heavy hand on this county. His newborn son was destined to succeed here. Henry gave suitable and generous hospitality to his French overlord and provided an impressive escort of bishops and abbots to the Mount.

The two kings crossed the tidal causeway, ascended the heights and then celebrated Mass together in the abbey, afterwards dining frugally with the monks. Later the two kings in amity and accord went out onto the terraces of the shrine and listened in the evening light to the swirl and swish of the race from the incoming tide cutting them off from the mainland until the morrow. Here it was that the kings of France and England were more at peace with each than ever they had been before or would be hereafter. The common ground that they each had in their respective present and one-time queen Eleanor was a subject of intense interest to both of them.

On his way home, Louis wished to see the great abbey of Bec, famous for its tradition of scholarship and from which Canterbury had gained two of its most gifted primates, Anselm and Lanfranc. Here Henry gave up his own bedchamber to his king in France, a gesture much appreciated by Louis.

In December Eleanor returned to Normandy and they both spent the Christmas season at Cherbourg. It was all too good to last. The new year, 1159, brought mixed tidings.

But before any trouble broke out, Henry received the best possible news from Frampton. Rosamond had become pregnant and this time she was brought to labour, albeit with her usual problems of managing to go to her full term. In the spring a son was born whom they named William after the founder of the Norman dynasty. Henry with his usual ability to cover immense distances managed to come over for the occasion. The child was baptised by Abbot Nicholas in the Abbey so close to both their hearts and where both their children had been conceived under such happy circumstances.

After the service Henry, Rosamond and their two children walked up to the high altar. They both knelt in prayer and then returned to the west end of the Abbey to be greeted by the abbot and his chapter before retiring to their apartments.

Outside on the northern side of the Abbey, Hikenai had wandered with her son Roger to the place where there had been bushes and where she had been tumbled by Hugh de Morville six years before. Now there were farm buildings and byres on the ground and the locality had been developed and was hardly recognisable. She was startled to see Hugh approach and also look at the place.

'We have memories of this area, do we not, dear Hickey?'

145

The girl shuddered slightly. Her involvement with him had been a mixed blessing.

'I too remember this place before that time.' Did the knight also shudder perceptibly?

A short distance away, Reginald FizUrse was standing at the very spot where he had stood when the fatal arrow had sped its way to its target, where a tiny chapel had now been erected. It was the mortuary place of rest for those monks who had died. He too felt uneasy. He looked away and saw William Tracy standing where he also had been on that fateful Christmas Eve. All three of the knights now realised that they had all returned to their stations to remember what each of them had been doing at that moment. One of them had a very guilty conscience still – unless there had been an outsider lurking in the forest. Richard le Breton also now appeared. He too was positioning himself carefully. He then moved towards the others and noted that each of them was within arrow range of the high altar, the site of Milo's murder.

'I feel in my bones that there is an evil feeling here and that each of you has something you wish to forget.'

'Come Brito, let us all go back to the refectory and remember the better things of this Abbey such as the ale and the wine.' William led the way.

* * *

The young Henry, now aged four, came for the first time to Flaxley and was able to get to know his half-brother Geoffrey. The King also took the opportunity to see how the domestic extensions to his properties at Woodstock, Clarendon, Windsor and elsewhere were progressing. He also gave a hand in planting the maze at Everswell.

Later in that summer, the simmering complications of the long-claimed territories surrounding and including Toulouse escalated. Eleanor's father had abandoned this territory after his matrimonial affairs had become entangled but had retained a loose suzerainty with some reversionary benefit to his daughter. The present Count of Toulouse now embarked upon an unwise quarrel with his southern neighbour, the Count of Barcelona, which was becoming ominous for the long-term benefit of the Poitevins. Henry was in a cleft stick after his diplomatic triumph with the

French king but he now had no choice but to embark upon a campaign to protect his interests. Becket embarked upon an expedition with gusto and Henry tried to contain the problem by explaining to Louis that it was primarily outside the influence of the French.

Unfortunately for Henry the monkish king for once outmanoeuvred him. Louis unexpectedly appeared on the walls of Toulouse with his reinforcements and declared his intention of defending the city. Louis, when his spirit so inclined, was ferociously brave and intrepid as he had already demonstrated twice on the Second Crusade. It was one thing to concede the Vexin, it was another to yield the important city of Toulouse to his ex-wife. Eleanor's claim was at best tenuous and Henry decided that discretion was the better part of valour and withdrew from the fray. Becket was displeased at this development and minor skirmishing continued throughout the autumn.

Eleanor came to France in December and she and Henry celebrated the Christmas season at Falaise.

In the early spring of 1160 Eleanor returned to England and resumed her suzerainty there. She made a considerable number of royal progresses and implemented many of Henry's functions with a just firmness. She impressed all those who saw her with the lavishness of her court life. Henry stayed mainly in France imposing his own brand of control in both his own estates and those of his wife further south. Unless one or other of the royals was seen at frequent intervals, sedition and rebellion was always likely to flare up. Eleanor made a fleeting visit to Normandy before Easter and she and the frugal Henry had a disagreement about her expensive tastes. Eleanor reminded her husband that her own revenues were more than ample to keep her lifestyle to the standard that she expected. She returned to England unrepentant and refused to amend her ways.

Affairs in France were not easy and Henry was keeping his ear close to the ground. The French queen was again pregnant and, after four daughters to Louis, there must be a strong chance this time that a child of the stronger sex would emerge. Henry was aware that her health was indifferent and Louis was considering a fall-back plan. Henry made his counter plans ruthlessly. In the early autumn he summoned Eleanor, young Henry and the little Matilda to come at once to Rouen with the intention that the latter would be immediately betrothed to the new infant Capet, should it be a boy. At a cost of seven pounds, vessels were hired and the Queen and her attendants landed in Normandy. Henry, ever mindful of the delicacies of diplomacy, represented his son and heir to his overlord in France and renewed both their homages.

Almost immediately afterwards, on 4 October, Queen Constance was delivered of yet another daughter and straightaway departed this life to join her Maker. Louis had hardly consumed the funeral baked meats when he married in mid-October Adele of Champagne, a closer by far relation of his than Eleanor. Next, the Archbishop of Reims refused to anoint Adele as queen. The Champagne family were not easy bedfellows of the Capet dynasty, but needs must when the devil drives and perhaps third time lucky would produce the much needed son and heir for Louis. Nor for that matter was this family on cordial terms with the Plantagenets. Henry was not a chess player for nothing. Matilda's presence had been necessary in case there had been a boy but the King's next move was quite outstandingly imaginative and shook the Capets to the core.

Whilst Louis was consuming his wedding feast, Henry upstaged him by celebrating the marriage of his son young Henry to the three-year-old Marguerite in Newburgh. But this move was only part of his plan. Without any delay he now annexed the castles of the Vexin held as a dower for Marguerite against the day of her marriage.

The French were incandescent with fury and claimed that the marriage was never intended to be implemented whilst the two children were so young. But Henry had been astute enough to make no reference or commitment to this vital aspect of the original agreement. The only English Pope, Adrian IV, had recently died and Rome was riven by two duly elected Vicars of Christ. The support of Henry was eagerly required for Alexander III who had by now fled to France. Two papal legates, Henry of Pisa and William of Pavia, were easily persuaded into giving the papal authority for Henry's action.

Louis expelled the Templars from Paris on the grounds that their order were the custodians of the Vexin. The Champenois leapt into action but Henry had made all his dispositions far in advance of the precipitate reactions from Paris. He seized not only Gisors but also the strategic stronghold of Chaumont. As Becket was heard to comment, 'Check mate.'

After all these excitements Eleanor and Henry spent a relatively quiet Christmas at Le Mans.

The Plantagenet dynasty at the end of 1160 had reached the zenith of its power and success. Prosperity abounded in all parts of its empire and its enemies were in disarray and confusion.

In the spring of the following year a simple, albeit not unexpected, event was to be the catalyst for a sea change in the affairs of the realm. The long ailing, aged and saintly Archbishop Theobald of Canterbury came to the end of his life on this earth. Theobald had been an ardent supporter of Henry's mother, the Empress Maud, and a wise counsellor to the youthful King, guiding him through all the pitfalls between Church and State. He had also trained in his household many young and intelligent men who were to provide the administrative backbone to all that had needed to be done to restore peace and prosperity to the war-torn England. But, as so often happens, the obvious successor was not apparent. Henry of Winchester was now very old, the Bishop of London had been senile for some time. Gilbert Foliot of Hereford might have been a contender but he had many enemies and had not yet reached the mainstream in the hierarchy. Richard of Chester was high ranking enough but had upset many as a result of the elevation of his own son, also Richard, to the see of Coventry. There was no consensus or support for any one outstanding leader at Canterbury. And Theobald had allowed, as age had crept up on him, many abuses to fester that needed addressing.

So Henry took counsel and for the time being sat on his hands. In September Eleanor gave birth at Domfront to a daughter whom they named after her. The family spent Christmas together as was their wont at Bayeux.

7

1162–1169

Henry was encouraged to go and see his mother, the Empress
Maud, now enjoying her retirement in France and spending the
evening years of her life doing good works, hoping that all this
would make peace with her Maker when the time came. Henry
was aware that underneath this façade her character had not
changed all that much and she was not unaware of what was
going on.

'You are seriously thinking of replacing the late Primate
Theobald with your friend and colleague Chancellor Becket?'
asked Maud.

Henry had indeed been taking soundings and was becoming
more and more enamoured with the idea. 'This suggestion has
many advantages, Mama, and we shall be able to tackle some of
the major problems between Church and State which need
urgent attention and modification,' he replied with some care.
When he was with his mother he felt the years fall away from
him and expected at any moment to be banished to his room
until he behaved himself.

'It won't work,' his mother answered sharply. 'It simply will not
work. He will know all your arguments which the pair of you
have worked out. Being the crafty man that he is, he will attack
all the weak points at once. His loyalties will no longer be yours
and he will do a volte-face. You mark my words. You are being a
fool.'

'I am the King,' Henry said, a shade more defensively than he
intended.

'You would not have been if those intolerable peasants from
London had not seen fit to rise above their station in life,' Maud
snapped back. 'Anyway,' she added, 'the Pope decides.'

150

Henry nearly reminded his mother that England might now have a King Eustace if his uncle had not played his cards with immense dexterity. However, he thought better of bandying words now. He remembered how his mother had ruined her chances of consolidating the throne by being so excessively rude and abrupt to the city fathers and the leading nobles and prelates. Her judgement was always suspect and her manners intolerable. It was not convenient to have been summoned and he had not considered seeking her advice – yet.

They spent some time discussing family matters. Eleanor was a dutiful daughter-in-law and she and Maud kept in closer touch than Henry was comfortable about. Maud was unaware of Eleanor's character defects and her lifestyle. Nor was Henry's mother informed about the closeness of his relationship with Rosamond.

*   *   *

Henry needed some relaxation after this spat with his mother so he went on his way to spend a few days at Frampton. Rosamond was as delighted to see him as always and he relaxed with his children. Geoffrey was starting a stammer which concerned them both. William was a tough little child who was into everything.

Far be it from Rosamond to raise affairs of state, but Henry respected her common sense. He took his time and edged the conversation round to the matter of Thomas.

'I must admit to being uneasy,' she said when pressed. 'You are such friends and I could see that your closeness could suffer. Thomas owes everything to you and he is quite brilliant in his administration of the country. Have you thought how you would cope if he were to become Archbishop?'

'He could do both jobs.'

Rosamond shook her head. 'It couldn't work. He would have to respect the Church's position. But there are heaps of bishops and so on who are on your side. It is just a matter of bridging the gaps. Both the Church and the country need a sensible solution.'

'That's where Thomas will do a marvellous job. Of course there must be some compromises. He and I know what I want and he knows what the Church needs.'

'You do remember that he needs to be ordained! He isn't even a priest yet.'

151

Henry laughed and assured Rosamond that this problem was the easiest one to solve. 'A layman one day and an archbishop the next. I like it. So will Thomas!'

'May I suggest that you speak to Thomas about all this and sound him out? I have to say though that Thomas, whom I immensely admire and respect, does not take kindly to not getting his own way – remember how cross he was over your withdrawal from Toulouse.'

Henry agreed that he would speak to Thomas. They then went on to talk about the children. Rosamond was asked how young Henry was settling in to his holiday arrangements in the West Country.

'I am not certain that being schooled by Thomas Becket is ideal for him. There is nobody of his age with him and Thomas is far too busy and involved to pay particular attention to the boy's training, unlike you with your uncle's interest and Brother Matthew's involvement. Young Henry takes quite a time to fit in with Geoffrey and his cousins when he comes down here. And he is behind them in his schooling. Brother Haymo is quite excellent with their lessons here. But Henry is rather a spoilt little fellow until the rough and tumble down here knocks some sense of give and take into him. By the way, Geoffrey is really bright and we are all well pleased with his progress.'

The King was devoted to the young Henry and would never take any criticism other than from Rosamond who had such a fund of common sense.

* * *

Henry's principal advisers were much more enthusiastic than Rosamond or Maud regarding his plans for Becket's elevation. Richard de Luci, chief justiciar, was overjoyed at the development. The papal legates were most supportive, but Henry was well aware that co-Pope Alexander needed friends, especially since he had been expelled from Rome whilst Victor IV was occupying the Holy See.

He also talked to de Bohun, FitzHerbert and de Braose, these three being married to the Milo daughters. He took soundings from his cousins William and Roger, two of Earl Robert of Gloucester's sons. Roger, who was his erstwhile schoolmate in Bristol and was a firm friend of Becket, was supportive. He was now in the Church and destined for preferment in the not too far distant future. William, now the Earl of Gloucester, was in Henry's view a real wimp and he prevaricated as he had always done. The previous year Henry had tried to persuade Gilbert Foliot to become the ancillary Bishop of London as the diocese needed some semblance of order and discipline to be reimposed. Gilbert had refused as he regarded this to be a retrograde step from his see at Hereford, but he was a sound and able bishop and, in his heart, had a poor view of Becket and considered that he, Foliot, had a better claim to the primacy. But Foliot was tactful and not too discouraging. Henry of Blois, King Stephen's younger brother and long since Bishop of Winchester, was always a family supporter, an admirer of the King and well aware of his problems. The bishop gave wholehearted and enthusiastic support and wished his cousin success in his plan. It has to be said though that Henry of Blois was not an admirer of the ambitious Foliot, especially as poor old Richard of London died on 5 May and the King had promised that bishopric to Gilbert as a reward for his support.

Eleanor thought that the King's solution was incredibly brilliant. She flattered him and was ecstatic about the future: 'It has everything that we have all worked for.' Henry was not sure that this effusion was genuine.

Finally, in the spring, the King had a long talk to Becket at Falaise. The latter had been apprised of Henry's thinking from an early stage and had displayed an irritating coolness which had disappointed the King. The general support for the King's unconventional plan had been so widely acclaimed that Henry was now quite sure that he could overcome Thomas' reservations.

The meeting was not easy. Becket reminded the King of all that they had done together, their friendship and cordiality, their common causes and ideals. Becket's own legal training and his organisation had given Henry a new dimension to his reign. Becket was intensely uneasy as his loyalties would now have to be divided. 'A man cannot serve two masters,' he said. 'Either he will love the one and hate the other or he will hate the one and love the other. How can the brocaded sleeve of the king's chancellor be reconciled with the hair shirt of the primate of all England?'

Henry deployed all his powers of persuasion and waxed

eloquent over the immense advantages that Thomas, the Church and, above all the people in his realm would all enjoy. 'It will,' he said, 'presage a golden era for everyone. Do not throw cold water on this incredible opportunity which is so widely acclaimed.'

They both tried to fathom the changes in each other that were becoming so apparent. Becket made concessions. He agreed to continue as chancellor and he would accept the archbishopric. Henry was overjoyed. But he was warned that life would never be the same again. They parted agreeably, clasped hands and gave each other the kiss of peace.

There was one more important assignment for Becket to undertake as chancellor before his elevation. Henry was meticulous in obtaining reaffirmations of oaths of loyalty and allegiance. Becket was to convene the lords temporal and spiritual at Winchester at Whitsun to swear recognition of young Henry as heir to the throne of England. Young Henry had been at Falaise for Easter with his parents and Becket escorted his protégé to England on this momentous occasion for the little prince. Becket procured a golden crown for the ceremony along with lavish and costly regalia. Neither the King nor Queen were going to be in attendance. This was solely an occasion for young Henry to take centre stage and Becket orchestrated the ceremony with his usual brilliance. Becket led the assembly in kneeling before the boy prince and swearing fealty first. It was a splendid occasion.

Before the chapter at Canterbury was to convene at the end of May to make their election, there was one more episode in this saga which was to change completely the course of subsequent events.

* * *

Becket returned to the Palace of Westminster to await his summons from Canterbury. He retired to his chamber after his quiet and modest evening meal. A steward disturbed him soon after this to say that an important person wished to see him urgently and alone. This visitor was shrouded in a cloak from head to foot and would not say who he was. Becket agreed to receive the visitor and dismissed the steward. The cloaked person entered and revealed herself to be the Queen, Eleanor.

Becket paled. He rose to his feet and his knees started to shake. Of all the people who it could have been, this was the least likely and potentially most embarrassing, if not dangerous. There could be only one subject that was likely to be raised. Rohesia, Becket's mother, had recently heard from Ayub and Becket had been advised by her of news of Eleanor's son Saladin. The boy was now fourteen and was developing extremely well. He was tall, handsome, very intelligent and clever. His schooling was superb and they all had tremendous hopes for an illustrious future for him. Becket gave the Queen the news of Saladin's progress. 'He has perfect manners and is being bred in courtesy and chivalry. Ayub says that he is a credit to both his parents.'

But this was not what Eleanor had come to hear.

She shook her long dark hair free and it fell in curls about her shoulders. Her dress was cut low over her bosom and her breasts were beguilingly full and exposed. Her eyes flashed. At the age of forty, Eleanor was still stunningly beautiful and she was aware that she was alluring. She knew that men found her irresistible and when she set her heart on a target she did not often fail. She enveloped Becket in a passionate embrace. And Becket surrendered.

It was dawn before the Queen left Becket's quarters.

For the next few hours, Becket sat quivering, his mind in turmoil. He, who was at the apogee of his power, whose success had melded the Plantagenet domains into a cohesion unknown for a generation, whose genuine friendship with the King was reciprocated, was utterly shattered. Now on the brink of the primacy, he was aware that the papacy would be within his grasp ere long, but now all this was hollow. His respect and platonic feelings for Eleanor were in disarray. The complexities and balances that had sustained him were now of no moment. His future had always been in the hands of others. And their power and their whims could crush him in an instant. He seized on the one thing that was within his control – his independence.

A messenger came clattering into the Palace of Westminster. The chapter at Canterbury had elected Thomas Archbishop in a meeting which had lasted until the late evening. He was later to know that the decision was not a foregone conclusion but ultimately unanimity was achieved. There was some irony to Thomas when he reflected on what he had been doing at that moment of decision and how the chapter might have reacted had they known.

155

On 23 May, Henry of Blois summoned the bishops, mitred abbots and clergy of the province of Canterbury and in the presence of young Henry and the justiciary endorsed the election of Thomas, Archdeacon of Canterbury, as their new archbishop. Only Bishop Foliot expressed reservations but he conformed to make the election unanimous.

On the day of the arrival of the messenger Thomas put off his gorgeous apparel, never to be worn again. He donned a verminous hair shirt and sackcloth and forthwith travelled to Canterbury on an aged nag. Upon arrival he washed the feet of fifteen beggars whilst kneeling and then sought to be scourged by each of the chapter in turn.

On 2 June, Thomas was ordained a priest by the Bishop of Rochester and on the following day he was consecrated as archbishop by Henry of Blois, Bishop of Winchester. Messengers were sent post-haste to Pope Alexander who, in conclave, immediately ratified the consecration. On the very day of Thomas's elevation he wrote to the King resigning from the chancellorship.

From this time on, Thomas was a transformed man. He was always frugal but now his meals were mainly of bread and his drink was of water. His celebration of the Eucharist was of the utmost sincerity and intensity as if the Lord's Passion in the presence of the consecrated bread and wine was literal. All who saw this marvelled the more so since this secular man had never been known for his piety.

The transformation of Thomas was sudden, complete and absolute to the astonishment and puzzlement of everyone.

Henry was enraged at Becket's resignation. He had not expected it; he had Becket's agreement upon which he placed immense reliance; and he thought that their whole strategy was in imminent peril. He foamed at the mouth, terrifying his entourage and there was no Rosamond available to quieten him.

Then he reflected that there was a strong probability that his erstwhile boon companion was playing a deeper game. 'I have seen him too often roistering with all and sundry, high and low; I have seen him in ribaldry, in gaiety, and sharing his lavish life far and wide; in eloquence, in wit and in devious and scheming negotiation; playing chess, in disputation and following the chase. No,' said the King to his entourage, 'it will not, it cannot last. He is getting onside in the inside. They, those devious, crooked,

156

nay criminal priests are being flattered into thinking that he is becoming one of them. You mark my words, he will be back when he has softened them up and we can finish off what we started. I shall give him a loose rein – for the time being.'

So it was that during the ensuing months Becket continued his austere and modest life and paid particular attention to his pastoral duties. Not all his appointments and promotions were to Henry's liking but the King chose to ignore these trifling irritations. Becket moved many of his more able entourage in the chancellery into his ecclesiastical offices and Henry began to become perturbed.

Henry concerned himself with the re-embellishment of his palaces at Woodstock and Clarendon. His country cottage for Rosamond near the former became ready for her occupation and the King was able to stay there whilst keeping an eye on the building work on the higher slopes above.

Rosamond was making certain that the tutorial systems under Brother Haymo were being implemented and the relaxations at Flaxley were enthusiastically enjoyed by all the children. Geoffrey was now ten years old and the eldest prince, young Henry, joined them as often as he could, as Becket had less time to undertake his tutorial duties in that child's upbringing. Milo's daughters' children, Earl Robert of Gloucester's grandchildren and the Clifford cousins were all part of these schooling arrangements. It pleased Henry and Rosamond that Geoffrey was by far the brightest and most intelligent. The youngest were William, now three, and Prince Richard, and these two were inseparable and as tough as they come.

It was about this time that the youngsters demanded their own tiny swords from the Flaxley iron works and both undertook that they would for the rest of their lives get their arms from that place.

Henry was immensely pleased. 'You, William, have the longer sword, as you are taller than Richard. I shall call you Longspee from now on. You Richard, although shorter, are stockier, you have the heart of a lion – *coeur de lion*.'

Henry was particularly anxious that all his extended family should become and remain friends. He remembered the networking through the younger generation established by his grandfather, King Henry I.

Henry and Eleanor spent some of the autumn in France to pay attention to their possessions across the water which were becoming neglected. They intended to return to England for Christmas but the weather was so inclement that they were stuck in Cherbourg and it was well into the New Year before they were able to rejoin their daughters who had spent Christmas with Rosamond and the Cliffords.

They landed at Southampton on 25 January and Becket came to meet the King. Henry considered that it was now timely to re-establish communications with the Archbishop. They embraced but with a singular and noticeable lack of cordiality. Becket pointedly turned his face away so that all present could see. This meeting was not in any way the start of any *rapprochement*. If Henry had been hoping to persuade Becket that it was time common sense prevailed he walked straight into a brick wall. Becket climbed immediately onto his high horse. The only concession achieved at this meeting was, following the King's earlier pressure, the Archbishop's resignation of his Archdeaconry of Canterbury.

As they parted Becket said heatedly, 'In the dread Judgement Day, we shall both be judged as servants of one Lord; for temporal lords should be obeyed.' Henry nodded. He thought that he could just see the beginnings of a breakthrough. Becket paused. 'But not,' he thundered, 'against God.'

Henry made an immediate tactical mistake – his only riposte was to threaten Becket with force. They parted with acrimony and their hearts each began to harden.

Henry had not noticed that there was a sense of unease between Eleanor and Becket. Henry was reluctantly persuaded by his Queen that the concession from Becket was a glimmer of light and that further time would be required to heal the breach. After all, Eleanor reminded him, 'You have raised him from obscurity to eminence, from being a mere clerk to the chancellorship. Everything that he has, he owes to you. Without you he would still be a mere clerk.' Eleanor expressed her sincere hope that Becket would come back into the fold. She was not noted for liking verminous men.

But Henry had other matters to attend to. He made a brief foray into Wales and took the opportunity to pass a few days of sport and pleasure at Frampton and Flaxley. He also spent more time finalising the building works at Woodstock and Clarendon.

On 29 April Gilbert Foliot was translated from the see of Hereford to London, and receiving a kind and supportive letter from Becket. Very soon, however, they were to fall out.

In July, the Scottish king Malcolm, Rhys from south Wales and Owen from the north of that principality came to Woodstock to reaffirm their homage to both Henry and his son. Henry was adamant in demanding these renewals of loyalty and fealty, which were reinforced by swearing on holy relics.

Becket meanwhile had continued his irritating attacks on what he now perceived to be his rights. Roger Clare, Earl of Hertford, was obliged to pay homage to Thomas for his castle and domain at Tonbridge. Conversely, the King's justiciars demanded that William de Ros owe allegiance to Henry and not Thomas. Becket installed his own nominee to the living in Eynsford who was immediately expelled by the lord of Eynsford who claimed that right of appointment. Becket responded by excommunicating that lord without informing Henry. In principle this was outrageous since the King must not be inadvertently exposed to contact with an excommunicant. All these problems exacerbated the tensions now growing between the two protagonists. But these were, in essence, side issues.

The primary problems that Henry and Thomas had been addressing with the Church, lay in the responsibility for dealing with secular crimes committed by the clergy. These, in the view of the King, should be dealt with in the secular courts, whereas, since the Conquest, the clerical courts claimed sole jurisdiction and had become incredibly lax and lenient. It is not altogether clear how these traditions had managed to grow up. Whatever the background, the current abuses were now quite intolerable and caused much anger throughout the country. As Chancellor, Becket had been adamant that reform was long overdue and when the opportunity arose for him to be enthroned as Archbishop the King had every reason to think that a sensible solution would speedily be found. But Becket had become totally defensive about the will of God and the laws and dignities of the Church.

In October Henry summoned an assembly of bishops and barons to Westminster to bring matters to a head and proposed that those clerks in holy orders who were found guilty of criminal offences should be handed over to the secular authorities for

159

punishment. Becket refused to consent. The struggle for judicial responsibility was beginning to escalate. Henry complained of the venality of the ecclesiastical courts and the indifferent quality of their judges. He reminded the assembly that many evil men were deliberately putting themselves forward for ordination and exploiting the mild penalties imposed upon them to the contempt of the country. The bishops were most conscious of the increasing and dangerous rift between Henry and Thomas and were anxious to obey the King's will without diminishing the role of the Church in matters spiritual. These affairs could not be settled in the time allotted and reflection and negotiation behind the scenes were necessary. Henry was not best pleased and stormed out of the meeting without waiting for the customary blessing from the bishops.

The next day Becket was summoned to the King's presence and personally humiliated. He was obliged to surrender his main sources of revenue which were the manors of Berkhampstead and Eye. The King then recalled his son, young Henry, and his child bride from the Archbishop's household, relieved Thomas of any responsibility for the children's further tutelage and put them formally into the care of Rosamond. To add insult to injury, the whole court celebrated Christmas at Berkhampstead.

The Pope, in exile yet again and anxious for support from his leading Christian kings in western Europe, advised Becket to give way to Henry. Henry had also worked on the bishops for their support, realising that many of them had many reservations about their new Archbishop who was far too pugnacious for the comfort of the kingdom.

In January 1164, Henry reconvened his assembly at his recently completed Palace of Clarendon. Becket chose to stay with his friend Bishop John of Salisbury in nearby Sarum and made a point of walking each and every day to Clarendon over what is still called Becket's bridge, which crosses the River Bourne near Laverstock in the lee of the Clarendon escarpment. Becket always made a point of arriving in time for the assembly, sometimes wet and always covered in mud.

The King tabled his weighty proposals contained in the Constitutions of Clarendon. The crux of the affair was that the King was demanding assent to 'the old customs of rendering justice as prevailed in the old days'. Becket was torn between his duty to the Pope and his loyalty to the King. He was aware of the antagonism from many of his bishops, many of whom had opposed his elevation. He was no fool and an experienced lawyer, and he realised that any concession would be ridden through roughshod. After all, he had worked closely with the King for far too many years to be naïve about the future. The arguments raged for several days and Becket was increasingly aware that he was losing sympathy and support. He finally gave way and acceded 'in good faith to the customs'.

Because Becket had spent so long coming and going by foot to Clarendon, he had not read the scroll with the attention that it needed. He went back to Sarum, went through the details and was horrified. The small print went far beyond what he thought that he had agreed to. He had thought that this document was essentially his original draft, made when he was chancellor, perhaps with peripheral and immaterial amendments. The new document, however, allowed the King to check appeals to Rome, to override excommunications, to control appointments of bishops and other senior preferments and be involved in many other details far removed from the root causes of injustice applying to the secular crimes of the clergy.

Thomas stormed back to Clarendon and withdrew his seal of approval: 'Never, never, while I have breath in my body, will I assent to these articles.' Grasping his copy, he marched out of the room with his entourage. The assembly was thunderstruck. Matters between Church and State were now critical.

All efforts at mediation were useless. The bishops inevitably were divided, those in the Canterbury archdiocese inclining towards Thomas – after all he was their spiritual overlord. Those in Normandy were behind the King. Foliot was privily pleased at Becket's humiliation. The Pope continued to have his own troubles and sat on the fence with mastery – each protagonist considered that he had the Pope's unequivocal support. All sought Thomas to come to terms but to no avail. At one point Thomas tried to flee the country – he who, as chancellor, had six vessels at his beck and call was refused a passage in a fishing vessel.

* * *

Eleanor spent Easter in London. Henry had considered whether

161

she might not have bridged the gap, but he found her unusually reluctant to become involved. Henry divided his time between the West Country and frenetically bustling about the country.

Rosamond craved a boon from the King during the early summer and stipulated that she was not to be asked the reason. The King was intrigued but it was not in his nature to refuse her anything.

'May I please borrow Reginald FitzUrse for a few days with a small escort for a special and very private affair?' she asked. She had always been aware that FitzUrse was smitten with her but she was confident that she could always contain any untoward approaches. And she trusted him, and he promised faithfully that he would respect the confidentiality of her secret mission.

They made their way to Canterbury. Rosamond left her entourage in a hostel and made her way to the Archbishop's lodgings. She persuaded the guardian to bring her to Becket's chapel where he was prostrate before the altar. After some time she removed her cloak and hood and made herself known, and to her astonishment Thomas began to shake uncontrollably. He begged her to leave at once.

She stood her ground and besought him to hear what she wished to say. Becket removed himself to the furthest corner of the chapel, still in a confused state. Rosamond fell to her knees and asked him to pray with her and to guide her in her mission. Becket, staying where he was, perceptibly relaxed.

Rosamond reminded Thomas of all the help that he had given her in the early days of her involvement with the King, of his interest and understanding of her equivocal position, of his support in every way. Then she asked if there was any possible way that she could help to restore goodwill between the King and his leading prelate. 'I do have his ear and he does listen to me.'

'And,' said Thomas, 'you are the only person in the realm who can defuse his tempers.' It was the first time in months that Becket had smiled.

'We, you and I, *have* to do something. This cannot go on. Please, your grace, lead me towards a solution for both Henry's and your happiness. What can I do?'

Becket came nearer. He had started to shake again. Rosamond looked at him and her violet eyes softened. Her instincts warned her that something dire had changed Thomas and he would never be the same again. 'You thought that I wanted to see you for another reason.'

Thomas broke down and wept. Rosamond now knew. She rose and took Thomas in her arms and comforted him in his distress. She did not shrink from his filthy and smelly body and clothes. She knew that this proud, able and most obstinate man would not compromise. He had been tempted and humiliated. And Rosamond knew who had done it. It explained everything.

'Thomas,' she said, 'all this is locked in my breast. You have my love and understanding now and for always.'

Her magnetic powers soothed the troubled Archbishop and he realised how much Henry owed to Rosamond. He disengaged himself gently and blessed Rosamond, adding that God would always be on her side and promising that he would always help her in any way he could.

They parted and Rosamond returned to Flaxley for the peace and quiet of that holy place. Henry never asked where she had gone but realised that she was unusually subdued and quiet and that, as always, she would have been pursuing his own best interests.

* * *

In October, Henry summoned Becket to Northampton to answer a charge of contempt. The famous and powerful Lord Marshal had not obtained justice in Becket's court and had complained to the King. Becket duly arrived on the appointed day but Marshal had remained in London to complete some urgent business. Henry had dawdled *en route* and deviated to enjoy some hunting. The lodgings customarily reserved for Becket had been allocated to some of the royal retinue. It all seemed to be deliberately spiteful.

Becket duly appeared in the castle on the following day. Henry had not risen from his couch. Becket waited. The King arrived and, passing Becket without any greeting, made his way to his chapel where he heard Mass and then broke his fast. The charge was altered in that it was not Marshal's injustice to be heard, but Becket's deliberate absence to answer an earlier summons. Becket claimed that he was ill and that anyway there was no case to answer.

Becket, whilst in an outer room, was found guilty and fined

300 pounds. The bishops found a surety for this, but no one was prepared to tell Becket. The King ultimately undertook this task. Becket calmly told Henry that he had no authority to try his archbishop in such a court. Henry then demanded the restitution of 300 pounds of revenues not accounted for in the handover of the Berkhampstead and Eye manors. Thomas found further surety but insisted that he was not subject to this either in this court.

On the following morning the King demanded restitution of revenues received by Becket whilst chancellor, amounting to 30,000 silver marks arising from surpluses from vacant sees and abbacies. Becket's sureties evaporated. There was likely to be no end to these fines. Becket, to the surprise of many, submitted, influenced by Rosamond's earlier impassioned appeal. Following his example some of his bishops also threw themselves upon the King's mercy. Henry gave not an inch – he was intent upon his pound of flesh and was going to break Thomas' spirit and tear his limbs, eyes and tongue out. The assembly broke up in consternation. Becket should resign, some said; Becket should hold fast to defend the Church from the royal secular fury said others. Sadly for all, Rosamond was not present.

Becket was sick on the morrow but on the day following was in complete possession of himself. He arose early, celebrated Mass and rode to the castle with his primatial cross borne before him. He carried this into the antechamber, ignoring the insult of the precedence accorded to the Archbishop of York. Foliot tried to restore some dignity to the proceedings and reminded Becket that he, Foliot, had the right to carry the Canterbury cross in his capacity as Dean of the province. There was an unseemly struggle whilst Foliot tried to wrest the cross by force from the Archbishop's hands and was unsuccessful.

'You have always been a fool, and always will be one!' Foliot exclaimed in wrath.

By now Becket had mastered the Constitutions of Clarendon and was aware that the King had the upper hand, albeit that he had not signed and sealed the document. He awaited the verdict, and when it arrived he spoke with clarity and firmness.

'I came hither to the King's court for one cause only, that brought by John Marshal. For none other will I answer. I was given to Canterbury free of all previous reckonings. I will bring no other sureties. I appeal, for myself and the Church of Canterbury to God and the Pope.'

Henry had thought himself in mastery, but this threw his plans into the turmoil. Those behind York suddenly realised how serious all this was becoming. Appeals were made in all directions to resolve the impasse. Henry played his next card and the chief justiciar, the Earl of Leicester, was enjoined to pronounce. Becket stood in front of Leicester and between them implanted his cross and forbade him to utter. Such was Becket's authority and presence that the justiciar was silenced. Becket reiterated that this was no trial and he would hear no sentence.

'The hour is past,' he said. 'I will depart.' And the Archbishop and his following departed with their heads held high.

As they marched out there were scenes of pandemonium and loutish behaviour. Becket's followers were pelted and there were both jeers and supportive cries. The outer door of the castle was found to be locked and the whole episode was rapidly becoming farcical. Then, beside the door was seen a key hanging on a rusty nail and Thomas and his followers emerged into the dusky streets of Northampton where the populace followed them to their lodgings.

Becket knew how the King's mind would be working and he expected a sharp and speedy reaction. The next few hours were spent in sanctuary and long before daybreak Thomas fled in disguise and under a pseudonym. He rested at one monastery after another on his way south and departed for Flanders from Sandwich in a small fishing vessel, manned by two oars only. He landed at Oye and struggled through the muddy roads of Belgium until he arrived at St Omer where he awaited the arrival of some of his clerks and servants who brought horses, raiment and treasure for his immediate needs. Becket immediately went to Sens where the Pope was staying and where he fortunately found Louis of France who gave him safe conduct and appropriate support.

* * *

Henry's reaction to Becket's flight was predictable: 'I have done with him.'

Every port was closed. It was forbidden that any person be allowed to fetch or carry letters, all travellers to and from France were stopped and searched. The penalties for disobedience were dire. An embassy of bishops, including Foliot, and barons were dispatched to Sens to prevent any support for Becket from the Curia. But the speed of Becket's flight, supported by luck in the weather, found them a few hours behind the Archbishop's progress. They sought an audience and a safe passport from the French king and learnt that Becket had been welcomed. Louis was courteous to Henry's emissaries but maddeningly sanctimonious.

'A prelate subject to the judgement of his king. How could this be? It would be far beyond my royal power to degrade the humblest clerk in my kingdom.'

The envoys pressed their cause but Louis played for time before they were permitted to wend their way to the Pope at Sens. The two parties met just outside Sens and Henry's ambassadors were enraged to see Thomas approaching with full panoply of office and mounted retinue, all provided by Louis. The English were accorded the first interview and Foliot presented the case against Becket with immense skill and consummate advocacy. The English were prepared to concede a number of papal levies which had gone by default and Alexander was reminded that he still needed friends in his own struggle with the anti-Pope who sat on St Peter's chair in Rome. The Pope and his cardinals sat and listened with an ominous and silent politeness. Becket had already pressed his case and the squabbling was beginning to pall.

'The wicked flee where no man pursueth,' Foliot declared with passion.

'Spare, brother,' responded Alexander.

'I will spare him,' answered Foliot.

'I said not spare him,' replied the Pope, 'but rather spare yourself.'

The envoys returned to England empty-handed to break the news to Henry at Marlborough where the court was to spend Christmas. The King had the father and mother of a rage and all those present were terrified. On Boxing Day a decree was issued banishing all of Becket's family, his household, servants and all his kin, young and old, male and female. They were all evicted from their lodgings, stripped of all that they had and dispatched on small vessels to the wintry and bleak shores of

166

Flanders, where all 400 of them were left to fend for themselves. The hospitality of the Capetian king and the monastic houses was stretched to the limit to cope with this invasion of penniless refugees.

Foliot was deputed to attend to the religious affairs of the province of Canterbury and the secular properties were looked after by the castellan of Dover, a man who always did what he was told to do.

* * *

During the last few months of that tumultuous year of 1164, Eleanor's two daughters, Marie and Alice, whom the world accepted as being fathered by Louis, were married to the brothers Henry of Champagne and Thibaut of Blois. Louis was anxious to strengthen his ties with that house, his third wife Adele being a Champenois daughter.

During the ensuing year a number of domestic issues were resolved. Henry went to Rouen to negotiate marriages for his daughters by Eleanor, Matilda and Eleanor. The German Emperor Frederick was a supporter of the anti-Pope, Victor IV, and Henry needed to put pressure on Alexander III for concessions in his struggle with Becket. He therefore arranged for Matilda to be engaged to Frederick's eldest son, Henry the Lion, Duke of Bavaria and Saxony. The marriage was not scheduled to take place immediately since Matilda was still only nine years old. His second negotiation was for the four-year-old Eleanor to marry the youngest son of Emperor Frederick. This came to nothing.

Queen Adele was again pregnant and Louis was determined to break the spell of his superfluity of daughters. The French king's generosity to the Church was dramatically increased; the clergy were enjoined to pray incessantly and a visit by Louis to Clairvaux where he prostrated himself and besought the Almighty for 'an heir of the better sex' was expected to pay off. In August Adele was delivered of the long-awaited son, to be called Philippe-Augustus. The joy and merriment in Paris were of legendary magnificence. And it closed a door in the diplomatic manoeuvring by Henry for the succession the French throne.

Eleanor spent Easter in London and in May she crossed to France and was briefly reunited with Henry in Angers where she became involved with Maine and Anjou problems. Henry meanwhile returned to England to try to suppress recurring troubles in north Wales but with indifferent success. In September he was in Chester and almost immediately departed for London. He would undoubtedly have spent time with Rosamond and the attendant children and indulged in as much sport as he could fit in.

Eleanor also spent time in Poitiers where she revived her intimate friendship with her uncle, Raoul de Faye. But the correspondence of the Bishop of Poitiers was responsible for spreading scandal and speculation regarding this relationship. However there was some mitigation in these allegations since Eleanor gave birth, in the autumn, to the youngest of her daughters, Joanna, although curiously for this family there is no actual recorded date for this event. Eleanor spent Christmas in Angers and this was the first Yuletide that she and Henry had been apart. Henry was probably at Woodstock for Christmas – he was certainly there in early January whilst he was busy updating a number of legal anomalies.

* * *

Many sources suggest that it was at this time that the Henry/Rosamond affair started. This was about the time that their long-established relationship began to be far more widely known. Hitherto they had come together in remote and isolated places such as Flaxley and Frampton, where their immediate coterie maintained a discreet silence. Now that Henry had completed his refurbishments at Clarendon and Woodstock, they were far more in the public eye and many more courtiers became aware of Rosamond and her children.

It is interesting to suggest that there may have been more than meets the eye in the birth of Joanna. As Henry and Eleanor were together at Christmas at Berkhampstead, Joanna's birth in October would be possible. But was Joanna born in October? She was born in the autumn with no firm date on record. It is not recorded where Eleanor spent Easter but she and Henry next met in May, so a 'late autumnal birth' for Joanna is impossible if Joanna was conceived then. Eleanor was certainly in Normandy in May – perhaps she came across earlier. Or did Uncle Raoul pay a private visit to England in the spring? In which case a child conceived at Easter could have had an early arrival in November or December. And why was the Bishop of Poitiers rushing into print – was he worried over something? And why did Henry not

*come back to France to see his newborn babe, even for Christmas? It
was March in 1166 before he rejoined Eleanor.*

* * *

After Henry's sojourn at Woodstock, he went to Maine to subdue a few rebellious barons with his usual ruthless efficiency
before rejoining Eleanor and his new daughter for Easter at
Angers. Pope Alexander III's fortunes began to revive and he was
able to return to Rome where his first action was to appoint
Becket legate for all England, excepting the province of York.
This encouraged Becket to send a delegation to Angers to
demand restoration to his see. Henry unceremoniously dismissed
this impudent group back to Pontigny where Becket was now in
residence.

Becket wrote three letters to his king in increasing dudgeon,
all of which were ignored. He concluded by giving the King until
Pentecost to repent, otherwise he would suffer the withdrawal of
unction. Henry remarked to his followers that the trouble with
Becket was his ability to mistake his will with that of Providence.
The withdrawal of unction was not something which worried the
King too much. However, he covered his back by reminding
Alexander that his cordial relationship with the German emperor
could be prejudicial to the Pope's new-found confidence. He also
reminded him that the English properties of the Cistercians
might have to be impounded if the Cistercian Abbot of Pontigny
continued to succour his rebellious archbishop.

Sabre rattling from the Church could be ignored by the King
but the common folk of England took it far more seriously and
Henry knew this. Henry himself had very good reason not to
push the Church too far. Excommunication would mean that he
could not crown young Prince Henry as King of England which
would ensure the succession.

In June the King negotiated the marriage between his son
Prince Geoffrey and the daughter of the Duke of Brittany. This
was a masterly move as he was continuing to have problems with
the Bretons.

In the autumn Eleanor returned to England and on 24
December their youngest, and last, child was born at Oxford.
This boy, John, was to become in course of time the controver-
sial king and, despite his many shortcomings, would be the ten-

uous link in the continuation of the Plantagenet line for the next 300 years. Eleanor paid a brief visit to nearby Woodstock and viewed with hostility Rosamond's cottage in the valley. Perhaps luckily for the latter, she was not in residence.

Henry spent Christmas with young Henry at Poitiers.

In the New Year 1167 Becket removed himself to a Benedictine monastery which, being under the personal patronage of Louis rendered his estates in England safe from any threat of confiscation. Bishop Foliot had another spat with Becket in Argentan in front of the Pope's legates. Their relationships had continued to deteriorate primarily due to Foliot's firm handling of the affairs of the Canterbury province and his rigid control of its finances which had cut off much of the revenues that Becket continued to need. Charge and counter-charge raged between them and Becket was reminded that his debts were not quashed at consecration 'as sins are done away in baptism'.

Eleanor continued to stay in England whilst Henry remained, always active, in France, dealing with a series of insurrections in almost every quarter.

In September Henry's mother, the Empress Maud, finally died at the age of sixty-five. She had ended her days doing a multitude of good works and living in the convent of Fontevraud. Despite her powerful personality and the difficulties that she had caused in her earlier days, she had been a prop to her son and she got on well with his tigress of a wife.

Eleanor meanwhile organised the marriage of their daughter Matilda to Henry the Lion, also in that September. She and Henry spent Christmas at Argentan.

1168 saw an escalation in other directions. In the spring Eleanor and Henry went to Poitou to subjugate Eleanor's vassals, the Lusignans. Henry won what was thought to be a resounding victory and he left Eleanor, accompanied by Earl Patrick of Salisbury, to restore order to the devastated area, whilst he went off to treat with the French king. Unfortunately, most of the Lusignan military élite had evaded capture and were still at large. Eleanor and Earl Patrick were on their way to Poitiers when they were ambushed by Guy de Lusignan. Patrick was slain whilst the Queen made for safety. Patrick's nephew, William Marshal, a young knight of immense ability and potential, fought furiously with the attackers and was eventually captured. Eleanor secured his release and, admiring his spirit, rewarded him generously and ensured his future and successful progress. He was soon appointed to be responsible for the continued upbringing of young Prince Henry as his first important upwardly mobile step.

* * *

Henry dispatched Richard Brito to Eleanor to discover the details of this attack by de Lusignan. Richard, the most recent of Henry's aides, was terrified of the formidable Eleanor. Eleanor was well known to eat those whom she desired and to spit out the pips with callous indifference, and she displayed her formidable charms to the unfortunate Richard. Richard was a Breton who came from a nearby part of her own countryside. She found him a malleable emissary and enjoyed twisting him round her little finger and watching his transparent discomfiture. On this occasion however she dispatched him to Becket, now at St Pontigny near Sens, with the instruction that she would follow in a day or so to demand an audience. She took as her escort William Marshal. She was well aware that Becket might not welcome her visit, but her message was diplomatic and persuasive.

Eleanor dressed carefully. She was not out to make a killing this time. She was in black, her still luxuriant dark hair modestly covered, and she kept her eyes modestly down. She entered Becket's presence and, aware as always, of the embarrassed vibrations from Thomas, knelt demurely at some distance from him so as not to seem threatening. There was a silence for some moments.

Eleanor was sad to see that the handsome and virile Archbishop was now a shadow of his former self. He was haggard and gaunt, pale and stooping. His eyes no longer had that fire that she remembered so well.

'I have sinned immensely and have come to crave your forgiveness. What has happened, has happened and cannot ever be undone. But I seek your forgiveness and the forgiveness of God.'

'This I can do but God's forgiveness can only come from your own real and genuine contrition which only He and you will know. It comes only from your heart, not from your lips.'

This Eleanor accepted and begged the Archbishop to make his peace with both God and the King for the sake of the whole country. They talked at length and sensibly about these problems.

171

Eleanor told Thomas that he was in very real danger of being found redundant. During his absence the Church in England had continued to function perfectly efficiently and successfully and he was, to put it frankly and brutally, not missed. Eleanor pressed for him to come back to reimpose his presence and authority, realising that he was not best pleased at this comment. They then reverted to talk about their mutual family affairs. Sadly, Becket's mother, Rohesia, had died soon after his family had been banished by the King. She had suffered badly following the privations that they had endured during that dreadful flight through Flanders. Thomas resented the circumstances which had led up to his dearly loved mother's premature death.

Becket's news from Palestine concerning Ayub and his family was joyous. Saladin was now a strapping young man going from strength to strength and a credit to all. 'Not least,' added Thomas, 'to you. He is honourable, fearless and brave and will have a distinguished future in his country. You, my dear Eleanor, are a veritable matriarch to all your lion cubs. They will all make their mark on history.'

'That is what Ayub told me when we parted all those years ago.'

'He sends his salaams and, dare I say it, his love. We share many things in life, not least our Kurdish involvements.' Thomas went on to say that he would make every effort, saving God's honour, to heal the breach with Henry and he gave Eleanor a blessing as they parted.

* * *

Henry concluded a Byzantine agreement with Louis whereby young Henry paid the French king homage for Anjou and Brittany – the latter being held by brother Geoffrey – and Richard for Aquitaine combined with a betrothal for the latter to Alais who was the sister of Margaret, young Henry's wife. The reasons for all this seemed obscure at the time except for Richard's betrothal – perhaps Louis did some horse trading for this.

Henry then returned post-haste to Poitiers after the Lusignan debacle, but had to deviate to suppress other uprisings within his lands and around his borders. It was during the autumn that the King suffered from a sharp fever which drained him. He remembered that his father had caught a chill which had proved rapidly fatal. This and his campaigns occupied him until Christmas which he celebrated at Argentan whilst Eleanor decided to stay at Poitiers.

*   *   *

The Christmas festivities were a short interlude in the hectic lives led by the close and intimate staff of the King. The four knights who organised Henry's intense travelling arrangements were able to relax and carouse without expecting to be sent to the ends of the two realms at the drop of a hat. FitzUrse, Tracy, de Morville and Brito the Breton were able to let their hair down. They were a motley crew but had worked closely and intimately together for a number of years and had much experience in common. Their loyalties to the King were intense and they each knew that their rewards would be invaluable. They had all struggled to maintain their positions in the early years of their partnership and Henry had always looked after them well, although he was an intensely demanding taskmaster. That year they were much more convivial than usual and were more indiscreet between themselves than was their wont.

Richard Brito had joined the team rather later than the others and had never been fully accepted, perhaps because he was a Breton and from a lower social caste than the others. After much wine had flowed, they all started to rib Reginald FitzUrse on his transparently obvious but unrequited predilection for the lovely Rosamond.

'Why is it dear old Reggio that it is always you who wishes to be sent to Flaxley or Frampton or Everswell? Is it because you are smitten? And does she ever give you any hope?'

'I am sorry Hugh that you now try to avoid this most pleasurable duty for our lord and master. After all there was once a woman now in the fair Rosamond's household who excited your own interest, or was it your passions? I always inform you of the progress of that young man, Roger, who is the onetime playmate and now the servant of our king's son, Geoffrey.'

This was all news to Richard and before the evening was finished he had discovered that the lad Roger was Hugh's by Hikenai and that the official story that Geoffrey was the child of the King by that servant was totally untrue and that Rosamond

173

was the real mother. This explained much that had puzzled him over the years.

* * *

During Henry's negotiations with the Emperor Barbarossa over the marriage of his daughter, Matilda, to the latter's son, Henry the Lion, it was mooted that the English king should aspire to the tenuously-held throne in Jerusalem. The Germans were disillusioned with the weakness of the leadership in the Christian kingdom there and were quite convinced that nothing useful or sensible could be done unless the leadership and military expertise could be properly reinforced. Barbarossa and his son were both firmly of the opinion that the Plantagenet king of England was the only solution. Henry was immensely flattered and saw much merit in assuming this important role in Christendom.

Henry and his three elder sons met Louis in early January at Montmirail to confirm the previous year's agreements. There was considerable flattery on both sides and the three young princes made their homage to the French king for all the Plantagenet lands in France. Hitherto Henry's position was secure and he was an able soldier who kept on top of dissident barons. Perhaps he was fearful that this transitory life could cut short his glorious reign long before his sons acquired sufficient maturity to cope with his complex empire. Having built a centralised organisation, he was in danger of decentralising and hence weakening his power base in a prejudicial manner. He was also very aware that he had three thrusting sons who were ambitious and dearly wanting to flex their muscles, and a move by him to Jerusalem could create space for them to take over control. In the context of Henry's possible aspirations in Jerusalem this extraordinary volte-face and change of tactics makes sense.

Becket, mindful of his recent meeting with Eleanor, still under pressure from some of his bishops and with the support and connivance of Louis then made a dramatic entrance to the assembly. Those present watched with trepidation. Becket, to the astonishment of all, cast himself weeping at the King's feet. Henry raised him to his feet, equally overcome. He pleaded the cause of the Church, renewed his vows of loyalty to the King, apologised profusely and begged for clemency and to be allowed to return to Canterbury. All present were convinced that the

174

rapprochement was genuine and there was joy apparent in all. Henry was beaming with pleasure. However, Becket ended by submitting his whole case with the words 'saving the honour of God and my order'.

The King exploded with rage and a flood of unsuitable language poured forth. Those present lost sympathy with the King following his intemperate outburst, but Henry rapidly changed tack and reiterated in a calm and conciliatory tone the affirmation conceded by Becket following the Constitutions of Clarendon. This swung the mood of those at Montmirail back towards the King's stance. Many of those present, including the bishops, continued to press the recalcitrant Archbishop to give way but to no avail. Thomas and Henry parted again having gained nothing, but with the King emerging with the sympathy of the assembly.

On Palm Sunday, Becket excommunicated Foliot, the Bishop of London, following a culmination of disagreements. This sentence was delivered by a ruse. A French priest attended Mass on Ascension Day in St Paul's Cathedral. He presented himself at the altar and handed a piece of paper to the officiating priest, who thinking it a part of the offertory, took it – upon which the visitor demanded that it should be read to the congregation before the celebration commenced. The priest opened it and read that his bishop was excommunicated. Meanwhile the Frenchman rapidly escaped before the wrath of those present manifested itself. Foliot was apprised and called all his diocesan clergy together and told them that he had been expecting this and had already appealed to the Pope, and that until it had been adjudicated the sentence was null and void. Henry was involved for his support and ultimately the sentence was overturned after a visit by Foliot to Rome.

* * *

During 1169 Eleanor decided that she would now spend most of her time in Aquitaine, and re-established her life mainly in Poitiers with some of her children. Young Prince Henry and Margaret his child wife, Richard, now twelve years old, Geoffrey, who was a year younger, and his bride-to-be, Constance of Brittany and her daughters Eleanor and Joanna were all with her and she much enjoyed their company. John, who was nearly four, was under the tutelege of the convent at Fontevraud. Aided by

Raoul, Eleanor started to restore the court to its former glory as a centre of learning, culture and chivalry. Eleanor's daughter, the young Eleanor, was married during this year to Alfonso VII, the King of Castile.

During the summer Eleanor again cornered poor Richard Brito who was always worried that she would seduce him. She plied him with drink and managed to extract out of him the real relationship between Geoffrey Plantagenet, Rosamond and her husband. She also was apprised of a problem that had emerged between FitzUrse and 'that Clifford girl' as she now called her. At last all these matters fell into place and she realised for the first time that Henry's first and seemingly true love predated her own marriage and that the King's son by Rosamond was older than her own surviving elder son, Prince Henry. She conveniently chose to forget her own affairs of days not long past. She began to feel threatened. She decided to make a visit to England privately and persuaded Reginald FitzUrse to be her escort.

*　　*　　*

Henry's moves during 1169 were more frenetic than he wished. In January he was at Montmirail. In March he went to Poitou where he spent a few days with Eleanor and his children, although his primary motive there was to silence some unruly barons. Then he went down to Aquitaine to subdue some more difficult vassals. In May he had to go to Brittany with Geoffrey who was to receive homage from his intended subjects in that country. Early in August he returned to Normandy via Angers for some tiresome meetings with the papal nuncios at Domfront, thence to Bayeux and Rouen. He was intensely conscious that he was not going to be able to go to England and deal with problems there, nor was he going to able to relax, see Rosamond and William Longspee and hopefully spend time hunting in Gloucestershire and Oxfordshire. Henry was not best pleased and this was to be the longest time that he was away from Rosamond. He dispatched FitzUrse to break the news to her and perhaps persuade her to come across for a few days to France, although his schedule was becoming more and more fraught.

Reginald sped across to Everswell near Woodstock. His mind was in a turmoil. He had always adored Rosamond from afar but had never had the courage to make approaches to her. His frequent visits to announce the King's imminent arrival had always brought such joy to her, ever enhancing her beauty. How he wished that he could have some encouragement. He approached the bower below Woodstock palace on the banks of the river Everswell. He had never been allowed to know the way through the maze which had now fully grown and was a perfect retreat. Hikenai and her boy Roger were the only ones who were allowed to know the route in. Roger blindfolded him and led him through to the centre where Rosamond was sitting by the splashing fountain. She looked quite stunning and Reginald was certain that she was expecting his arrival to be the advance notice that Henry was close behind.

She started up to her feet crying, 'Is he on his way? When will he be here? Reginald, you are always the bearer of such good news and I am always so very glad to see you.'

Reginald advanced, took her outstretched hands and said softly, 'I am not today the bearer of welcome news. The King has immense travelling commitments and asks me to say how very sorry he is but he does not know when he will be able to come across. He is devastated.'

Rosamond gave a cry of distress and Reginald took her in his arms to comfort her. She responded and clung to him, sobbing quietly. Then she pulled herself together and, still in his arms, kissed him gently on the cheek and thanked him for his help. Reginald had never held her so closely and for so long and, after some moments, still holding her closely, his emotions suddenly got the better of him. He kissed her passionately again and again. At first he thought that she was responding demurely and without any rejection and even, he thought, with some appreciation. Then he became aware that his overtures were unacceptable and that she had gone limp in his arms with no reaction. He was aflame and hoped that she would succumb and respond to his advances with favour. Such was the vanity of man, he convinced himself that it would be but moments before she capitulated to his ardour, having displayed such reticence as would be appropriate.

Rosamond tore herself from his embrace in distress, fell to the ground and covered her head with her arms crying out, 'No, no, no, what are you doing? Please leave me. Now, now. Don't touch me. Go, man, go.'

Reginald stood in confusion, rooted to the spot. He moved

closer to the weeping woman and bent to pick Rosamond up. She cringed away in terror. He realised that the King's paramour had rejected him but he knew not the way out of the maze.

'How do I leave?' he asked, now nervous and shaking.

Rosamond rang a handbell and her son Geoffrey came running from the house. Rosamond asked him to take the knight out at once, but before he was blindfolded she said, 'Reginald, I promise you that this is between us, no one will know, but only if this never, never happens again.'

Geoffrey looked askance at the emissary from his father, but his mother signalled him to lead him away. Geoffrey led the discomforted and discouraged FitzUrse out of the maze. Roger the servant was waiting and watching by the riverside.

* * *

Rosamond now decided to go with her two sons to her haven of Flaxley where she had always felt safe. She had not been to see her relation, the anchoress, for many years and now felt the need to seek solace and comfort from her. This saintly lady was now very aged but greeted Jane, as she always called her, with affection, albeit with some sadness that she had not come more often.

'I am glad, dear child that you have been blessed with two such fine lads. They will be a credit to you and the King; their father will find that their loyalty and courage will give him much solace in the tribulations that he will suffer. I have to tell you that you will not be blessed with any more children and I know that you have had many difficulties in going to your full term. Your life will go through many vicissitudes and you will face a very great danger. If you are brave and understanding you will survive and I shall pray for you and the good Lord will determine what will happen. Have courage and wisdom, dear Jane. Henry will be wanting from you that which will be most unwise for all of you. Your common sense will guide you into how to handle all this. You have a pallor that is new to your complexion. You must take much care of your health as I am fearful that your days may not run their full course. Never fail to render to God all that He is due.

'Now, the King promised that a goodly church would be built at Westbury and the excellent and efficient Thomas saw that this was done. What the villagers there have not yet been given is a

178

priest worthy of them to minister to their needs. It is a pity that nothing has been done to rectify this omission. There is an excellent and able young cousin of ours well known and admired by that excellent father of yours. Henry will like him and will enjoy his wit and ability. Walter Map is his name and it is high time that he have some experience of the pastoral care of souls here. Pray speak both to your father and the King.'

Rosamond, Geoffrey and William were then blessed by the aged soul who told them that she would soon be called to join her Maker and that they would not see her again. They parted with tears and much sadness. Rosamond was much perturbed. They all returned to Everswell where she knew that Henry could find them. A few days later Eleanor arrived at Woodstock with FitzUrse.

8

Eleanor was by now in a simmering rage. She remembered all the high hopes that she had had and the children that she had borne this boor. She had brought him possessions, lands and wealth from far and wide. Now she knew that not only had he a lady love who had shared his bed and who was raising his children, but also this love, the Clifford girl, had been much involved in tending this brood with her own cubs. They were taught together, they played together, they hunted together and they all had a loving relationship with her. And more importantly, Geoffrey Plantagenet was the eldest and Henry was a devious devil who would do anything to ensure a succession. Illegitimate succession was part and parcel of the tactics of the dukes of Normandy.

Eleanor had the ability to forget that she had had many affairs and at least two children sired by other fathers – but then, the succession to her lands was not prejudiced by these.

FitzUrse was nervous. He was suffering from the pangs of unrequited love and felt spiteful and vengeful. No man likes being rejected, but the wrath of Henry would be quite devastating and his whole career and future was locked into Henry's generosity. He trusted Rosamond's discretion but was aware that if the story became known she might find it difficult to convince Henry of her own innocence. And he knew that he was playing with fire. In addition, Eleanor was becoming more and more angry by the hour. He surmised that she had been told something that should not have been revealed to her.

'Now Reginald,' the Queen said, 'that woman is in residence and I want to see her to have certain matters out. I am going to clear the air. How can you arrange this? It must never be known

– ever. Otherwise a little bird will whisper not very nice nothings into the King's ear.'

Reginald knew what the Queen was getting at. 'Go,' she said, 'and find out the weak points of this impenetrable maze which protects her.'

Rosamond's servant Roger was seen up at the palace from time to time and Reginald summoned the lad to come to him. He soon found out that Roger was not at all pleased with his station in life nor at the treatment that he received. 'After all,' he said bitterly to FitzUrse, 'my father is from the same station in life as you, but I am treated like a servant. When I was born, it was put about that my mother had produced the King's son. We were both born at about the same time. This was to save the Queen's feelings about her newly-wed groom, the Prince Henry, as he then was. She could not be allowed to know that her husband preferred another to this dark beauty from southern France. So I and Geoffrey Plantagenet were brought up together and as children we were playmates. He is now treated as the King's son and spends much time in the King's household. I am just a lackey and my mother, who sullied her name for the King's sake, is still a skivvy. Sir Hugh de Morville, my father, made a small provision for me and my mother, which I never share in. It isn't fair.'

Reginald could see a way to infiltrate the Queen into the maze, so he brought Roger to Eleanor. She cross-examined him and satisfied herself that he could be persuaded to help. He described the movements of Rosamond who had recently been taking morning rides generally in the direction of the convent of Godstow near Oxford. Eleanor promised Roger a small sum of money now, with more when her plan was executed and a final payment when she emerged from the maze after her meeting with his mistress. When Roger helped Rosamond to dismount, after she had returned from one of her visits to Godstow, he was to snip a thread from her silken riding gown. This he was to hold whilst his mistress re-entered the maze. Reginald and the Queen would be secluded in some thickets nearby and at a signal from Roger would come to the entrance of the maze. Eleanor would follow the thread through to the centre for her confrontation.

* * *

Margaret Clifford, Rosamond's dearly loved mother, had been for

181

many years closely associated with the nunnery on the banks of the Thames just outside Oxford. Following the anchoress's strictures, Rosamond had visited this haven of peace and tranquillity as often as she could after her return from Flaxley. The nuns welcomed her and she persuaded them to put her to useful work wherever there was a need. She did not mind what she did or however menial a task was given to her. She helped in the kitchens, she fed the poor and she nursed the sick and the suffering. She sat with the dying and held their hands in their last few hours of this transitory life. The nuns loved her and she became an integral part of their lives. And she enjoyed herself as she had never enjoyed herself before.

She made a habit of riding over early in the morning and often stayed until the long summer's evenings began to fade. There were other occasions when she only remained for the morning, when she would return for an afternoon of gainful employment by the water garden in the middle of her secure maze.

It was on one such sunny afternoon that she returned and was helped to dismount by Roger just by the banks of the Everswell. She was an adept horsewoman but she had wrapped herself up for the journey as the days had been very changeable recently and she had been suffering from an annoying and persistent cough for the past few days, probably brought on by a soaking that she had recently undergone. Roger was rather clumsy, but then he was a clumsy fellow at best. He fiddled about with the hem of her silken dress which he said seemed to have caught on a thorn bush. Then he said that he had cleared the obstruction and she hurried into the maze.

Eleanor and Reginald were waiting in a nearby copse. There had been several abortive attempts on previous days to implement their nefarious plan but they had been thwarted by Rosamond's erratic timing. This had put the Queen much out of humour. It was with some difficulty that the knight persuaded the Queen that this was in no way the fault of the unfortunate Roger. Eleanor had intended to reduce her second payment but Reginald was able to restore the original agreement.

The pair now approached the entrance to the grounds and, alone, Eleanor followed the thread through the maze. Sensibly she did not pick it up as she progressed as she realised that she would need it to secure her line of retreat. She heard the sooth-

182

ing sound of the fountain and realised that she was near to her victim. The maze then turned away and she thought that she was going back on her tracks and soon found herself on the outer edge again. She wondered if she had been trapped as it was much further than she had expected, but the path twisted again and she again neared the secret garden.

Then, when she was least expecting it, she entered the bower and stood amazed at the beauty and tranquillity of the place. Rosamond was sleeping on a seat. Three interconnecting fountains were playing and there was a round pond at one side with water lilies and other water plants. It reminded her of her own palace gardens in her beloved Aquitaine where the Arabic tradition of the delicate effects of water had been introduced by her father and grandfather. She too had followed and developed these ideas. Becket and Henry had with superb taste imported these concepts into this most English of settings. There were two niches just by the seat into which had been installed fine little statues. In one corner was an abundance of fruit trees and bushes with the fruits ripening but not yet ready for eating. A wicket gate led to a path leading up to a tower, which in turn led to the house which was the trysting place for Rosamond and her Henry.

Momentarily Eleanor's resolutions weakened. She paused and looked again at this fair beauty with her tresses falling around her waist, sleeping so peacefully, who had stolen her husband's heart so completely. Eleanor's heart hardened. Rosamond had such a seraphic and serene face in repose. She was not quite as Eleanor remembered her, although it was some years since she had seen Rosamond. She seemed paler and looked less robust than before.

'It's we the dark beauties that keep their looks and their fire,' thought Eleanor. 'These fair sirens become careworn and lined long before their time. Henry will soon tire of this hussy who ensnared him before he was old enough to know better.'

Rosamond flicked away a fly which had settled on her face, stirred and, aware that she was no longer alone, awoke with a start and saw Eleanor. She leapt to her feet as Eleanor continued to look menacing.

'What are you doing here? How did you get in?'

'I must be blunt,' Eleanor said. 'I have come to kill you and rid this world of your pestilential presence. I will give you a choice of how you die.' She withdrew a jewelled and curved dagger from her bosom. She then showed the frightened Rosamond a tiny, exquisitely chased silver goblet with a lid, which she carefully removed. 'You die by poison or by stabbing to the heart. Think before you choose, I will give you a little time to reflect. But die you shall and I will do it within this hour.' Eleanor had not appreciated the irony that both these weapons of death were presents from Ayub.

Rosamond crossed her hands in front of her and looked Eleanor fully in the eyes. 'I know that I have wronged you and what can I say to ask for your forgiveness? We have so many things that we share in common. We have above all Henry who has shared both our lives for so long. We have both borne our dearly loved children who are all adored by their father. These boys and girls have grown up together and shared teaching, play, games and hunting together. They all love each other, they all love you and I like to think that they all love me. We are each so different. I am softer and give them a gentle home life which they all so much appreciate when they are with me. You give them culture and fun, music and drama, poetry and intellectual stimulus. You are the Queen and you have your duchy and you are admired from far and near. You give them glamour and ritual. I am the stay at home to whom they can all come when they are hurt or bruised. Your children will all have an inheritance or dynastic marriages. My sons are destined to serve and support your sons in whatever roles they may have in the future. Do we not each have a part to play in this life? And would not my departure leave an unfillable gap in their young lives? Not to mention that quite extraordinary man, that genius, who has done so much for you and me and yours and his lands. You do not know how often I have managed to defuse his rages and calmed him when no one else can. Somehow he always tries to come to me for my calming effect. I do not know why, but I do have this influence upon his troubled soul. I beg you not to throw all this away. I promise you that I shall never, never be his wife or agree to supplant you as Queen.'

Eleanor was amazed and began to respect her rival, but she had not weakened in her resolve. She also knew how trustworthy and steadfast Rosamond had always been and she now knew that her own role as Henry's wife would continue to be honoured by this extraordinary woman who inspired so much love. 'But your Geoffrey is the eldest child and I cannot accept that he could ever have any precedence over my sons. We both know our Henry.'

'Never fear. Geoffrey would never want to be king. He is not like your sons who are thrusting and bursting to rule. Henry and I have planned that he will be a churchman and, through God's will, we need in this land of ours and yours a steadying and loyal hand at the top of the Church. You will know that a priested man can never become a king in this land and you can rest assured on that and, if I am alive, I shall see that this will be done.'

Eleanor suddenly realised that Rosamond had touched upon a course of action which would save her own face. She was weakening. And she was beginning to like this person to whom Henry had for so long lost his heart.

Rosamond continued, 'It is possible that I may not be as long in this life as I would like. I am conscious that this is a very transitory life and that when the good Lord summons us, we come and it is not for us to anticipate His will or intentions. But if you were to cut short my life, you may be anticipating God's call and your sin would not be acceptable to His will.' Rosamond coughed and Eleanor thought that she saw a tiny fleck of blood appear on the white silken dress that she wore. With a flash of understanding, Eleanor realised that Rosamond's paleness could indeed be the early signs of that dread wasting disease that was the scourge of so many. Was not this, her sudden realisation, a Divine intervention? Eleanor made up her mind and put the goblet and dagger on the ground. She could not proceed and preempt God's Will and incur the dire consequences that must ensue. Rather to Eleanor's surprise, she took Rosamond in her arms and the two women embraced each other for a long time with a respect neither would ever have believed possible.

Reginald, still standing outside the entrance to the maze, had started to have misgivings. He was not privy to the Queen's innermost thoughts and feelings and had been given no idea concerning the thrust of this meeting between Eleanor and Rosamond. But the longer he stood there the more worried he became. If harm befell Rosamond, the King's rage would know no bounds.

His real, albeit unrequited, love for Rosamond which had been so bluntly rebuffed did not now extend to a desire for revenge and he was becoming more fearful by the minute. With trepidation he entered the maze and followed the silken thread warily. He knew that the path was lengthy and tortuous and that he would approach the centre several times before he finally came upon it. So it was that he could occasionally hear voices but not clearly what was being said, but the odd words and phrases that he could hear were not reassuring. He hurried on. The hedges of the maze were now thickly grown and he was not visible on the other side as he progressed. Then he came to the bower but kept himself concealed. He could see a dagger and a lidded cup upon the ground and realised with horror that Rosamond's life had indeed been under threat. He started to go forward to render succour, but paused as he heard the two women talking in muted voices. Neither seemed to be in any distress. Something had happened between them which had defused the tension. He heard Eleanor begin to take leave and to his astonishment saw the two women embrace each other with a tenderness that left him utterly astonished. Reginald returned quickly, thanking his luck that the silken thread had guided him in and out of the maze. He awaited the Queen's return and she emerged, pale and flushed, but calmer than he had seen her in recent days. Roger the steward was still in the nearby copse looking after the horses and now came forward to claim his final reward. Eleanor handed a money bag to FitzUrse to pass to Roger, mounted her horse and rode back to the palace at Woodstock, outlined proudly on the brow of the hill before them. The knight dismissed the disloyal servant with disdain and followed Eleanor back.

They returned to France as soon as they could and between them never referred to this episode again.

* * *

Rosamond was still shaking with the terror of her ordeal when her two sons came upon her lying on one of the seats in the bower. Geoffrey was most solicitous and demanded to know what had occurred. William, now a child of eleven, hugged his dear mother and dried away her tears as he comforted her in her distress.

Rosamond refused to divulge all that had happened, but

186

Geoffrey, now a young adult and frequently with his father's court in France, arranged for the dismissal of both Roger and his mother. De Morville had provided a small property for their benefit and the two of them were banished to that place.

Rosamond was sad about this. Hikenai had been a loyal and dutiful servant to her ever since Geoffrey and Roger had been born, and Hikenai's family had been serfs for generations on the Clifford estates at Frampton. Geoffrey too was sorry at this break with his early days, especially those childhood days when he and Roger had shared many escapades. William, on the other hand, had suffered, generally in silence, when Roger had bullied and teased the much younger boy whenever he could. All three of them were aware that Roger had become increasingly morose and disaffected as well as loutish. Both Roger and his mother were reminded forcefully by Geoffrey that their continued good behaviour would not prejudice their family at Frampton, but if they did not observe the terms of banishment the consequences would be dire for all.

* * *

It is difficult to date this episode. There is some evidence for Reginald's love for Rosamond. Alfred Lord Tennyson's play Becket *involves a dramatic occasion bringing in Henry, Geoffrey, Thomas Becket and FitzUrse. There is also much obscurity about Eleanor's movements in 1169.*

Becket did not return to England until December 1170 and would have had no time to be involved with this episode, quite apart from the obvious fact that the attempted murder had to take place in clement weather and therefore in the summer months.

If, of course, FitzUrse was not involved, then Eleanor's attempt to murder Rosamond could have taken place in the early 1170s, but then there would be no intervention of either Becket or Reginald. It is more probable that there was an intended murder involving Eleanor, Rosamond and FitzUrse at the maze in Everswell and that Becket subsequently became aware of it.

Hikenai now disappears from this story but we do not hear the end of Roger. However, there is one further vignette about Hikenai which needs addressing. We revert to the unlikely legend that Henry had the child Geoffrey Plantagenet by the 'base and low born' Hikenai. All these suggestions turn on the fact that Henry met Rosamond years later than

187

he did (said, as it happens, to occur about 1169, when Henry was far too involved in Normandy, as we have seen), and therefore Rosamond could not possibly be the mother. But there is a wealth of evidence as I have already promulgated that Rosamond met Henry in 1151 and the story was put about to assuage Eleanor's feelings when she married Henry a year later.

It is said in many sources that Hikenai had another child called Peter, 'possibly a bastard by Henry or a half brother to Geoffrey by another of her clients, a man to whom she was not married' (hence her reputation for being loose-living). It seems that in 1193 Geoffrey considered giving a preferment to Hikenai's son, who would have been Roger's half-brother.

I reiterate therefore that Geoffrey Plantagenet was Henry and Rosamond's child. Hikenai was probably the wet nurse and also had a son, Roger, fathered by one of Henry's entourage. Hikenai had a second son, Peter, probably about 1170 after she had left Rosamond's household, fathered by someone irrelevant to this story. Thus it was that Geoffrey took an interest and helped his impecunious younger half-brother Peter, who had nothing.

The timing of everyone's movements in the summer of 1170 was too complex for all this to have taken place then, although it might just have been possible. I have therefore placed this episode in 1169.

188

9

1169–1171

Eleanor returned to Poitiers and bade farewell to FitzUrse who had taken a leave of absence from the King's court and now had to return to England to attend to his estate at Williton in Somerset, which he had inherited upon his father's death the previous year. Eleanor felt much unease at what she had so nearly done and considerable relief that she had avoided the drastic actions she had originally intended. Her marital relationship with Henry would never be the same again and she would lead her own life and spend as much time as she could in her own patch. Her sons would be encouraged to take on their birthright and flex their muscles. Eleanor was now forty-seven years old and probably past child-bearing age. She had produced her quiverful of children for Henry. She was still stunningly beautiful with her dark hair as luxuriant as ever and her maturity and presence gave her a poise and attraction which was not yet to diminish with age. Her contemporaries could and did become old ladies but all those in her court continued to marvel at the allure of her perennial youth. Eleanor also included in her entourage her uncle Raoul.

She would continue to give her support to Henry providing her own interests were paramount. She was disturbed at the ongoing conflict between Becket and the King and would continue to try to ease matters between them, but as both grew older their attitudes hardened. She also wanted to hear news of Saladin who was now nigh on twenty years old and she was certain that he would now be on the threshold of exploiting his great potential.

So she sent William Marshal as her emissary to pave the way to meet Thomas at his retreat at Ste Colombe near Sens. Becket was now far more relaxed when she came into his presence and to her surprise she found that he was much better informed about her activities than she expected. To her chagrin, he was not forthcoming about his sources. Perhaps someone had been indiscreet when she was staying at the Palace of Woodstock, perhaps Rosamond had been in touch, or Geoffrey Plantagenet. Could it have been FitzUrse who was part of that team of Henry's aides who galloped about organising the King's moves and messages, or even one of the others in that close-knit little band? Be that as it may, Becket pre-empted her and asked Eleanor for the full story and she felt much relief in unburdening herself. Then, to her own astonishment, she fell to her knees and begged the Archbishop's absolution, which he readily gave. Eleanor felt an intense relief for she was not an unduly Godly woman.

The news of Saladin gave immense pleasure to Eleanor. Ayub had sadly died, Becket knew not when, and the upbringing of their son had been transferred to and undertaken by his brother Shirkuh. Eleanor recalled that it had been the hands of that very formidable warrior who had slain her dear uncle, Raymond of Antioch, nineteen years earlier. Shirkuh had recently blooded Saladin in a successful campaign involving the invasion of Egypt. At the culmination of that expedition Saladin had been appointed vizier in Egypt, a well-merited and deserved honour for such a young man.

As they came to their parting, Eleanor asked Thomas, 'Was it what we did together on that fateful night which changed your whole life?'

Becket nodded as tears sprang to his eyes. 'I could never have given you what you wanted. What has to be, has to be. Let it be thus.' And he put his hand into hers and they each went on their respective ways.

* * *

Geoffrey Plantagenet rejoined his father's court and brought his mother across for a few days so that she could spend time with his father in France. Henry's schedule had been intense and it was a pleasant interlude for them all. Upon Rosamond's return she had taken the opportunity to see Becket. Thus it was that Becket had been apprised of the happenings at Everswell. She too implored the obstinate Archbishop to be conciliatory.

190

Rosamond took the opportunity to remind Henry of his long-unfulfilled promise to the hermit at Westbury to appoint a priest for the cure of the souls of that village where Becket had ordered the new church to be built. She reminded the King of her kins-man, Walter Map, whose family had rendered service both to the Cliffords and to the Empress Matilda's cause during the sad and rebellious times of the previous reign. Map had studied in Paris during his teenage years under distinguished tutors and had returned to England in 1162. Henry had noticed the clerk's potential and had employed him in his household as an itinerant member of his justiciary. Henry had always found him an amus-ing and stimulating man and much enjoyed his company, so he agreed that Map needed an extra dimension to his responsibili-ties. He called him in and charged him with the living of the vicarage at Westbury.

'This is not to say that I am sticking you in a rural backwater to rot with the locals. You are far too valuable to me here and I have noted you always except Jews and Cistercians from your oath to do justice to all men, as you say that it is absurd to do justice to those who are just to none. Be that as it may, I have promised that a priest of calibre will be appointed to Westbury and you will find yourself a curate who will be answerable to you for the discharge of his duties. You already know that I often hunt the nearby Vale of Castiard and stay as often as I can at Flaxley Abbey some three miles away. My lady Rosamond spends as much time as she can there with my children. She will give you all the help and advice that you may require.'

Walter was duly grateful and sped on his way to fulfil his mis-sion. Rosamond had a mild unease about his prejudice towards Cistercians and whether this would cause problems at Flaxley later on. However, she also knew that, with the continuing ban-ishment of Becket, the duties that he had undertaken so suc-cessfully as chancellor had gone by default. Henry had still not replaced Becket and far too many matters both great and small had failed to be done and many had begun to notice this. But the King was not overly receptive to advice of this nature and his temper, especially where it concerned his relations with Becket, was not to be trifled with.

* * *

There was yet another meeting in November between Louis and Henry near Paris to see if the simmering row between Becket and his king could move towards an acceptable resolution. Becket presented a petition which, to some extent, was conciliatory but Henry objected to two aspects. There was a limited submission by the Archbishop and many felt that a breakthrough could be imminent. But Becket's final words destroyed all that had taken place. He qualified his plea which included some form of arbitration by adding the rider, 'saving the honour of God'. Henry knew what this could mean and immediately flew into a rage. Further efforts at bridging the gap were made but Becket reverted to his trait of obstinacy, whereas Henry, who had earlier lost much sympathy, regained the support of those present. They parted in rancour and with no sign of the kiss of peace. If anything Henry had made more progress than Becket.

But Becket still had a card to play: he proclaimed that unless Henry withdrew his banishment and reinstated his archbishop before 2 February 1170, the kingdom of England would be placed under an interdict.

Another appeal to the Pope went winging on its way. But Alexander was again in trouble and his palace at Rome was under threat from the German emperor's forces, who were protagonists of the anti-Pope. It was suspected that English money was subsidising this expedition. Alexander played for time and responded by sending two cardinal delegates to report on and, if possible, resolve these issues. Becket was evasive and could not be pinned down. Henry gave the delegates a rough ride, telling them that he gave not a fig for them.

Henry was now desirous of effecting a reconciliation without the intervention of the Pope. He took his legitimate son, Geoffrey, who had been invested with the title Count of Brittany, to Paris. This was ostensibly not only for Geoffrey to pay homage to Louis for his investiture but also to pray at the shrine of St Denis and to meet Louis' long awaited son, Philippe-Augustus, now a precocious three-year-old infant who had the temerity to advise Henry to love the French, honour the King and show more devotion to the Church. Luckily for all Henry took this in good part.

Henry and Geoffrey spent Christmas at Nantes. Eleanor probably spent Christmas with some, if not all, of her children at Poitiers.

In January 1170 Henry spent a few days in Brittany, then moved to Normandy where he suggested a meeting with Becket at Caen. But whilst Becket was on his way he learnt that Henry had suddenly departed for England, arriving in mid-February much delayed by a stormy crossing. Henry's intention now was to set in motion the coronation of Prince Henry as his nominated successor to the throne of England and decided to avoid meeting Becket for this reason. This matter was fraught with difficulty as the only prelate licensed for a coronation was the Archbishop of Canterbury and Becket was still in exile. Henry knew that there was no English precedent for such a coronation when there was already a reigning king on the throne. It was, in his opinion, simply a device to ensure that upon his demise an orderly succession would ensue besides giving his eldest son some responsibility and experience of governing. In fact it was intended to be an exercise in decentralised management. Henry was ready to trample on Becket's feelings and reactions and there were to be additional personality problems which would intrude.

Eleanor meantime was busy, with Henry's support and agreement, with the arrangements for the solemn installation of Richard as the Duke of Aquitaine for much the same reasons. Under Aquitainean practice this was to be a far more sacred installation than the English ceremony. Prince Henry was staying with his mother during the early stages of these negotiations.

Henry had some delicate negotiations with his nobles and prelates in England to secure their support for his plans and Becket soon became aware of what was going on. Henry decided to close all the ports to prevent any unlicensed landing by Thomas or his followers.

On 31 May Richard was enthroned at Poitiers and then, in Limoges, took the virgin martyr Saint Valerie's ring which symbolised his marriage to the dukedom of Aquitaine. It was a most solemn occasion. Eleanor then returned post-haste to Normandy to reinforce the Channel port blockade. The young Prince Henry was dispatched on 5 June to London with an entourage which included two Norman bishops supportive of Henry. As the Pope had not sanctioned the coronation, Becket was on strong grounds to instruct both the Bishop of Nevers and Henry's cousin Bishop

Roger of Worcester (son of Earl Robert of Gloucester) to impose proscription and excommunication on all prelates who were intending to be involved in the ceremony. But Eleanor was a match for this ruse and the two bishops were prevented from crossing the Channel.

The rivalry between the Archbishops of Canterbury and of York had long been an intense matter of dispute. A compromise had seemed to solve some of the problems. York was made Primate of England and this was intended to give him country-wide authority. Then to compensate, Canterbury became Primate of *all* England. So the two arch prelates were back to square one. In Becket's early days whilst he was in the household of Archbishop Theobald, his career suffered a distinct setback when he twice crossed swords with Roger Pont L'Eveque who was also a cadet member in the same court. Roger told him then in no uncertain terms that he, Becket, was consumed with envy and would frequently break into unseemly language. He added that this clerk was nothing more than a '*baillehache*', which literally means 'a water-axe', and that Becket was either a bellyache or a ball's ache. It took Becket many years to put his career back on course. There never was and never would be any love lost between Roger and Thomas. Roger Pont L'Eveque was now the Archbishop of York and had willingly agreed to crown Prince Henry.

On 14 June Prince Henry was crowned King of England by Roger of York supported by a goodly array of bishops and nobles and in the presence of the young king's father. There was one notable absentee – young Henry's wife, the child Margaret, Louis VII's daughter who might also have been expected to be crowned as Queen at the same time as her husband. This slight was soon capitalised upon.

There was no expense spared for the festivities and the crowds were suitably and indeed lavishly entertained. During the ensuing banquet for the magnates in Westminster Hall, an interesting episode occurred which would be the precursor of future problems. The centrepiece of the feast was to be a dressed boar's head which was brought to the principal guest, the young king, by his father as a signal of honour to his first-born, now the 'king' of England.

Roger of York said, with a quick wit, 'Not every prince can be served at table by a king.'

To which young Henry riposted, 'It is no condescension for the son of a count to serve the king.'

There is no comment how this insult was received but young Henry was not presented with the sceptre after this feast and was kept in England to resume his studies under the auspices of William Marshal.

After the coronation Hugh de Morville was sent on a judicial mission to Cumberland and Northumberland during which assignment he was allowed to spend some time with the wife whom he had recently married, Helwis de Stuteville, an heiress through whom he had acquired the castle of Knaresborough. By the early autumn de Morville was back in France with the King.

Henry returned to Falaise at the end of June to rejoin Eleanor and chanced to meet his cousin, Bishop Roger of Worcester, and rebuked him with characteristic anger at his absence from young Henry's coronation, reminding him not only of their kinship but also of his duty as a prelate to be present. Roger sought to allay the fury by explaining that the royal mandate forbade him from seeking a passage. Henry retorted angrily that his Queen would hardly countermand his own summons, at which the Bishop with great diplomacy refused to implicate the Queen in any way, saying that he would prefer to take the full blame himself rather than the King should blame his wife: 'Better I should lose a leg than she should suffer one harsh word from you.'

Nevertheless Eleanor *had* stopped Roger from going across with his authority for imposition and excommunication and she was not going to accept this effort to stop the coronation of her eldest son. Had Henry known this there is little doubt that he would have approved.

Henry's next diplomatic problem was to pacify the irate Louis who was furious at the absence of Margaret from the crowning ceremony. Louis now invaded Normandy to show that he was not to be trifled with. Henry reminded Louis that the timing of young Henry's coronation could not be delayed any longer and he was conscious that his liege lord in France would not have been happy for this ceremony for Margaret to have been undertaken by anyone other than the primate of all England. As far as young Henry was concerned they had had to use the services of the remaining Archbishop who had been deputising for Becket for so many years. Thus, the sooner that Becket could be brought to his senses the better for all, and then he could fulfil the duty that was his to perform and both of the young sovereigns could be recrowned with due pomp and ceremony. Louis had the grace to accept this explanation and undertook yet again to orchestrate another meeting on 20 July at Freteval.

Both parties showed much more restraint and goodwill than they had for a very long time. Unusually for Henry he was most contrite and promised to make amends. His insult to Canterbury would be rectified by the recrowning of both young Henry and Margaret. He did quote a precedence for the use of York but re-iterated how much pleasure it would give him to see Becket crown the young Prince who had been brought up in his household all those years ago. He reminded Thomas how much love and respect the new king still had for his mentor. He went on to say how he was aware that he had wronged the Church in so many ways and looked forward to a much happier future for both of them.

There was only one sticking point in respect of the absolution for those bishops under excommunication. It was agreed that this would be subject to reformation by those bishops of their errors. The delicate agreement held but the flashpoint was all too near. Each of them had kept something back – Becket kept his author-ity over his bishops and Henry withheld the kiss of peace. As Henry and Thomas parted, the King shed tears, as he could so easily do, and held the Archbishop's stirrup to help him mount.

Henry immediately had second thoughts as he felt that he had conceded too much. As was his wont, when these feelings came upon him, he undertook a series of unpremeditated visits with-out disclosing where he was going. Becket was unable therefore to tie him down and make suitable arrangements for their return to England together. Almost immediately afterwards Henry suf-fered a severe fever and, at one stage, this was so serious that all despaired of his life.

However, he recovered with his ebullience undiminished so that in October he and Becket finally met at Chaumont, where the final terms were at last agreed although Henry still refused the kiss of peace until they were both back in England. The King wrote to his son, the young Henry, authorising Becket's return as he had made his peace with him. At this stage neither pushed for this last act of reconciliation. Becket was about to be on his way back to Canterbury at last.

Becket's parting words were prescient: 'My heart tells me that I shall see you no more in this life.'

They were due to meet at Rouen for the crossing but Henry could not be present as he had to quell an uprising in the Auvergne. He had deputed John of Oxford to accompany Thomas on his voyage of return which was hardly tactful. John had been excommunicated by Becket a few years before for damnable traffic with schismatics and they were still implacable enemies. Becket's expectation of a triumphal return to his archdiocese accompanied by the King with due honour and affection was in tatters. He did not have any means, so the Archbishop of Rouen gave him enough money to hire one ship only.

He landed on 1 December at Sandwich virtually six years to the day after he had fled from that very port. He immediately suspended Roger of York and excommunicated yet again Gilbert Foliot of London and John of Salisbury who promptly departed for France to complain to the King. Becket was welcomed with acclamation by the townsfolk and many from the countryside flooded in to greet his return. The nobles took no notice whatsoever. The young 'king' did not make any move to come and see him but stayed pointedly at Winchester.

Becket then wrote to the Pope telling him that he had excommunicated those bishops until they submitted to his authority but that they had refused unless and until the King's wishes were made known. He then departed for Woodstock where the young 'king' was to spend Christmas. The warmth of welcome from the citizens of London where he stayed *en route* was most reassuring. On 18 December, young Henry sent a message that Becket was not welcome at Woodstock and that, on behalf of his father, he instructed the Archbishop to return forthwith to Canterbury where he was to celebrate Christmas in his own cathedral church. Becket entered his city on bare feet amid acclamation and tears of joy from the common folk.

On Christmas Day, Thomas celebrated Mass in the cathedral during which he prayed for the Pope, the King and the common people. Then he delivered a sermon in which he reiterated his condemnation of the recalcitrant bishops whom he had suspended and excommunicated and added to this list one Nigel, denigrated by him as a violent oppressor of the Church, the Vicar of de Hardres and Robert de Broc, the castellain of

Saltwood Castle who had impounded some victuals destined for the chapter's Christmas table.

* * *

Henry had gathered with his family for the Christmas season which was to be celebrated at the castle of Bures near Bayeux. There he was joined by Eleanor, being the first time that she had been with him for three years, and she brought with her Richard, Geoffrey, Joanna and John. It was intended to be a joyous family Christmas. Young Henry was holding his own court in Woodstock as was befitting of his new rank. The court was also gathered together in strength.

On Christmas Day there burst upon this happy family scene the three angry bishops who had sped from England in protest and they poured out their story of Becket's perfidy and continued arrogance. They described his questionable actions and the suspicions of those in London, who considered that he was intending an uprising and they described a number of armed clashes.

Henry was uncontrollable. He flew into paroxysms of rage, he foamed at the mouth, his grey eyes glowed like coals of fire, he gnawed the rushes. The assembled company, used to similar scenes, had never seen him so angry and they even worried for his survival.

The King cursed the ingratitude of his erstwhile friend and colleague. He cursed those whom he had promoted and upon whom he relied. He cursed those whom he had succoured and helped and who broke his bread and drank his wine at his table and helped him not in his hour of need. He cursed the cowardice of his entourage. He cursed the baseness of those contemptible associates who were men of no action, when action was so essential.

To allay and assuage this wrath, one of his barons said ill-advisedly, 'So long as Thomas lives, you will never know an hour of peace.'

And said another, 'Maybe plait a rope around this traitor's neck and hoist him upon the gallows.'

'Who will rid me of this turbulent priest?' roared the enraged King.

Eleanor almost wished that Rosamond could have been there

198

to calm Henry's dreadful spasms. She had often wondered if her husband did not suffer from the dreaded falling sickness.

His four closest aides, Reginald FitzUrse, William Tracy, Hugh de Morville and Richard le Breton slipped out from the assembled throng. These four men of court had shared so many fortunes and misfortunes over the years that they had now formed a close and natural bonding besides needing the support of their King. Three of them had been present at the death of Earl Milo and each suspected that one of them might have been his murderer, so their conduct each to the other had always been suitably wary. Reginald and his family had been close to the de Mandevilles who had played such an equivocal part in Stephen's reign. That family was now beginning to be restored to favour but there were still many reservations about their loyalty. FitzUrse had tried to seduce Rosamond and that was very dangerous especially as Becket had been made aware of what he had tried to do. Becket could so easily tell the King, whose rage would be devastating to both Rosamond and himself. Becket's death would surely solve a problem for FitzUrse. William Tracy's mother, or perhaps it was his aunt, was an illegitimate daughter of Henry's grandfather and hence may have been a cousin of the King who always treated him as part of his kinfolk. William's family loyalty to the King was transparent and was never questioned. De Morville had been an ardent supporter of Stephen and an associate of that king's disreputable son, Eustace, who had been murdered under questionable circumstances thus clearing the succession line for Henry. Hugh had come out of this episode with some skill and much credit but his family were not respected and considered untrustworthy. De Morville was always treated as an outsider. None of these three knew much about Brito, who had been thrust upon them. He was said to have rendered a service to the King, possibly saving his life, for which he was continuing to be rewarded and he never wavered in his adoration of Henry. But he always had his own agenda which he kept close to his chest.

All four of them still needed to have the major rewards due to the close servants of the King and were always struggling to prove themselves. They had been trained to implement the King's wishes and commands without any delay. Here at long last was their golden opportunity for reward and glory.

199

They now sped towards Canterbury.

The party at Bures suddenly became aware that the hot-headed four 'in the flower of their age' were missing from the gathering. Three of the court were dispatched to intercept them and a sense of foreboding further dampened the festive season.

*   *   *

On the evening of 29 December 1170, Thomas was praying in his chamber with some of his monks when the four knights burst in upon him and presented an ultimatum that he immediately absolve the three bishops under interdict and restore them to their sacred duties. Becket refused point blank saying that he had the support of the Pope whose authority he could not override unless the bishops submitted completely to his command. The knights then withdrew with anger in their hearts.

Thomas then prepared himself for vespers in the cathedral. His staff implored him not to go for his safety's sake but he refused. They wanted to lock the doors of the church but were rebuked as the House of God was not to be made into a castle. The knights, now fully armed followed him in the gloaming with dreadful menace. They entered the church and shouted, 'Where is that betrayer of the King? Where is the Archbishop?'

Thomas came down the steps of the presbytery and turned to them and replied, 'If you seek me, I am here. I am no traitor, I am a priest of God.' He then made the sign of the Cross and fell to his knees in prayer.

'Wretch!' cried Reginald. He struck off Becket's cap with his sword and they again demanded the absolution of the bishops.

'I am no traitor,' Becket repeated. 'I will not stir hence. I shall not absolve these priests who have defied me and God.'

They threatened him again and he responded, 'Slay me here if you will, but if you touch any of my people with me you shall be for ever accursed.'

The monks in the cathedral now fled in terror except for Edward Grim, who bore the Cross and now tried to protect the Archbishop. An incredible calmness came over Thomas who now realised that he was facing martyrdom. He bowed his head, covered his eyes and said, 'To God and the blessed Mary, to the patron saints of this church and to St Denys, I commend myself and the Church's cause.'

200

FitzUrse struck the first blow, removing the crown of Becket's head and leaving a gash, the blow having been partly diverted by Grim springing forward and taking the main force of the sword upon his arm, which was nearly severed. Thomas received a second and a third blow on his head administered by William Tracy. Richard le Breton then administered the fourth and final blow with such force that his sword was shattered on the pavement. As he did this, he cried out with venom, 'Take that for love of my lord William, *my king's brother*, whose marriage with the Countess de Warrenne you prohibited!'

As he died, Becket said, 'Lord, I am now ready to embrace death. Into thy hands I commend my spirit.'

His blood poured from his grievous wounds, staining the floor with red mingled with the white of his brain.

Hugh de Morville had been guarding the door to prevent the entry of those without and did not take part in the actual murder.

A treacherous subdeacon, one Hugh Mauclerc from Horsea, who had given the knights the access that they had needed now entered and, with a macabre gesture, put the point of his sword into the Archbishop's skull and extracted the brains intermingled with blood and scattered them all over the chapel. He then led the knights to their escape from the scene.

Within minutes of the outrage the heavens opened and a storm of unprecedented ferocity broke upon the city. Rain fell and lashed the ground, thunder rolled about the heavens and the sky became blood red, seemingly as a protest at the unspeakable crime that had been committed.

The body of Thomas was recovered by the monks and placed on the high altar overnight. They became aware of the horsehair shirt that he wore beneath his canonical clothes and the privations that he had endured and the mortifications of the flesh to which he had subjected himself. On the following day he was buried temporarily and privately in the crypt as the church had been desecrated and would need to be rededicated. Within a remarkably short time the grave became a place of pilgrimage, visions and miracles.

* * *

Henry dismissed the Christmas court and moved to Argentan to

201

await news, which was brought by messengers from Canterbury late on the last day of December 1170. Their description of the scenes in the city and their cathedral were graphic. The populace were stunned and appalled and the monks were in terror. All were in panic. Such a crime in God's house had never taken place within living memory.

Henry was utterly shattered. His intemperate words had borne fruit but they were as far from his intentions as they could be. Those who knew him always realised that his rages passed and calm returned as quickly as the storm had erupted. Henry's grief was terrible to behold. He went into solitude and refused all food and drink. He threw off his clothes and went into sackcloth. His retreat was absolute and no one could approach him. His groans, prayers and lamentations were terrible to hear – so much so that his household feared for his life such was the intensity of his sorrow. It is said that he was in solitude for forty days.

The shock that permeated Christendom was appalling and all leaders reviled Henry and demanded that the direst penalties be imposed upon him. Even young Henry, who had rejected Becket's approach for Christmas with such coldness and abruptness, denigrated his father's appalling behaviour to his archbishop, 'his very dear friend and foster-father'. He distanced himself from any involvement in the murder. The rift between the young king and the old king began to widen perceptibly.

Henry immediately dispatched envoys to the Pope pleading his innocence and reassuring him that all that his words were given in anger and not with any intent of causing death to one who had been for so long his friend and confidant. The Archbishop of Rouen came to Henry to give him spiritual comfort and the Bishop of Lisieux interceded for him with Pope Alexander, who was said to have had a vision of Becket's chasuble changing its colour to blood red.

Henry submitted himself with all humility to the judgement of the Church and accepted whatever penance might be imposed upon him. Pope Alexander reacted with remarkable restraint despite the pressures placed upon him by Henry's enemies. At Easter he excommunicated those 'satellites of Satan', as he described Becket's murderers. He placed Henry's Continental possessions under interdict but not England – after all it was not England that had perpetrated the crime. He soon lifted the

Continental interdict. He did not excommunicate Henry as he was expected to do, but forbade him to enter consecrated ground until he had been absolved.

* * *

The four knights fled first to Saltwood Castle where they sought immediate shelter and safety with Robert de Broc, he who had been excommunicated so recently by Becket. They were said to be glorying in their deed although William Tracy said afterwards that they were overwhelmed with a sense of their guilt. Two days later they went to South Malling near Lewes in Sussex, where it was said that on undoing their armour and placing it upon a table, the table cast these from its surface onto the floor – a veritable miracle.

At Easter, when they were excommunicated by the Pope, they fled to Scotland where they were threatened with hanging. They then returned to England and found refuge with de Morville in his castle at Knaresborough where they remained for the next year in some comparative safety, albeit in misery and increasingly straitened circumstances, shunned by all those in the neighbourhood. It is said that even the dogs refused to eat the morsels of meat that fell from their plates.

Then in some desperation they approached Henry for mercy, but he was nonplussed about what to do with them and much embarrassed, especially as they were outside his jurisdiction, having murdered a priest. So he referred them to the Pope.

* * *

What now follows in the lives of the four knights is much obscured. There are a number of legends. But first we shall look at that extraordinary statement made by Brito as he administered the coup de grâce on Becket's skull with such ferocity. The source is from William FitzStephen who wrote a life of Becket in 1180 and was not only his one-time secretary but claims to have been an eyewitness of the murder. But the Lord William was not Henry's brother but Stephen's younger son and brother of the vicious and useless Eustace. William was an amiable and totally unambitious man who was, in effect, bought off by Henry and married to the wealthy heiress Isabel de Warrenne. They had no children and William died at the siege of Toulouse in 1160. Subsequently the widow Isobel married Hameline, Henry's illegitimate half-brother. So Brito's cry of rage is inaccurate on several counts, not least that Becket stopped the marriage. This story gives the only account of Brito's murderous intent, even though the reason for it still eludes us.

Reverting to the legends, the first is that they all died within two years of their crime. The second is that Reginald FitzUrse fled to Ireland and founded the Irish family of McMahon on the somewhat specious theory that both his Norman name and the Irish name, McMahon, mean 'the son of a bear'.

William Tracy is said to have confessed his sins to the Bishop of Exeter in whose diocese the Tracy lands in Devonshire lay. He is also said to have stated that they had been compelled to swear to the King that they must slay the primate – but this story is extremely improbable. Tracy is also reputed to have become a steward or seneschal in Normandy from 1174 to 1176. The most likely story is that he was in the papal court in 1172 and that he went from there to the Holy Land on his penance, but upon reaching Cosenza in Sicily he was smitten with a dreadful wasting disease whereby his flesh decayed whilst he was alive and he died in agony praying all the while to St Thomas. The Tracy family survived in either the direct or the indirect lines and during the seventeenth century a barony was conferred upon a Tracy of Toddington. This peerage became extinct a hundred years later.

A further story involves their banishment to the Holy Land to expiate their sins, perhaps for fourteen years. Before going, FitzUrse gave half his manor of Williton in Somerset to his brother and half to the Knights of St John. All of them did their penance on the 'Black Mountain', a site never located but probably in the Holy Land. They were reputed to have died there and were buried in Jerusalem before the door of the Templars' church.

De Morville is reputed to have returned to Knaresborough, obtained a royal pardon and a licence to hold a market at Kirkoswald in Cumberland. His wife was still alive until the new century and Hugh is alleged to have died in 1204 leaving two daughters who both married well. It is more probable that this Hugh de Morville was a namesake of greater respectability and probity. The sword of de Morville was said to have been long preserved in Carlisle Cathedral.

Of Brito nothing more is recorded. William Brewer, a powerful justiciar in the reigns of Richard and John acquired half the fee of the house of Brito. Brewer's nephew married one of the daughters of the above de Morville. But that is all we know and it is all very tenuous, except that the great and the good of those times all knew each other and were often interconnected in one way or another. So they all probably took a low profile, and a trip to the Holy Land gave them good cover until they were called to account by the Good Lord.

We react to what actually happened in history and the life and death of Becket is a classic case of something that went disastrously wrong. Perhaps it is worth a mild speculation on what might have happened if Henry's incredible inspiration of choosing Becket for the see of Canterbury had pursued the course that he and Becket had always wanted. There is no doubt that the abuses by the clergy in civil crimes were in need of a major overhaul, but would it have worked out as they wished?

Thomas was an extremely intelligent man and trained as a lawyer but he was not an intellectual. He was an excellent adjutant and administrator, his attention to detail was meticulous and his industry remarkable. He was also a good delegator and his ability to choose a high standard of clerk in his civil service took much of the humdrum workload off his shoulders, but he always kept a close eye on what was being done in his name. He was not a mover and shaker. When he accepted the archbishopric he was his own master and he became a barrack-room lawyer. It was much easier to resist and say 'no' than to initiate reforms or create a new deal to the general advantage. It is possible that he thought that the abolition of long-standing laws and their replacement by hastily conceived and ill-drafted legislation would create more problems than it solved.

Then there is the curious legend concerning the origin of his mother. The Dictionary of National Biography says that she may have been a Saracen emir's daughter who liberated his father, Gilbert, who was being held to ransom after the First Crusade. We tend to forget that the Near East always had a strong Christian tradition. The Churches in Egypt, Syria and the present Lebanon are particularly noteworthy. There would have been many cross-faith marriages and Rohesia, Becket's possible Saracen mother, could have had a Christian mother, thus exposing her to this influence. Becket's visage was swarthy and he was tall, dark and handsome and there is a stained-glass window depicting him thus. Becket had a powerful ascetic streak and a fanaticism commonly associated with Muslims and Christians in the Near and Middle East. There are many of mixed blood in all generations in every country but Thomas may not have been easily accepted in England and, as a consequence, have developed a chip. Bearing in mind that we consider that

205

Eleanor had had that affair with Saladin's father, she would have understood this problem and found much in common with Becket when they first came together.

There is also the astonishing and unexplained personality change that he underwent between his, albeit reluctant, acceptance of his new role and his consecration. This I have suggested was due to the intervention of the full-blooded and still lusty Eleanor. It certainly makes sense and explains much that then came to pass. Eleanor kept herself very much in the background during his long banishment but she still had communication with him and she would have had to maintain a rigid discretion. There is no reason to suppose that she may have seen him far more often than the extant records show.

Thomas certainly was not universally loved or respected by his peers. Gilbert Foliot called him a fool. Thomas was an obstinate man with no idea of compromise. He was, paradoxically, a simple and abstemious person and although he enjoyed the luxurious trappings of life with the King, he had a puritan streak. He was a showman, an actor, who enjoyed the dramas of life on the stage. These were the Saracen traits in his character. When he lost Henry, as he would have had to lose Henry, he lost the decision maker and he became directionless.

So what would have happened if he had conformed to Henry's concept? Sooner or later, I suggest, he would have fallen out with the King and events would not have been much different.

10

1171–1174

Eleanor was devastated by the death of Becket. She had to a great extent distanced herself from Henry's running battle with his archbishop but had always kept herself informed of what was going on. She had a great regard for Becket's abilities and, during the early years of their reign, had worked closely with him and had admired his considerable ability, taste and energy. She had made no secret of her own support for Becket's elevation to the primacy and had been more than secretly pleased that she had won her point of view over that of Henry's mother, who had steadfastly opposed this issue. Henry had almost always asked for the Empress Maud's advice and Eleanor was often irritated that her husband listened to his mother rather than herself. On this occasion she was delighted when Henry had agreed with her and was absolutely convinced that she had been right. But she was sadly all too aware of her own part in Becket's sudden volte-face and she had many times tried to bridge the gaps between these two obstinate and wilful men of such enormous ability. What is more, she had realised the potential these two had for correcting the evils that were bedevilling the relations between Church and State. Eleanor admired the fundamental sense of justice that Henry had always insisted upon for the country and she understood the administrative and practical flair that Becket possessed. She saw that the reconciliation, fragile though it always seemed, would recreate their original concept. The potential teamwork between them was one of those missed opportunities that would never now recur.

Becket's death removed her access to his private lines of communication with his Saracen forebears. She had never known how he knew what was going on in the Near East, but it was surprising how much trade activity took place and trusted couriers were always available to carry messages.

Eleanor understood all too well that the appalling outburst of her husband, however unbalanced, had reaped these dreadful consequences. There would always be those who would react as these four knights had done and she blamed Henry for what he had done. She was not such a fool to think that he, in any way, meant it and she would support him in his genuine efforts to mitigate the disaster. In her inmost heart she would never forgive him and she, for her part, would ensure that her sons would be guided and encouraged to run their own parts of the unwieldy Angevin empire. She was sufficiently wise and experienced to know that the four boys were intensely quarrelsome but she was determined to perform the matriarchal function and provide the focal point for them to succeed. She knew that she was embarking upon a dangerous strategy, but she was disturbed that Henry could lose everything by his inability to avoid making enemies and his tendency towards precipitating conflict. He rode a knife-edge and was continually upon the brink of disaster. His health had given them all a fright recently and he was beginning to age perceptibly.

Her first step was to distance herself from Henry and to lead her own life in her power base at Poitiers. This was the easiest to accomplish. She had, since the birth of John in 1166, made it clear that she was no longer prepared to give him his conjugal rights. Whether Eleanor was past childbearing age after John arrived is a moot point – she was forty-four at that time and some women can continue to reproduce well into their late forties or even early fifties. In any case Henry's affair with Rosamond was now well and truly out in the open after so many years of subterfuge and, although her background made her realistic, she was not best pleased that they had been living a double life for so long and that she had been so blind and unaware of it all. She was glad that she had had it out with Rosamond. She cast her mind back to her affair with Ayub and the warnings that Uncle Raymond had given then about the problems of harems in the Muslim world and her equivocal position in such surroundings. Ignoring the question of differing religions, she could see that she and Rosamond, in a Saracen context, would have been a powerful force for good in Henry's lifestyle. She was fond of

Geoffrey Plantagenet who had so many of Henry's characteristics. Her own children had a deep-rooted love for that Clifford woman who had provided far more of a mother figure than she had ever done, especially in their infancy. Rosamond had given them fun and games and organised their schooling and holidays and they all got on well with both Geoffrey and William Longspee. As an example of this, she knew that Rosamond and William Longspee had been welcomed in young Henry's Christmas gathering at Woodstock. She also remembered that Henry had always said that his grandfather, the first King Henry, had been adept in encouraging the extended family to keep together as a cohesive unit.

So it was that Eleanor reassessed her strengths and her weaknesses and analysed the opportunities and the threats to her position. She had refurbished her castle at Poitiers and brought it up to date. This made it not only comfortable but very elegant, unlike the Spartan and chaotic mess in which Henry lived. It gave her an especial pleasure to convert the tower which her lecherous grandfather, William the Troubadour, had built for his mistress into her own private quarters. Into these rooms, redolent of the seamy side of her grandfather's life, she admitted only those whom she particularly favoured.

She set about recreating the tradition of music, poetry and chivalry and to this end invited her daughter, Marie of Champagne, to host the revelries. Her court now was to include not only her young and nubile daughters, Eleanor and Joanna, but also her daughters-in-law: Margaret, who was married to young Henry; Alys, the daughter of Louis who was engaged to her son Richard; Constance of Brittany, the intended of Geoffrey; and Alix of Maurienne who was pledged to the six-year-old Prince John. Besides these, Henry's sister Emma of Anjou, her niece Isabel of Flanders and Ermengarde of Narbonne were all young and spirited beauties adding lustre and style to these gatherings. As many as sixty young ladies were known to throng the halls of pleasure intent on having fun and games with the young bloods. Eleanor's own sons were always coming and going as well as the young sons of the nobility in Aquitaine. Uncle Raoul's clan of relations were also enthusiastic participants.

Marie brought with her a talented and liberal cleric called Andrew the Chaplain who was deputed to write a book on the arts of courtly love (*Ars Amatoria*). This codified the tradition of chivalric behaviour and how it should be conducted. It was based upon the Roman affairs of the heart and went into considerable detail concerning the procedures for seduction. It described what should be worn, how to initiate an introduction, how to develop the acquaintance, how to pursue the target. The tactics of when to cool and when to inflame, when to please and when to torment were laid down to the last intimate detail. The value of gifts both from the emotional and the material viewpoint was important, and the frequency and timing of these should be meticulously planned. For instance, a lace handkerchief bedewed with wet kisses presented from a kneeling position at the right time could be of more value than a brooch or jewelled gift. This work of etiquette in noble society was intended to be followed exactly, without deviation.

Marie then superimposed the traditional Poitevin codes of courtly practice called 'courts of love'. Here the suppliant lover would bring his case to a court of ladies for their adjudication but always keeping a strict anonymity over the identity of his loved one. The jury would deliver their verdict and their judgement created a precedent. One said that 'mortal love is but the licking of honey from thorns'. And another asserted that 'ideal love can never exist between spouses'.

Marie also organised masques, jousts and tournaments which used up the surplus energies of all the young men and kept them out of mischief. The court also became a centre for troubadours to congregate and they were much encouraged to come.

All these escapades were intended to highlight the unassailable position of women in the life of the Poitevin nation and to give them a status not accorded elsewhere in the Western world of the time.

These frolics, and it should be said that there was much intense seriousness by many participants, became conspicuous and memorable for immorality, lechery and licentiousness. Eleanor's own reputation continued to be, not surprisingly, under intense scrutiny.

Eleanor now decided to build a small chapel at Mons near Belin to the south of Bordeaux on the pilgrim route to Santiago de Compostela. This was near a family château where she was reputed to have been born.

*   *   *

This admirable expression of filial duty has now given rise to the legend that this place was where she had innumerable of her bastards buried. Eleanor's fecundity in wedlock does not give her much time during her marriage to Henry to implement this alleged aspect of her life. It is possible that she may have had a bastard or two during this later period and the chapel may have been sufficiently near and discreet enough for some of her court to have wanted to use these facilities.

*   *   *

After Henry's recovery from his grief, he decided to resume his active life and to embark upon a series of manic activities. This was part of his tactics when under pressure to deviate attention from pressing problems that he was expected to attend to. He also took the view that, by allowing time to intervene, these pressures would diminish.

First he ensured an orderly takeover in Brittany for his legitimate son Geoffrey, who had now inherited that land upon the death of Count Conan, as arranged. On 6 August Henry landed in England and just arrived in time to be present at the deathbed of his cousin Henry of Blois, who had been Bishop of Winchester for so many years. Despite the bishop's frailty and age, he did not lose this opportunity to rebuke Henry for his part in the martyrdom of Becket. Henry and Rosamond then went to Frampton for a few days of hunting and relaxation and were joined by Geoffrey Plantagenet and young William Longspee. During this interlude serious news came from Ireland, then as always a thorn in the flesh of the English Crown.

A deputation of Irish nobles had approached Richard de Clare asking for assistance in bringing order and method into the prevailing turbulence in that country. Richard's mother was one of the many mistresses of Henry's grandfather, Henry I, but there is no record as to whether she had any children by him who would have been half-uncles or aunts to the King. But Henry was always loyal to his grandfather's memory and activities and he treated Richard as a kind of cousin and had a great admiration for his abilities. Moreover there was a relationship between the Clifford and the de Clare families. Richard had brought a force across the water and soon restored some semblance of order in

211

the province of Leinster which surrounded the pale of Dublin. As a result of his resounding success Richard became known as Strongbow, the name by which he is universally known to history.

As a reward from the Irish he was persuaded to take for his wife Eva, the beautiful daughter of Dermot McMurrough, one of the leading warrior kings in eastern Ireland. This led to Strongbow declaring himself to be king of Leinster, an action which was now to be violently opposed by Henry. Ireland was always regarded as a province of the English Crown and whilst the subjugation was very much in Henry's best interests, the unauthorised marriage and subsequent declaration of independence were most obnoxious to the King.

Strongbow was summoned to appear before Henry at Newnham at once. He dragged his feet so Henry threatened to confiscate all the de Clare properties in the west of England and, more importantly, the urgent reinforcements needed by Richard were to be stopped from going.

In September Strongbow deemed it expedient to arrive at Newnham where he was instructed to proceed at once to Flaxley, the resident hermit having made the appropriate arrangements for horses and advised Henry's party at the Abbey of his guest's landing. A good relationship was soon re-established between the King and Strongbow, not least due to the benign influence of his cousin Rosamond. She always had this extraordinary ability to defuse a potential explosion.

Henry decided to become personally involved with these problems in Ireland despite the fact that his mother, the Empress Maud, had dissuaded him from becoming embroiled in that country some years ago. Her reasons were cogent: she took the view that the Irish could never be controlled from England and that it was always a waste of time and resources to intervene. But to Henry now, it seemed opportune to mount a campaign especially as a diversionary tactic to draw attention away from his problems with the Church.

An agreement was made whereby Strongbow was to retain Leinster, and those nobles who joined and supported the conquest of Ireland should be rewarded with appropriate lands, estates and titles. The expedition was planned meticulously and 400 vessels, 5,000 men at arms and 500 knights with their horses

212

and accoutrements gathered to embark at Milford Haven in October. This force landed at Waterford a few days later where Henry was duly welcomed and due homage was paid to him.

The slight resistance was soon overcome when the Irish realised that Henry's military reputation and the strength of his army were far too great to be engaged in serious battle. Henry made his way to Dublin where he was proclaimed 'King of Hibernia', a title ratified in due course by the Pope. Strongbow was appointed chief justiciar of Ireland. Hugh de Lacy, a powerful West Country supporter of the Earl Robert, was appointed Lord of Meath and a justiciar of Ireland. Other notable personages who settled and contributed to the immediate stability of the country were Philip de Braose, whose cousin William had married Bertha, Earl Milo of Hereford's daughter, and Robert FitzStephen. Both were soon to be ennobled in the counties of Limerick and Cork.

Henry, ever the opportunist, reformed the Church in Ireland to correct a number of irregularities to bring it into closer alignment with the rest of Christendom. He knew that the timing of his zeal would ensure some considerable mitigation in his penances which would have to be exacted in due course.

Henry spent Christmas in Dublin and in April decided to make his way back to England and from there to Normandy. He had spent far too long away on a peripheral matter and had allowed too much time for his puppies to get up to mischief. Bad weather and contrary winds delayed him longer than he intended, but there were certain affairs that he wished to attend to first and papal legates could wait. He spent a few days with his old friend Gerald Cambrensis, recently appointed Archdeacon of St Davids, a younger son of the Pembroke family of de Barri. Gerald was tutored at Gloucester Abbey and later became a prolific writer on the stirring events that he witnessed. Henry was committed to cultivating the West Country mafia which had given so much support to his family during the disastrous reign of his predecessor, Stephen. Gerald needed the King's support for, upon taking up his duties, he tackled with great vigour many abuses in the Church in west Wales. Tithes had seldom been collected; he excommunicated not only a sheriff of Pembroke who had seized some cattle belonging to the Pembroke priory but also an archdeacon taken in concubinage. These excellent activities appealed to a king who was so dedicated to efficiency, energy and justice.

Henry also spent a stimulating few days with Walter Map who had already taken up his responsibilities at Westbury. Walter was a dreadful gossip and had a great sense of humour which lightened the seriousness of much of Henry's daily life. Later on, Map too wrote much about those times.

Before returning to France Henry and Rosamond spent a few days at Frampton and Flaxley. Rosamond took the opportunity to suggest that it was time for arrangements to be made for their son Geoffrey's involvement with his career in the Church to be initiated. Henry agreed and their son was anointed to minor orders as a deacon and made an archdeacon of Lincoln as well as endowed with a prebend at St Paul's. They both agreed that this would be the first step in a career that they knew to be full of promise and potential, besides giving him a sufficient income for the time being. Henry said that as soon as something suitable for his status became available he would be promoted accordingly. Rosamond now knew that she had taken the first step to fulfil her promise to Eleanor when they had had that extraordinary meeting at Everswell.

* * *

The day of reckoning for Henry's alleged crime could not now be avoided. His appearance was unexpectedly sudden. Communications with Dublin had been virtually non-existent but when he arrived in France Louis commented that 'Now in Ireland, now in England, now in Anjou, he rather seems to come on wings than by horse or boat.'

Henry went first to Savigny and found that the papal legates were unfriendly and uncompromising. He made it perfectly clear how far he was prepared to go and that he expected some concessions. He was prepared to be contrite but not as contrite as all that. With that, he left saying that he had plenty of important affairs that needed his immediate attention. He was persuaded to attend a second meeting at Avranches Cathedral at which young Henry would be present and the cardinals were also apprised of how far they could go. Both parties listened carefully.

The meeting was more reasonable on both sides. Henry submitted to an intense cross-examination and acquitted himself with

214

dignity and contrition. He swore that it was never his intention to seek the death of Becket and admitted that his intemperate rage was a factor which had led his evil associates to take the law into their own hands. His shock and sorrow when he was advised of the consequences were most grievous. He would submit himself to whatever penance the cardinals decided to impose and he was prepared to accept any Christian discipline. The cardinals accepted that Henry was not guilty of plotting or planning the death of the martyr and that he had purged his conscience. A substantial fine was imposed whereby the King paid an annual sum to maintain 200 soldiers in Jerusalem. Some of the Consitutions of Clarendon were mitigated. The estates of Canterbury were to be restored and all those who had been banished were to be allowed to return.

Finally the King was taken to the porch of the cathedral where sinners were flagellated. The King's outer garments were removed, under which it was seen that he wore a hair shirt. This too was removed to expose his bare back and the many monks were each instructed to give the prescribed number of lashes, at the end of which 'there was not a dry eye amongst those present – not even the cardinals'.

On 11 June Eleanor arranged for a further ceremony for her favourite son, Richard, at the abbey church at Limoges. He was invested with the ring of St Valerie, symbolising his marriage to the dukedom of Aquitaine, the title by which he was now to be known. Unlike his less fortunate elder brother, young Henry, he took over most of his duties from his mother. However there was one vital difference between them. Eleanor remained his guide and mentor and he took her advice from time to time. The young king wanted entire independence from his father and was not inclined to pay any attention to the freely proffered advice.

Arrangements were now made to crown young Henry with his wife Margaret, to fulfil the promise made by Henry after the first crowning of the young king in 1170. This was done on 21 August 1172 by the Bishop of Evreux – the see of Canterbury being still vacant. Roger Pont L'Eveque of York, Gilbert Foliot of London and John of Salisbury, who had all participated in the first crowning of young Henry, were tactfully encouraged to be absent; a stratagem endorsed by both the Pope and Louis whose support was so vital.

In November Louis invited his daughter Margaret and her husband, young Henry, to pay a visit to Paris. Ostensibly this was to be a family gathering but Louis was well aware that there was a growing revolt between Henry and his children, mainly focused upon his son-in-law. The opportunity for mischief was too good to miss. *En route*, young Henry called upon his father and delivered an ultimatum demanding full responsibility for his inheritance, complaining at the same time how his expenses far outstripped his meagre income. He added fuel to the fire by comparing his lot with his younger brother, Richard, the Duke of Aquitaine. Henry refused outright and rebuked his son for asking before he had learnt his business.

Louis naturally took the part of young Henry and encouraged him to pursue his request. Henry, now very suspicious, summoned them back to him for Christmas. Young Henry departed from Paris with anger in his heart and refused to stay for Christmas. Instead he invited all knights named William in Normandy to attend a banquet at his expense at which 110 appeared. By this time young Henry was under the pernicious influence of an itinerant and sinister troubadour called Bertran de Born. However, young Henry did make an attempt at bridging this show of independence with his father. He asked his mentor William Marshal to approach the King and ask whether his half-brother, William Longspee, a strapping lad now aged fifteen, could participate. Henry's immediate reaction was one of anger at this impertinent suggestion, but Marshal was diplomatic and persuasive and, more judiciously, obtained Rosamond's support. She defused Henry's fury and suggested that this would be to Longspee's advantage and of immense benefit to keeping relations and communications on an affable basis between the two families. She reminded the King how his grandfather had always achieved amity in similar circumstances. Henry, somewhat to his own surprise and certainly to the surprise of those in his immediate entourage, agreed. Willliam Longspee, armed with a new sword from the foundry at Flaxley, covered himself with credit in the preliminary jousting and acquitted himself well on this happy occasion. William Marshal kept a fatherly eye on the lad and young Henry was most impressed with his junior half-brother.

Henry and Eleanor, with Richard and Geoffrey, spent a subdued Christmas at Chinon. There were serious signs of dissension in the air and the impertinent and juvenile reaction from the King's eldest son created a hostile atmosphere.

In January young Henry was summoned back to Anjou. Henry was quite determined to train his son into his duties and was disinclined to allow any leeway. Young Henry was marched off to Auvergne where there were preliminary discussions over a complex series of negotiations which Henry was adept at undertaking and which often confused the participants. The elder king however omitted to tell his son of one significant aspect. The court then migrated to Limoges on 21 February for a series of festivities combined with serious business which lasted a week.

Four powerful potentates attended: Alfonso and Sancho, respectively the Kings of Aragon and Navarre, together with the Counts Humbert of Maurienne and Raymond of Toulouse. Raymond, at long last, agreed that he owed suzerainty to Eleanor and paid due homage, but it should be noted that this volte-face was due to a violent disagreement with Louis arising out of the Count's refusal to marry the King's sister. Raymond played a masterly double game by encouraging Eleanor, his new overlord, to continue her plotting over the future of her sons' interests and to listen to her devious uncle Raoul's machinations with greater attention. He then privately tipped Henry off to watch his back: 'I advise you, king, to beware of your wife and sons,' he said with astonishing duplicity.

Humbert and Henry then delivered their shock to young Henry and announced the betrothal of his youngest brother, John, to Humbert's daughter Alix. This, in itself, was not too dispiriting for young Henry but it was the ancillary deals which made him furious. John was allocated several estates in the Midlands of England as well as three important castles in Normandy – those of Chinon, Loudun and Mirebeau – all of which were part of his own possessions. His father had omitted to tell him that he was to give them away. And to add insult to injury, young Henry was obliged to sign the marriage treaty.

On the day that all these negotiations began, Pope Alexander canonised Becket in response to popular demand. The scale of attested miracles at the shrine and the vast number of pilgrims who flocked to Canterbury were incontrovertible evidence that Becket was in the great tradition of Christian martyrs. Canterbury Cathedral's finances were now restored to a firm footing after many years of negligence and raiding by the King's representatives.

Young Henry was incoherent with anger at the contempt with which he was being treated by his father. He complained vociferously that his father had no right to give his own properties to John and that he continued to have no responsibilities or control in his own kingdom, let alone any adequate income to support his court and lifestyle. He continued to compare his lot with his two younger brothers who were going from strength to strength. Henry refused to give any concessions but he was firmly reminded that Louis had made his wishes and support for young Henry quite clear. Henry now realised that his back certainly needed watching but it was still inconceivable to him that Eleanor would forget her marriage vows of obedience to her wedded husband, a heinous sin against the laws of the Church.

Early in March he reduced young Henry's entourage which would go some way to controlling his expenditure and remove some seditious influences. His son's fury escalated further and Henry became convinced that his main problem of loyalty was with his eldest son. Eleanor, accompanied by Richard and Geoffrey, now went to Poitiers. Henry took young Henry back to Chinon. His son accompanied him with anger and reluctance. On 5 March Henry made young Henry sleep in the same room, thus intending to keep him in his sight the whole time, a naïve idea little likely to succeed.

Young Henry bribed the castle guards to lower the drawbridge during the night and fled towards Paris. Henry awoke in the morning to discover that the bird had flown the nest. A posse was dispatched to catch up but young Henry had had too much of a start and had craftily laid a false trail. The pursuers were led to believe that he was aiming for Normandy and then discovered that he had crossed the Loire. Henry gave chase towards Le Mans, Alencon and Argentan but the fugitive swung east to the safety of Paris.

Henry sent an embassy of bishops to Louis to demand the return of his son, and they immediately fell into a neat trap set by the French king.

'Who sends this message to me?' asked Louis.

'The King of England,' responded the spokesman of the deputation.

'This cannot be so,' was the reply. 'The King of England is here with me as you see.'

The prelates expostulated, but Louis rubbed salt in their wounds. 'You may be referring to your King's father, the one-time King of England who is no longer your King, but who still endeavours to act as such, having resigned his kingdom to his son, here present.'

Louis was on weak ground in his argument, as the French practice had always been for the reigning king to arrange for his successor to be crowned during his lifetime to ensure an orderly and accepted succession upon the death of the reigning monarch. Louis' father had done this for him, although he had only survived for a very short time. The Normans had imported this procedure to England, but the bishops were not empowered to argue this case, or perhaps they felt that their status was insufficient to negotiate with the French king.

They returned to Henry and warned him that hostilities were likely to break out very soon and that he should mobilise appropriately. A number of discontents on both sides of the Channel, sensing a weakness in the King's position, declared for the young king, including both William Marshal, his mentor, and the troublesome troubadour, Bertran de Born. Richard and Geoffrey immediately gave their support for their eldest brother and they were encouraged to throw in their lot by their mother and her uncle Raoul. The latter went at once to Paris to bring the news of the spreading revolt which now included an invasion into the northern counties of England led by William the Lion, King of Scotland. The rebels were soon joined by the Counts of Flanders, Boulogne, Champagne and Blois. The forces ranged against Henry were indeed formidable and the situation looked dire. Louis orchestrated a series of bribes to all these soldiers of fortune now getting ready to pounce. Flanders was promised the earldom of Kent, Boulogne the county of Mortmain, and Blois some estates in Touraine. Louis provided the young king with a seal to replace the one he had left behind in Chinon when that young man had fled from his father's bedroom so precipitously.

Henry's astonishing military prowess and genius reacted with alacrity. He instructed Archbishop Rotrou of Rouen to write to Eleanor and remind her of her duties to her husband: to support the King and to bring her erring sons into submission to their father. Otherwise the censure of the Church would bear upon her and the punishment of excommunication be imposed.

Eleanor does not seem to have replied. She decided that she would be safer in Paris with her sons, and accompanied by an escort she disguised herself in man's clothing and rode astride her horse. Unfortunately she was betrayed by four spies planted in her court, intercepted, arrested and put into custody at Rouen. Now there started her long period of imprisonment. Henry now knew that she was the instigator of his family's rebellions. During the rest of that year (1173) Eleanor was moved from place to place but almost certainly confined in Normandy. The records are non-existent but the most probable prisons are Rouen, Chinon and Falaise, all castles in strong positions and always loyal to the Angevin cause. By moving her around and suppressing details of her place of confinement, Henry was able to keep his foes guessing. In the following year Eleanor was moved across the Channel where she would be even safer from any attempt at rescue. Henry's coup in capturing her removed the centrepiece of the revolt by his sons.

Meantime, Louis was not sitting idly. He orchestrated a meeting in the spring where all his plans were confirmed and due fealties sworn including the refusal of allowing any partner to make independent peace with Henry.

Henry meantime still found time to make two administrative appointments. It was incredible that in the midst of all these military preparations he should not forget that he was still running a kingdom. Firstly he had been long aware that since Becket's banishment the post of chancellor had never been filled. An obscure priest, Ralph de Warneville, who held the treasurerships of Rouen and later, in plurality, of York (from 1167) assumed this responsibility. But the other appointment, in April, was the elevation of Geoffrey Plantagenet, now aged twenty, to the bishopric of Lincoln which had fallen vacant. Henry leant on the chapter at Lincoln to confirm his election in that same month. Geoffrey was not ordained, other than in minor orders as a deacon, but this was no bar to holding this senior episcopal appointment. This promotion, long since flagged, now gave Geoffrey a status in the land and his abilities were beginning to be recognised far and wide. It was an inspired choice not only in recognising his worth but also in the timing. It also gave him a more than adequate independent income.

Henry also started the process of electing a new Archbishop of Canterbury as the see had been for far too long vacant. Gilbert Foliot of London, who had been fulfilling the duties virtually since Becket's banishment convened the chapter and the King stressed that he wanted an uncontested and trouble-free election. The monks, in conclave, considered two candidates. The first was Odo, the prior of Canterbury and the other was Richard, the prior of Dover. The monks recommended their own prior, Odo, but the bishops were strongly in favour of Richard. Neither contender was of the stature of previous holders of the primacy of all England, but they were both safe pairs of hands after the contentious St Thomas, and although the election was not uncontested as was desired, Richard was duly consecrated.

Coordinated hostilities began in earnest in May. Flanders attacked Pacy in Normandy. Louis infiltrated the Vexin, assisted by Geoffrey of Brittany, took Aumale in June and hoped to aim for Rouen. Philip of Flanders went for Verneuil, but had to withdraw when his brother, the Count of Boulogne, was killed in action – Philip deeming it politic to secure his own succession in Boulogne. Louis deviated to take on the Verneuil attack.

Henry sensed an opportunity to attack through the weak link. Louis, although brave, was not the best of generals. Henry moved with powerful forces towards Verneuil, breathing vengeance. Louis retreated and made his escape at great speed towards the safety of Paris. So far the war had consisted of the besieging of castles combined with a plundering of the land and the burning of crops, with little open warfare. These tactics enunciated by Louis were expensive and wasteful in manpower and the scorched-earth policy removed the source of supplies for the armies. Henry's strengths lay in open battle, tactical manoeuvring and speed of reaction. The first serious skirmish was a victory for Henry but the war was far from over. However, a wedge had been driven and his enemies' battle plans were not working as they would have wished or intended.

In Anjou and Maine the revolt was in full cry. Count William of Angouleme, Geoffrey de Rancon (he who been ignominiously dismissed so contemptuously by Louis on the Second Crusade) and the de Lusignan brothers joined in the fray here. Henry switched his forces and turned his attention to this front. His internal lines of communication were much to his advantage. He pummelled large areas between Tours and Poitiers with such savagery that they capitulated. Then he turned round and crushed the rebellion in Brittany and imprisoned his captives there at Dol. The speed and decisiveness of his campaigns was simply astounding and completely baffled the forces arraigned around him. On one occasion, in July, he is said to have marched his armies from Rouen to Dol in a day, a distance of 140 miles. This is patently impossible for footsoldiers since they could hardly cover more than five miles per hour and there are not twenty-eight hours in a day let alone allowing for rests and sustenance. Mounted troops would need changes of horses. Even King Harold had been unable to do this distance in his time before the Battle of Hastings. But Henry himself could cover huge distances in a day and his armies would not have been far behind. The surprise element of his sudden appearance in force would have an immense influence on the success of his battle tactics.

Louis was in command and he was never the best commander in war. Young Henry was totally inept and too inexperienced to coordinate the disparate forces trying to bring his father to his knees. Divisions sprang up between the attacking forces. An effort was made to sue for peace and the venue for an armistice was the traditional elm tree at Gisors where the kings of France and England had always met to sort out their differences. Henry offered exceptionally generous terms to his sons, but Louis, smarting over his defeat, persuaded the English princes to reject the offers. Young Henry was least satisfied and saw further mileage in continuing the conflict. There is little doubt that, although Henry was having a series of successes, his forces were very stretched and his reaction to events was frenetic. Louis was convinced that Henry would crack at any moment. It was therefore premature for a victory to be conceded to Henry just yet.

Young Henry was aware that William the Lion of Scotland was on the rampage in Northumbria although he had had some setbacks following a counter-attack in Lothian. The rebellions in England, mainly in the Midlands, had not yet borne fruit. An invasion of England from Flanders in late September 1173 led by the Earl Robert of Leicester had an initial success in East

Anglia, but was surprisingly cut to pieces near Bury St Edmunds in Suffolk in the following month by a rabble of peasants led by Humphrey de Bohun, Earl of Hereford. Humphrey's wife was Margery, eldest daughter of Milo, and through her he had inherited Milo's earldom. His friends and relations from the West Country still remained intensely loyal to his cause. Earl Robert of Leicester was captured and imprisoned at Falaise, perhaps to rub shoulders with Eleanor.

Hostilities went into suspended animation during the winter. Rosamond was now spending more time in France. Her younger son, William Longspee, was now fifteen and attached to his father's court and all the legitimate children were growing up. With the incarceration of Eleanor, Rosamond was now acknowledged as the King's official companion and played her part in court life. She made it plain that she was not to be regarded as deputising for the Queen but she gave a stability to life and continued to mitigate Henry's temper to everyone's advantage. She was conscious that Geoffrey Plantagenet's elevation to the bishopric of Lincoln was not quite as she had promised Eleanor since he was still not yet a fully ordained priest. This would have removed him from any possibility of succession to the throne and this in turn would have satisfied Eleanor that her own sons would have undisputed rights. Rosamond suspected that Henry still wanted to keep his options open and did not want to show all his cards, certainly at the present time.

This part of Henry's family together with John spent Christmas in Normandy. Eleanor was imprisoned, Richard and legitimate Geoffrey were in Poitiers and the young king was with Louis.

Early in the following year, 1174, young Henry attacked Sees but resistance was more stubborn than he expected, so little success was achieved. He then considered that he might go across to England and coordinate the disaffection of the many nobles in the Midlands and encourage the Scottish King William to renew hostilities after his limited success of the previous year.

Henry began by consolidating his position and popularity in Maine and Anjou. He spent Whitsun in Poitiers where he disbanded Eleanor's effete court and took with him his daughter Joanna, the two French princesses, Margaret and Alys (the betrothed of Duke Richard), Constance of Brittany and Alice of Maurienne. Meanwhile he learnt that Duke Richard was powerfully ensconced in Saintes, so Henry marched far more speedily than expected and repelled his son's forces from there.

His court in England was becoming increasingly worried at his continued absence as affairs were becoming much more threatening. The Scots were again on the warpath and the Midlands' nobles were militant. The rebels had invested Carlisle, Northampton was being battered and Nottingham Castle fell to the insurgents. Young Henry had sent a force to England. In all, the King's situation was dire. His officials in England were beseeching him to come, and come quickly.

He returned to England from Barfleur on 8 July, taking with him all the Poitevin ladies as well as Eleanor, whom he now considered would be more safely confined in England. It is not known whether Rosamond was in this party but she was back in England either just before or very soon afterwards. As the ships left the harbour, the gusts of wind worsened and the sailors became terrified. They appealed to the King to return to the safety of the port. Henry lifted his eyes to heaven praying, 'If you, good Lord, desire that I restore peace to my clergy and my people, then, in your mercy, grant me a good journey and a safe landing. May your blessed saint, the merciful St Thomas, intercede for me, a miserable sinner. If it is not to be your wish and if you are hostile to me and my cause, may it never be my fortune to reach the shores of my country.'

The good Lord, in his wisdom, listening to the intercessions of the martyred archbishop, caused the storm to ease and the vessels all reached Southampton safely. Henry knew a good omen when he saw one, so he went at once to Canterbury to the shrine of St Thomas to give thanks, arriving on 12 July. He put off his royal clothes, donned a hair shirt and joined the pilgrims flocking to the martyr's tomb. Gilbert Foliot was preaching to the crowd and Henry protested to the congregation of his innocence in the death of the saintly Thomas. He begged the bishops present to grant him an absolution for his unintentional part in the martyrdom. He insisted that the monks present, of which there were some seventy, should chastise him with at least three strokes each, which they did. He then retired to prayer and fasting for three days saying again and again that he had sinned against the Lord and begging for forgiveness. He was at long last at peace with Thomas Becket.

He returned to London, tired in body, lacerated from the scourgings but refreshed in spirit. He retired to his chamber to rest and get some sleep. Suddenly there was a hammering on his door and the guard went to quell this unwelcome intruder.

'Begone!' he said. 'Begone at once! The King is asleep and must rest.'

That old soldier, Henry, always kept one ear open for disturbance or danger, and was immediately awake and alert. 'Let him in,' he commanded.

The young courier, hot and sweaty from riding all day and night, staggered into the room. Henry knew the lad, Abraham, a trusted servant of his justiciar, Ranulf de Glanville, but feared the worst.

Good news poured out from the messenger. Ranulf and Henry's son, Geoffrey Plantagenet, had achieved a resounding victory after many vicissitudes. Geoffrey had raised money and forces and led them personally north. He had trounced Roger de Mowbray first at Kincardferry, then at Kirkby Malzeard, before capturing de Mowbray. Then Geoffrey had had a contretemps with Bishop Puiset of Durham, who had connived with the insurgents although he had remained ostensibly loyal. Geoffrey forced the Bishop into pledging his loyalty to the King and had then marched without hindrance towards Alnwick in Northumberland where he forced William the Lion to abandon his siege there and retreat. Outside that town Geoffrey and de Glanville had surprised the Scottish King and captured him on 13 July. With this capture the revolt collapsed. William the Lion was now imprisoned in Richmond Castle.

Henry was overjoyed with this news. Coming as it did but the day after his prostrations at Becket's tomb, he was convinced of divine intervention. 'Now may God be thanked and St Thomas, the martyr and all the blessed saints.'

Henry's stock in the world rose and his enemies quaked with fear. 'Was it another miracle?' said they. Henry called Geoffrey Plantagenet to him and said, 'Baseborn you may be, but you alone of all my sons have shown yourself as my only true son.'

An additional source of pride and pleasure to Henry and Rosamond was not only the brilliant success of their elder son but also that the young William Longspee had taken part in the campaign under the auspices of Geoffrey and had emerged with much credit as well as being very brave in battle. They delighted at the boy's obvious potential and Henry decided to give him his spurs and knight him for his contribution to their cause.

'It would give us both much pleasure,' said Henry to Rosamond just before the ceremony at Woodstock, 'if you would yourself bestow the accolade on William's shoulders.'

Rosamond demurred as she was unsure about the legitimacy of this procedure, and the last thing that she wanted was for the ceremony to be disputed later on. She reminded Henry that she had no official standing. Henry tried to allay her worries. 'After all,' he said, 'I am the King and what I command to be correct cannot be gainsaid.'

Rosamond suggested a compromise. William knelt before them and they both held the sword, their fingers intertwined, and laid it on each of his shoulders in turn. Thus all three of them played a part on this very special occasion.

The rebellion in England was now crushed and the insurgents sued for peace which was concluded on 26 July. But all was not yet over. Louis revitalised the war on his side of the Channel. Henry returned to Barfleur on 8 August and marched menacingly upon Rouen, now under siege.

Rouen was in a powerfully defensive position. The Seine protected it on three sides and the hills around gave added support. Louis decided to attack on the only narrow front available. For two weeks they hammered on the gates to no avail. The defending forces were able to resist with ease and conspicuous bravery. The feast day of St Lawrence was on 10 August. He was a saint held in particular veneration in Rouen and also by Louis. A truce was agreed, so that all Christians could celebrate this holy day.

The gates were opened and the citizens debouched upon the river banks and made very merry. They sang and they danced, they played music, jousted and fenced with their swords. But they did worse than that: they cocked snooks at the encircling French forces to the mortification of the besiegers.

'Behold,' said Philip of Flanders, 'the city, for which we have sweated to no purpose is wide open for attack. Let us take ladders and our arms; let us scale the walls and teach these impudent burghers a lesson that they will not forget. They will not flaunt us again in a hurry. Besides, Rouen is the jewel in the crown of Henry's Normandy.'

226

'Heaven forfend,' replied the monkish King, 'that would stain my honour! I have given my word that the day of blessed St Lawrence should be a day of peace and goodwill.'

But he was overruled and the Frenchmen secretly collected their weapons and their scaling ladders and moved under the lee of the walls. Some monks celebrating the day on a church tower saw these suspicious movements and rang Old Rouvel, the ancient bell that always warned of danger. The disporting citizens poured back through the open gates, closed them and gave the dishonourable Franks a sharp drubbing so that their 'perfidy was turned against those who devised it'.

Henry arrived the following day. The gates of Rouen were opened and all the bells of the city including Old Rouvel rang out with joy and celebration. Louis was utterly demoralised. One moment he was on the brink of a momentous victory. One moment he was near to capturing the capital of Normandy, which would have opened the whole dukedom to his troops, the next he was in complete disarray. He struck his tents, destroyed his engines of war and fled back to Paris before suing for peace.

The protagonists met at Montlouis in September. Henry was again magnanimous, albeit less generous than he was the previous year. Young Henry was cut from half the Normandy revenues to 15,000 pounds. Richard still received half the revenues of Aquitaine but only two ungarrisoned castles of Henry's choice instead of three fully manned ones. Geoffrey kept Brittany. John's provisions were all to stand.

Richard was the last to cease fighting but when he finally came to terms he threw himself weeping at his father's feet, begging for forgiveness. Henry reiterated that all he did was for their benefit and that he loved them all dearly. Then he gave them the kiss of peace.

11

Henry announced an immediate amnesty and released all his prisoners, amounting to about a thousand. Young Henry released his too, but these were only about a hundred in number.

There was one vital exception however. Eleanor was in captivity and she remained thus for fifteen years. She had been moved to England in 1174 and how perceptive Henry had been to take her there when he did. When Louis had besieged Rouen, it is probable that he was hoping to find Eleanor imprisoned there. Henry was always careful not to reveal where she was being kept at any time so that any attempt to engineer her escape could be thwarted. She was moved around with some frequency and Henry charged Ranulph de Glanville with this responsibility. She was probably kept at Winchester to begin with and later on was at Sarum, Ludgershall (in Wiltshire) and safe houses in Berkshire, Buckinghamshire and Nottinghamshire. It is almost certain that she would not have been kept in close confinement or incarcerated in dismal surroundings. She was permitted to have certain luxuries and her standard of living would have been similar to that to which she had been accustomed. She certainly had one personal maidservant and her quarters would have been well staffed to cater for all her needs. As time went by there must have been certain agreements regarding parole so that she could take exercise and go riding. Eleanor was only just over fifty when she was first imprisoned and she had been well used to an active life. She was not, by any stretch of the imagination, an old lady and she needed and got both physical and mental stimulus. Fifteen years is a very long time to be shut up in a tower. De Glanville was an astute gaoler and although he did not live at her prison on a day-to-day basis he selected sensible, firm and competent castellans, one of whom was Ralph FitzStephen. Not only had he to live with this charge but also he had to remember that, in the fullness of time, Eleanor might outlive the King, and upon her subsequent release he would not wish for any angry retribution. She was still a powerful person and her favourite son was not known for kindness.

Ranulph was emerging as an important member of the King's administrative team. He had been Sheriff of Nottingham and had played a leading part in the defeat of the King's enemies in England. He had given support and guidance to Geoffrey Plantagenet and they had achieved success with an extraordinarily lucky sense of timing. De Glanville was by training a lawyer but he was also a diplomat and was appointed justiciar. He was intensely loyal and a man of wide abilities.

In September catastrophe struck Canterbury Cathedral only two days after Archbishop Richard had returned from his visit to Rome. A fire destroyed the choir. It has been suggested that it was caused by arson but this has never been proved. However this did concentrate the minds of the monks on the site of the shrine for their new, and highly profitable, saint. There had been acrimonious arguments about this and they continued with greater ferocity now that the choir needed reconstruction. Finally a Frenchman, William of Sens, took over the planning; he raised the altar and the ambulatory to a considerable degree so that the pilgrims could perambulate with ease and the entire congregation of the nave could view the shrine and the scalp of the martyr which was to be displayed. Unlike similar disasters the question of funding did not arise – the money was there both from the wealth of the cathedral and the huge riches pouring in from the visitors to the tomb of St Thomas. But despite all the hopes of a speedy completion of the works, the shrine was not installed for another forty-six years and St Thomas remained in his temporary tomb in the crypt. This delay was partly caused by the funding running out. Overspend has always been a problem.

* * *

Henry now turned his attention to his domestic affairs. In 1174 he made over the Everswell estate to Lord Walter de Clifford 'for the love that he bear for Rosamond, his daughter'.

King William of Scotland, having been kept in chains, made

his peace with Henry on 8 December at Valognes. The terms were onerous: he had to do homage to Henry and to bind his heirs and successors similarly. The Scottish Church would become subject to the English Church. The Scots were not to harbour hostile fugitives from England and Roxburgh and Berwick were to be ceded to the English crown.

Henry next gave his half-sister Emma of Anjou in marriage to David, Prince of North Wales, who desired that his descendants should share the blood of the Plantagenets and thus make his enemies realise that his new-found relations were of considerable power and consequence. Henry's father, Geoffrey of Anjou, had produced Emma, a bastard, from a liaison with a lady in Le Mans.

In May 1175 the two Henrys travelled across from France together and all observed how close they had become. They seemed inseparable, travelled together, ate together and slept in the same room. They went to Canterbury and made a joint pilgrimage to the martyr's shrine and spent the night in fasting and prayer.

On 1 July Archbishop Richard attended the kings at Woodstock and presented Henry with the papal dispensation for and confirmation of Geoffrey Plantagenet to the see of Lincoln. The main obstacles that had to be overcome concerned not only his youth but also his bastardy. No mention was made of the fact that Geoffrey was not ordained yet. This was a matter of great joy to Henry and Rosamond and some relief to the young king in that a bishop was debarred from succession to the throne. It was however not lost on the young king that his half brother was not yet a priest. Henry always liked to keep a card up his sleeve.

In early July Henry spent a few days of relaxation at Frampton with Rosamond followed by hunting at Flaxley. After young Henry's submission and forgiveness, his father convened an assembly at Gloucester Abbey so that the Welsh and the West Country nobles could render homage to their future king. The Welsh sailed up the Severn, landing first at Arlingham where William the hermit provided horses for them to proceed to Frampton where they were splendidly entertained by Walter and Margaret Clifford, together with Rosamond's brother Richard and Rosamond herself. The next day they all gathered in Gloucester where Henry had included William the Lion in these celebrations. The magnificent ceremony was conducted by Archbishop Richard with the support of many bishops, abbots, priors, archdeacons and robed clergy including Gerald Cambrensis who described the event and Walter Map, rector of Westbury. Also present were Richard de Luci, chief justice, Ranulph de Glanville and Ralph de Warneville, the recently appointed chancellor. Young Henry approached the abbey upon a white charger much bedecked whilst William the Lion was on a grey charger. The nobles led by the Earl of Gloucester were on chestnuts. By one of those quirks of fate, Henry had reinstated the de Mandeville family into a position of trust and authority. William de Mandeville, a younger son of the dreadful Geoffrey and a brother of the obsequious Ernulph, had been restored to the family title of Earl of Essex and had recently fought with distinction during the rebellions in France and was now part of Henry's inner circle of advisers. He too participated prominently in the Gloucester celebration and procession which also included Geoffrey Plantagenet and William Longspee in conspicuous positions.

All those present paid homage to the two kings at their seats by the high altar, swearing fealty and kissing hands. Archbishop Richard then celebrated Mass and preached a rousing sermon. Afterwards the Welsh repaired to Llanthony Secunda without the city walls to continue their junketings. The citizens of Gloucester made very merry as did many of the English nobles.

Gerald and Walter returned to Westbury where they spent a week. They joined the King's party at Flaxley for sport and many discussions of a more serious nature, all of which Henry much enjoyed. He still missed the intellectual stimulation that he had enjoyed with Becket in those far off days before everything got so serious and tense between them.

However, Walter Map told the King that he was becoming disenchanted with Abbot Nicholas of Flaxley and the behaviour of the Cistercian monks there. When he had been first appointed to Westbury he had found them most cooperative and cordial. They had collaborated over several grants of land and donations to the mutual advantage of the abbey and the parish. Their arrangement was that all these should emanate from outside Westbury. Recently Abbot Nicholas had tried to bypass him and negotiate substantial legacies from within his parish, when Map had expostulated the abbot had dug his toes in. Walter was excessively angry at this incursion into his patch and against their hitherto amicable understanding. He now accused the monks of greed, drunkenness and gluttony and went further by vilifying the whole Cistercian order. He reminded Henry that the order was under strict supervision and annual visitations from Cîteaux which should have reimposed their traditional disciplines of chastity and frugality.

Henry was disturbed at these allegations and spoke sternly to Abbot Nicholas, telling him that he did not want to hear any more complaints. Nicholas made an excuse that legacies sometimes took many years to come to fruition and his negotiations for these had been initiated long before Map's appointment as rector of Westbury in 1170. Henry reminded the abbot of his great regard for Walter and as a mark of this Map was appointed to the prebend of Mapesbury at St Paul's soon afterwards.

The party was broken up soon after when Rosamond received bad news from Castle Clifford to which her parents had returned. Her dearly loved mother was seriously ill and she and Richard made haste on horseback to be with her. They had always been a close and affectionate family unlike the quarrelling Plantagenets. Margaret Clifford died later in the summer to the distress of Rosamond. The family made the long and arduous journey to Godstow nunnery, so close to all their hearts, where she was to be buried in the chapter house. This was indeed an honour as normally only abbesses were interred there. The Clifford family continued to give generous endowments to Godstow, augmented by the King.

On 1 August Geoffrey went to Lincoln where he was received in procession by the monks and acclaimed by the people. He then went to Tours for a course of instruction after which he would be consecrated.

Now Henry turned his attention to the validity of his marriage with Eleanor. He had decided that he now wished to marry Rosamond. What a Pandora's box of scorpions he unleashed! Eleanor had her views, Rosamond had always maintained her position. The legitimate sons could be about to be disinherited. Geoffrey Plantagenet, the eldest son, whom they all feared, might become the heir. The inheritance of Aquitaine would be a prize of invaluable worth. Louis was poised to exploit the break up of the huge Plantagenet empire. Last and not least, William Longspee was emerging with potential.

Henry and Eleanor were as closely related as Louis and Eleanor had been. The Louis divorce had been, officially, due to their consanguinity. There was, in addition, the acceptance by most parties that Geoffrey of Anjou, Henry's father, had had prior carnal knowledge of Eleanor. Geoffrey had a vivid birthmark on a part of his body which is private. Henry had seen this when he and his father had had that nude bathe in the river, from which Geoffrey had subsequently died. Eleanor had taunted Henry with her own knowledge of this which seemed to be an admission of guilt. This was an aspect which, if true, would be an invalidation of the Henry/Eleanor marriage and would render all their children illegitimate.

In the summer of 1175, Cardinal Pierlone came on a mission from the Pope. He had an official assignment to try and resolve the antagonisms between the Archbishops of York and Canterbury. But he had a hidden agenda which was to solve the marital difficulties between Henry and Eleanor.

In the first place he reminded Henry that they both knew the consanguinity issue when they married so they could not claim ignorance. The fact that Louis and Eleanor had the same problem was avoided because everyone knew that it was not the real issue and a diplomatic solution needed to be found. It was not easily provable that Geoffrey had had an earlier affair with Eleanor. After all, Geoffrey had tried his best and Henry had seen his father ejected from Eleanor's room, but Eleanor's contention was that she had escaped with honour intact even if she had seen the tell-tale birthmark. Eleanor had undoubtedly said more than she should have done and she was probably economical with the truth, but it was not an admission of guilt.

Pierlone then pointed out that if the marriage was annulled, Henry would be obliged to release Eleanor and send her back to Aquitaine. Once there she would be able to resume her machinations against Henry as well as stimulating her sons into a further rebellion. And a catastrophic scenario could be that she would be free to remarry a partner totally at odds with Henry. Henry's kingdom would be halved in size and the balance of power could shift dramatically.

Henry then had an inspiration. He suggested to Eleanor that

she should retire from an active life and take the veil. She would be appointed abbess of Fontevraud. The marriage would be annulled and thus Henry would not have to surrender her Aquitaine lands. To Henry this seemed to solve all his problems. But Eleanor refused. Quite apart from Fontevraud being in Angevin territory, she was not ready to retire, nor had she any vocation and she certainly was not going to abdicate her inheritance. She did not draw Henry's attention to the reaction of her sons to all these outrageous machinations.

She was quite sure that Rosamond's health was still suspect and, in any case, the Clifford woman was not going to produce any more children. If Henry subsequently married another this too would prejudice her own sons' future. She awaited developments.

Rosamond was also quite adamant that she was not going to marry Henry and assume the mantle of queen. She reminded him of her original refusal all those years ago at Castle Clifford, of her intense love and loyalty to him and that she always had his best interests at heart and would continue to fight for them. As always the possibility of a class-one Henrician rage was avoided by her softness and understanding. Her love and closeness to all the children whom she had nurtured and seen grow up were also vital to the well-being of all. She was not going to see her sons, Geoffrey Plantagenet and William Longspee, exposed to this sort of danger. They too had been bred to give loyalty to their half-brothers and sisters. Rosamond also knew what Eleanor had realised – that her health was not good. She had suppressed this from Henry and all those close to her. So even if she had agreed, she knew in her heart that she would not have enjoyed any long-term benefit.

Henry was in a cleft stick and his substantial present of silver to the papal legate to ease and encourage him to be sympathetic in his recommendations had not achieved the desired result. Pierlone refused to agree to an annulment, pointed out the difficulties that Henry would encounter, and returned home.

In the autumn Henry at last agreed to discharge all the considerable debts of young Henry which had been escalating over the past three years. As the year drew to a close, famine and plague hit the land and misery prevailed. Henry, young Henry, Rosamond and her family spent Christmas 1175 at Windsor.

234

*   *   *

The Christmas festival of 1175 witnessed a dire and dreadful episode in the chronicles of that time, which was to have serious repercussions in later years.

Bertha, the daughter of the assassinated Milo, Earl of Hereford, had married William de Braose soon after her father's death in the late 1140s. The marriage had been a happy one, probably far happier than the union proposed by her father with the de Mandeville heir, Ernulph. In due course she bore a son, also called William, who had been brought up and educated with his cousins including Rosamond's children at Flaxley and elsewhere in the West Country. Later on, owing to a concatenation of circumstances, William inherited large tracts of Brecknockshire on the borders of the Welsh Marches. These fell into his hands following the death of two of Milo's sons – Henry, who was murdered, and Mahel upon whose head a large stone had conveniently fallen from a castle tower. William the younger's seat was at Abergavenny and he decided that the nearby Welsh chieftains needed to be taught a sharp lesson as well as seeking revenge for the death of two of his uncles.

In 1175 he invited the leading local chieftain, one Seisall of Dynfall, his son and many of the other leading figures who owed allegiance to Seisall together with their retainers to Abergavenny on the pretext of Christmas feasting and bridging local differences in the spirit of goodwill and accord. It has to be said that Seisall had instigated the death of William's Uncle Henry some ten years earlier.

The visiting party left their arms and armour outside the hall and joined in the feasting and drinking with much gusto and relish, totally at the mercy of their hosts. At a given signal William's retainers swarmed in and massacred their guests, leaving no survivors. On the following day William and his men marched to Seisall's castle at nearby Arnallt, slew another son, Cadwallader in front of his mother, and then seized her as a hostage.

The Normans were distrusted from that day onwards for their treachery and butchery under the guise of friendship and hospitality. To this day the affair is not forgotten by their descendants, some of whom are still the inhabitants of Abergavenny and the surrounding neighbourhood.

235

Nowhere is it recorded that William de Braose was married at this stage. In 1175 William would have been in his late twenties so it would have been more than probable that he was married by then. His wife was Maud de St Valerie whose family came from Hay-on-Wye very near to the Clifford stronghold on the troubled Welsh borders. She was reputed to be rapacious and brutal as well as, perhaps rather surprisingly, a good military commander. It would seem therefore that it would be entirely in her character to have orchestrated this dreadful deed but there is no evidence to support this idea. Both William and Maud re-appear later on in this history of events.

*   *   *

To return to Henry's problems, on 26 January 1176 the two kings went to Northampton to reorganise the administration of justice. The country was divided into six areas and a considerable number of judicial appointments were made to implement these provisions.

The country was gripped in an iron frost, followed by appalling weather which lasted until the end of February. This weather was not confined to England and there was a serious famine in Anjou and Maine. Although there were privations in England, Henry sought to alleviate conditions across the water by supplying as much grain as could be prudently spared. Rosamond suffered far more than usual and she did not look at all well, so that even Henry noticed and became worried.

Richard and the legitimate Geoffrey came to England to join the King, young Henry and John for Easter which was celebrated at Winchester. Rosamond and her two sons were also present. They were all horrified to realise how ill Rosamond had now become. She was coughing, very pale and obviously in much pain. As always she was delighted to see them all and gave them their usual warm welcome. Her spirits rose as the days went by and she seemed to improve visibly. But they all knew that this reunion was likely to be the last time the family would be together with Rosamond. She had played such a large part in bringing them all up and organising their early schooling and their holidays in Flaxley. They all knew that their father had always been living with her. Eleanor had also lived her own life and had never been a dedicated mother and it had been useful

236

for them to have had such a stable family childhood. Henry also had been a peripatetic father and had never had much time for them when they were children. But when he was there he was always so relaxed when they saw him in the company of Rosamond, usually at Frampton or Flaxley on holiday, and this they had grown to value. They were all devoted to her and realised now that they were unlikely to see her again. It was also useful for them all to bond together, although there were still tensions among the older legitimate sons.

On 20 May there was an embassy meeting in London from King William of Sicily who was seeking the hand of Henry's daughter Joanna and much negotiation took place to cement relationships between the two kingdoms. An agreement was satisfactorily concluded.

Young Henry, who was still complaining about his lack of authority and lack of funds, despite his father's earlier generosity in discharging all his injudicious debts, now asked to go on a pilgrimage to Santiago de Compostela. Henry at once realised that this could be a ruse to renew his dubious friendships in France. Young Henry was allowed to go to Paris only and then to stay for a short time with Richard in Poitiers to assist his brother in suppressing further rebellions. However, Henry strictly controlled the funds that the young king could take with him.

Both of them were well aware that the tournament season was about to begin and the young king enjoyed this sport. It was also a useful source of additional income from prize money. Despite the support given to young Henry by his mentor William Marshal during the rebellion, Henry still trusted this excellent and straightforward knight and hoped that his considerable sense would keep the wayward young king from going off the rails. But the King took the additional precaution of sending in the young king's party his vice-chancellor, Adam Chirchedune, to keep his eyes skinned and to report back.

Unfortunately for Adam, he was caught with an incriminating letter in his possession and the young king was keen on flaying him alive. However, upon an appeal for clemency, this drastic punishment was mitigated and Adam was publicly flogged and returned in ignominy to Henry who was not best pleased. The young king was still up to his tricks and did not seem capable of learning a lesson. However he was persuaded, almost certainly by William Marshal, to abandon his machinations against his father and to spend his time in France going from tournament to tournament and enjoying a life of frivolity and irresponsibility. It was certainly an expensive way of passing the time but young Henry was an accomplished jouster and the prizes could be and were considerable. At least it kept him out of mischief and away from undesirable friends who had tried to lead him astray.

Joanna spent a few days with Eleanor before her departure to Sicily and wedded bliss. The Bishop of Winchester had agreed to meet the expenses of the journey and to provide a proper retinue of servants in accordance with Joanna's station in life. She set off from Southampton on 27 August and her entourage was instructed not to return before the princess was duly wedded. John, lately Dean of Sarum and now the newly elected Bishop of Norwich, was deputed to travel independently to Palermo and to participate in the betrothal ceremony. The poor bishop had a hair-raising journey from which he was very lucky to survive. Storms, insurrections *en route*, famine and fleas in his bed caused him immense discomfort. To be fair he found time to be much distressed by the many scenes of starving peasants. He had intended to visit Rome before arriving in Sicily, but the routes were impassable due to the bandits who were preying upon those unwise enough to travel. The vessels that he chose for his journey were small and powered by rowers, for he hoped thus not to attract the attention of pirates. He was violently seasick and most uncomfortable all the time. But he eventually arrived and concluded the negotiations for the formal betrothal. He returned to England arriving at Nottingham Castle on Christmas Eve, where the King was celebrating Christmas.

On 28 September Prince John was betrothed to his half first cousin (once removed), Hawise, the granddaughter of Earl Robert of Gloucester. Earl Robert had brought up Henry and had been a staunch supporter of Henry's mother, Maud, during her epic struggle against Stephen. Hawise was the sole heiress of the immensely wealthy Gloucester estates. However, the consanguinity was far too close. John's earlier betrothed, the infant Alix, had long since died.

Sadly the King's court at Christmas was not in the best of spirits. During the late autumn, Rosamond's health had continued to deteriorate and she had now gone to the nunnery at Godstow where she was looked after by the nuns and her decline continued.

* * *

On 13 February 1177, the marriage of King William and Joanna Plantagenet was celebrated in Palermo by the Archbishop. The bride looked stunning and the concourse of bishops, priests, nobles and populace were hugely impressed. Henry's negotiations had strengthened his influence in the Mediterranean. Joanna then disappeared from view to all intents and purposes. Her most Christian and devout husband had long since espoused the practices of his Turkish subjects by maintaining a lively and fully staffed harem to keep his sexual appetite in constant practice. Joanna may have thought that she was his only wife and she would have witnessed the activities of her mother's court in Poitiers but she had not been expecting a role as 'she who may be summoned upon a whim'. The senior concubine initiated the young Queen into the procedures of the harem and the comeliest told her what went on in the swimming pool within. All the ladies were expected to disport and bathe when the King so wished and he would watch them with interest and expectation. He would throw an apple to the lady of his choice in the pool and she would repair to his chamber for his delectation.

'Hence,' said this beauteous one, 'we have an expression here that the lady of his choice is the apple of his eye.'

The tempers of her Plantagenet father and Aquitanean mother which Joanna had doubtless inherited may have given an added spice to her life in the Sicilian court.

* * *

In the early part of 1177, the Abbess of Godstow sent an urgent message to Henry. Rosamond was unlikely to live for very much longer and she wanted to see him. Henry galloped as fast as he could and arrived just in time.

His dear Rosamond was in a very poor way and was intermittently conscious, but she knew him from time to time and they were able to spend a few precious moments together. She commended their sons to his safe keeping and encouragement. She made him promise to see that Geoffrey fulfilled his high promise in the Church.

'He is so very like you and has the same temper and impetuosity. He will always love you and be loyal. William will be the soldier and again will always be loyal. You need loyalty. Always love and forgive your other sons but they will continue to fight you. Ask Eleanor's forgiveness for my sins against her.'

And she turned her face to the wall and died in his arms.

Henry was desolate.

The funeral was taken by Geoffrey, in whose diocese Godstow lay. He was in tears. The robed clergy included Gilbert Foliot, Bishop of London, Henry's cousin, Bishop Roger of Worcester, Abbot Nicholas of Flaxley, Gerald Cambrensis and Walter Map of Westbury, plus many others. Henry and William Longspee were inconsolable. The ten-year-old Prince John was in floods of tears. The young king came across from Tours. Rosamond's family included her distraught father, Walter and her brothers, Walter and Richard of Frampton. Her many cousins through her Earl Milo relationship, also attended: Humphrey de Bohun, Earl of Hereford and his wife Margery, Milo's daughter; Sir William de Braose; Bertha, another daughter of Milo; and Herbert and Lucy FitzHerbert, Lucy being the third of Milo's daughters. During the service a cloaked priest was seen standing at the back of the church. He was later identified as Eleanor's chaplain.

Rosamond was buried in the place of highest honour in front of the high altar. Her tomb was splendidly and richly embellished with silk hangings and lamps and candles perpetually burning. On it there was only a simple inscription: 'Tumba Rosamundae'. The tomb became a shrine of veneration.

* * *

The story of Rosamond is one of the most romantic in English history. After well over 800 years the full truth will never now be known. But it is embedded in folklore. Most historians dismiss the length of Henry's affair with her by saying that it was a middle-aged man's lust for a young woman and lasted only a few years from the late 1160s until her death in the middle 1170s. From this argument it is incontrovertibly stated that Rosamond could not possibly be the mother of Geoffrey Plantagenet or William Longspee.

The Clifford family history is clear that Jane/Rosamond was probably born in the late 1130s. The verbal traditions handed down from time immemorial to Henriette Clifford's family give three quite clear

240

and separate stories that Rosamond was contemporaneous with Henry and that they knew each other as children. Mrs Clifford is a descendant in the direct line from Richard Clifford, Rosamond's younger brother, whose family have been at Frampton for over 900 years and are still there.

Gerald Cambrensis says that Rosamond was very young when Henry started his affair with her. If we assume that he is right and if we accept the Clifford family dates that Rosamond was born in the late 1130s, then it all falls into place: Henry and Rosamond began their liaison in 1151 or thereabouts. This is the clear contention in Baden Watkins' book and the Clifford family legends and from this it follows that Rosamond could all too easily be the mother of both Geoffrey and William.

If Rosamond had been born in the late 1130s, it is inconceivable that a woman of that beauty and presence would have not been much sought after and probably married and there has never been any suggestion of this. I have explained how the Hikenai story could have come into this equation.

Geoffrey Plantagenet was the eldest son of Henry, the most dearly loved and the most loyal of all his children. Geoffrey was also extremely able and immensely talented. It is unlikely that his mother would have been of 'degraded character'. A wet nurse, probably yes; mother, no. He was brought up and nurtured in a civilised society and mixed with the brothers and sisters of the full blood with ease and familiarity. This would not have been the case if his mother was 'degraded'. He was also feared as a possible contender for the throne.

Historians generally say that Rosamond was a young bimbo when Henry started his lustful affair with her not earlier than the mid 1160s and that he kept her in seclusion at Everswell. None of this seems likely as Henry's movements during the late 1160s until 1170 were mainly out of England.

The court of Henry was discreet and in the early days the relationship was mainly conducted in the West Country where there was less chance of tongues wagging. Rosamond was undoubtedly a character of immense vitality and strength of purpose, who had an enormous influence upon one of the most able kings this country has ever known. She was also stunningly beautiful with long fair hair and a real English complexion. What she certainly was not was a mere king's concubine who was here today and gone tomorrow. Instead she has spawned a huge amount of speculation and literature.

241

The strengths of the legends and the innumerable stories about Henry and Rosamond ought not to be lightly dismissed and the thrust of this book is that it all could be true.

And if it is not true, it ought to be.

12

1177–1189

Henry was now in some pain from his leg. During his rapid progress from Nottingham to Godstow, he was agitated and paying less attention than was his wont when mounting his horse to continue his journey. The horse shied and caught him a nasty blow on his leg. Despite this he continued on his way, but the wound did not heal as quickly as he expected. This wound was to cause him problems for the rest of his life and he always had to hobble from then on.

On 19 June 1177, the young king's wife, Margaret, gave birth to their first child in Paris, who lived for only a few days. Henry was still at Woodstock when he received this news. A few days later he obtained confirmation from Rome that his application to annul his marriage to Eleanor had been refused. His plan to marry Rosamond was now of no consequence following her death. As he had been warned he was well aware that the control of Eleanor's estates would be highly contentious should his marriage with her be negated.

But his enemies were never far from barking at his heels even at this time of deep sorrow for Henry. The long-standing arrangement that Louis' daughter Alice should be married to Richard had never been implemented and the girl had been under Henry's control in his court since 1168. The gossip was rife and scandalous, stirred no doubt by the young king and Margaret and fanned further by Eleanor. Louis now demanded a full explanation and immediate action. The allegations were that Alice was by now the mistress of Henry and that the King was most reluctant to lose his paramour to his son. The timing of this was distressing to Henry. Alice was by no means a beauty and had very few qualities or abilities which would have appealed at the best of times to him. But the rumours persisted and included the suggestion that Henry would now marry Alice, raise a new family and declare John as his successor.

Richard was overtly angered by all this but it is probable that he too was dragging his feet over a commitment for which he had very little heart. He also played the card that it was invalid for him to marry his father's mistress. No doubt he had been put up to this by his mother.

Henry met Louis at Ivry on 18 August and they resolved their differences amicably. Henry reminded Louis that Alice's dowry arrangements concerning the transfer of the county of Berry had been hanging fire and as soon as Louis had sorted this out Richard would be married at once. The inheritance of the Count of Berry who had died the previous year now became much more urgent. When Henry was put into a corner, he came out fighting vigorously.

During the middle of 1177 young Henry and Richard were supporting each other in campaigns in Poitou suppressing the endless insurrections. Richard was a ruthless campaigner who was always fighting. The turbulence in Aquitaine never ceased, so Richard savagely annihilated his vassals, razing castle after castle with a brutality not easily forgiven. He combined this with rape and pillage and his appetite was seldom assuaged. Once he had finished with the unfortunate women whom he captured he gave them to his followers for their satisfaction. Richard's reputation as a soldier was in the ascendant and he was more and more feared in Aquitaine. Henry joined his sons from Ivry later in the summer. The elder Henry had expected the young king to consolidate the Berry territory, but this had been neglected. Young Henry made a lackadaisical attack upon Chateauroux but the infant heiress of Berry had been spirited away from under his nose. Henry moved quickly, caught up with her and took her into what might be euphemistically called his protection. Henry then had a further coup by purchasing the county of La Marche which consolidated his neighbouring territories neatly.

In the midst of all this Henry allocated Ireland to his youngest son, John, then aged ten, and appointed Hugh de Lacy as viceroy. He also agreed to subscribe to a crusade with Louis – never a difficult decision for the latter to take. In September he dispatched his daughter Eleanor to Castile for her marriage to

King Alphonso in Burgos Cathedral. Before she went she spent a few days bidding farewell to her mother in her place of confinement. Eleanor's marriage to the Castilean king was happier and more successful than that of Joanna, her sister in Sicily.

* * *

Meanwhile, in Palestine, the crusading skirmishing continued. The Christian army now included Earl William de Mandeville who had gone to the Holy Land. This army besieged Hareng on 4 November, a place on the borders of the principality of Antioch.

Saladin thought that Jerusalem was denuded of soldiers, so he collected a substantial force, invaded at Ascalon and attacked the town of Ramlah. The king in Jerusalem, blessed by the patriarch, gathered together the few remaining knights and soldiers. The defending army was outnumbered but God was on their side against the infidel.

Saladin was unusually overconfident and had relaxed his vigilance. He had allowed some of his formations to pillage the countryside at the very moment that the Christians were grouping for a counter-attack.

On 25 November morning came and the Christians were in the better position on top of the high ground. The four ranks of soldiers were formed into a single wedge shape. This formation successfully resisted the repeated onslaughts. Odo, the commanding Templar, led a cavalry charge of only eighty-four men, preceded by a cross, straight to the heart of the Saracen forces, scattering them to the four winds. This victory was regarded as being solely due to divine intervention.

This was an unusual defeat for Saladin who only just escaped with his life, and his reputation was dented for the time being.

* * *

Christmas 1177 was celebrated in style at Angers. It was the most lavish affair witnessed for a very long time. Henry and his eldest sons were present. Henry's realm was on the crest of an economic boom and the country was encouragingly prosperous.

1178 was a year of consolidation on both sides of the Channel. Henry returned to England in July and again made a pilgrimage to the tomb of St Thomas. Towards the end of that month

Archbishop William of Reims fulfilled a long expressed wish and vow to make his own visit to the shrine of the martyr. The trip was a great success and William was fêted by both Henry and the Church with many gifts and tokens given in honour of the French prelate. On 6 August Henry knighted his legitimate son Geoffrey at Woodstock.

One of the penances imposed upon Henry following the martyrdom of St Thomas was an obligation to found monasteries. He responded to this with great assiduity. The one that is of some interest is the Carthusian friary at Witham in Somerset. Probably a few years earlier than 1178 Henry persuaded La Grande Chartreuse near Grenoble to send some monks across to establish themselves in this remote part of the royal forest of Selwood. The Carthusian order was most ascetic, forswearing meat and living on bread, water and salt on one day in the week. They wore hair shirts and were not allowed to leave their precincts. The monks lived in wooden shacks and initially lived in penury. The dispossessed peasants suffered intolerable privations and were implacably hostile so that the morale both in the village and friary became dispirited. The first abbot asked to be recalled and the second died soon after his arrival. To save Witham from an ignominious collapse Henry now asked for the secondment of their Carthusian procurator, Hugh of Avallon. Hugh was most reluctant to come but the monks were overjoyed as at last something was being done. Hugh immediately realised that this house of God needed money. This money was initially used to rehouse the miserable peasants properly. Then the friary needed proper stone buildings. Hugh bearded Henry and a substantial sum was at once made available to rectify these injustices.

Hugh's ability to get Henry's support was legendary. Having re-established the house upon a proper footing he next bought the hovels with Henry's money and then offered them to him as worthy properties for a king. Henry was puzzled as to the use that he could make of them. Hugh suggested that the King buy the hovels from him so that he could use the money to build something more worthy for everyone. The King saw the joke and gave a further substantial sum as compensation.

The ready access that Hugh had to Henry, both then and later, gave rise to the rumour that perhaps Hugh was Henry's illegitimate son, but this is impossible as Hugh was born in 1135 and was thus only three years younger. Henry always enjoyed the company of able and intelligent men who could stand up to him, and Hugh's star continues to cross the path of this story.

On 26 February 1179 the young king returned to England and was greeted most fondly by his father.

On 1 May Richard decided that he must teach Geoffrey de Rancon a lesson that he would not forget in a hurry. Geoffrey had refused to render homage. Richard's tactics were to taunt the defenders with cowardice so much that they left the safety of their powerful defences and sallied forth hoping to catch the Aquitaineans unprepared. There was fierce fighting and the garrison was forced back to their gateway which they were unable to close in time. Thus entrance was achieved and the hitherto impregnable Rancon Castle at Taillebourg capitulated within nine days to the astonishment of all. Richard proceeded to completely demolish the castle. This further strengthened his reputation as one of the finest soldiers of his time. Richard returned to England and was also greeted by his father with great joy.

Louis was now fifty-eight and not in good health. He expressed the wish 'to prepare for his migration from this world'. During August Louis and his son went hunting together in the vast forest of Compiegne. The hounds had raised a wild boar and the party had all gone deep into the forest when Philip became detached from the main group and then got lost to the consternation of Louis and his escort. Darkness fell and Philip was out of earshot of all. The solitude was frightening and the sound of his calls for help only echoed off the trees. Now distraught, he saw a charcoal burner's fire and made his way there. The grubby man was as frightened as the Prince when he appeared, but he was kindly and took the terrified Philip to safety, to the relief of the King. Philip suffered a severe fever as a result of his ordeal and at one stage his life was in danger.

Louis realised that his succession had very nearly been cut short and there was no credible substitute for his throne. He had a vision on three successive nights of St Thomas of Canterbury so he determined to make his own pilgrimage at once, appropriately dressed, following the route taken by Thomas on his return to Canterbury.

On 22 August Louis landed at Dover where he was met by Henry and they went in solemn procession to St Thomas' shrine accompanied by Archbishop Richard, many bishops and nobility. Louis spent three days in fasting, prayer and solitude. As a token of his appreciation he gave one hundred measures of French wine to be given each year in perpetuity for the sole use of the monks of Canterbury. He also gave gifts of gold and silver and a magnificent ruby known as the 'Régale de France'.

On 26 August Louis returned to France to find that Philip was well on the road to a full recovery. The miracle had worked. Louis then organised, in accordance with long-established French custom, the coronation of his successor, Philip Dieu-Donne, who was an unprepossessing youth of fourteen.

Louis then suffered a stroke which left him completely paralysed on his right side, which made it impossible for him to attend his son's coronation which was now set for All Saints' Day. Henry did not attend primarily because he did not wish to pay homage to this tiresome youth. His three elder sons attended and were asked to play a conspicuous part in the splendid ceremony.

Louis lingered on for a further nine months, unable to play any significant part in the affairs of his realm. Towards the end of his life he collected all his gold, silver and rich clothing and instructed that these be distributed to the poor and needy. On 13 September 1180 he 'paid his debt to nature' and 'his spirit fled to the skies to enter upon its eternal reward', expiring in the abbey of Notre Dame. He was buried in the Cistercian abbey of Barbieux, which he had founded. Fifty-nine strokes of every church bell in Paris tolled in his honour, one for each year of his life.

Thus died the monkish King of France after a reign of forty-two years. He had many saintly qualities, few of them appreciated in the rough and tumble of the times. Walter Map described him as 'gentle, kind-hearted and simple, but indecisive too often. He mixed well with all stations in life, perhaps listening too much to those whose advice was suspect. He was a strict judge, albeit lenient'. Other contemporary commentators of the time, such as Gerald and William of Newburgh, all agree with Map's views.

Philip, his successor, was a far different man. He was crafty, devious and determined. He was utterly ruthless in his determination to curb the power of the Angevin empire, was more intelligent than his father and remarkably successful in his achievements. He was a past master at playing off one faction against another and all the Plantagenets underrated him to their disadvantage. He was physically unattractive, scruffy and smelt. He was not nice to be near.

In 1180, Henry appointed Ranulph de Glanville justiciar. Young Henry returned to England and suggested that they might make a useful visit to Philip who was already showing signs of rocking the boat. But first the young king was made to swear at the tomb of his great-grandfather Henry I that he would follow all his father's instructions. This was an unwise move by the elder king as it irritated the younger unnecessarily just at the very moment that he was showing some sense and responsibility.

The two kings returned to France and celebrated Easter at Le Mans. They then met Philip II at Gisors in June and renewed the treaty signed between Louis and the elder Henry three years earlier. Sometime during 1180 the French king married Margaret, a daughter of Baldwin, Count of Hainault.

* * *

Probably during 1180, when Henry was in England, prior to the two kings' return to Normandy, the elder king had an affair with Nesta, the wife of a North country knight, Sir Ralph Bloet. There were Bloets mentioned in the Dictionary of National Biography *during the early part of the twelfth century, one of whom was a bishop. There are several spellings of this name. Ralph was probably of this clan and this is the only mention of him. He would have been part of the Norman establishment. It is said that the Bloets were living in the Welsh Marches and that Nesta was from a noble Welsh family. They had a son called Morgan who was brought up in the Bloet household.*

The date of Morgan's birth is not recorded but he appears later on both in 1201 and 1213. It would seem that he would have been about twenty years old in 1201 and was always acknowledged as an illegitimate son of Henry. The dating of the affair is also not unreasonable since Rosamond had died in 1177 and Henry would have got over this loss by then and Eleanor was still imprisoned.

I have dismissed the story that Hugh of Avallon could have been an early illegitimate son, as Hugh's birth is far too early. I have also dismissed the tale that Henry had an affair as well as a child by Alice, the daughter of the deposed Count Eudo de Porhoet of Brittany in 1168. Alice and Henry were step-second cousins once removed, well within the prohibited degrees. Alice's great-grandfather was Henry I and Alice de Porhoet's great-grandmother was one of that king's many mistresses.

It is my view that Henry had no other liaisons during Rosamond's lifetime. There will be other mistresses who will appear later on. Henry was said to have lusted after Roger de Clare's sister in his youth. But there was always much gossip about Henry's affairs with remarkably little tangible evidence. The affair which was much believed concerned Alice, the daughter of Louis by his second wife who was still engaged to Prince Richard of Aquitaine and who had been in Henry's household since 1168, when she was eight years old. It was also said, from one source only, that she had had a daughter by Henry who did not live. I am confident that there is no truth in this whatsoever.

William of Newburgh states that Henry had no affairs until Eleanor was past childbearing age. However, I do not accept this – Rosamond was certainly his mistress very much earlier.

I now turn to the illegitimate children of Henry's three elder sons. There is no evidence that either the young king or Geoffrey of Brittany had any illegitimate children. If they did, there is no evidence that they had any impact upon the Plantagenet dynasty. Prince Richard, Duke of Aquitaine, has always been regarded as homosexual. The evidence for this will emerge later. In his youth he was noted for his sexual appetite and for the rape of his female prisoners. It is said that 'he carried off the wives, daughters and kinswomen of his freemen by force and made them his concubines; and when he had sated his lust, he handed them over to his knights for whoring'. But about 1180, Richard fathered one bastard, Philip de Cognac. Very little is known about Philip although he will appear briefly at the death of his father in 1199 when he was about twenty years old. Nothing is known of Philip's mother nor where, when and how he was brought up.

* * *

In July 1181 legitimate Geoffrey married Constance of Brittany thus consummating his right of inheritance in that county.

Henry spent most of his time in 1181 in England. He was still as frenetic as ever and his travelling programme gave no indication of slowing down. He simply took his government and justiciary with him wherever he went and grew less able to delegate as he grew older. It was obvious that he could not keep up this pace indefinitely. He was beginning to show his age. He began to put on weight and his hair was greying. His old leg wound continued to trouble him. He was still addicted to hunting and because he rode so much he had become more and more bow-legged. Although he made every effort to take exercise, he suffered from various maladies from time to time.

Problems arose in Normandy when Philip of Flanders decided that it was now opportune to attack, although he had already agreed with Philip of France to a truce in that area. He initially negotiated with Frederick Barbarossa of Germany to join forces with him. But Barbarossa had too many problems of his own to become involved other than peripherally. The Fleming forces had some initial successes round Noyon and Senlis but young Henry, Richard and Geoffrey decided to combine their forces and repel this impudent Philip as well as demonstrate to their father that they were capable of a successful military action. It was a confusing campaign. The Count of Sancerre was defeated and deposed and the three brothers were poised, with a large force, to thrash the armies of Philip of Flanders. Just in time he capitulated and asked Philip of France for diplomatic support, which was given to him.

Young Henry then turned his attentions to the tournaments. His mentor, William Marshal, had been an impecunious youth and when he had joined his uncle, Patrick Earl of Salisbury, had found it necessary to make his fortune in the lists. The practice was for the winner in any joust to take the horse and equipment of the vanquished. The winner then sold these back to the loser and by this means could make an excellent living providing he was successful. By this means William had done very well. Young Henry followed on the coat-tails of William and had also done very well. But the trouble was that the young king was on a very limited allowance and liked to maintain a large entourage of hangers-on who were very expensive to keep. These rich young men were as irresponsible as young Henry and they were a bad influence which William Marshal always tried to curb. Of course, as time went on, these expenses irritated Henry's father, who became less inclined to give his eldest son any authority. The pace of Henry's life in England had no attraction to the idle and bored younger king. Richard of Aquitaine was in full authority and was not slow to rub salt in his elder brother's wound. Thus the rifts widened.

The anomaly of Geoffrey Plantagenet's bishopric of Lincoln

still required a solution. Pope Alexander III demanded that this unsatisfactory state of affairs needed regularisation. Geoffrey had been bishop now for eight years and had not yet been ordained or consecrated and the largest see in England, whose diocese ran from Lincolnshire to the Thames, was in limbo. In fact the matter was more serious since Geoffrey's predecessor, Robert de Chesney, had died in 1166 and the see had been to all intents and purposes vacant now for fifteen years. Geoffrey wrote an impassioned and plausible letter to Alexander pleading for a further respite. This request was granted by the Pope and Geoffrey was allowed another three years before he had to conform. But Henry now had other plans for Geoffrey, whose efficiency was outstanding. Robert de Warneville, who had been temporary chancellor since 1173, was appointed Bishop of Lisieux in July 1181 and agreed to relinquish the chancellorship. Henry now decided that Geoffrey should assume these duties, the second highest position in the royal administration after the justiciar.

Although Geoffrey seemed to neglect Lincoln he had been assiduous in many administrative matters. He had redeemed the cathedral silver and ornaments which had been pawned to Aaron, the famous Jew in Lincoln, and had augmented these with generous gifts and two fine and tuneful bells from his own resources. He also recovered estates which had been unwisely mortgaged. He had encouraged learned men from abroad to come to the cathedral school and thus promote a high standard of scholarship – a reputation which was maintained over several decades. His detractors nevertheless claimed that he was more adept at fleecing the Lord's sheep than feeding them. Geoffrey agreed to resign the bishopric and would become chancellor, as well as receiving substantial compensations of lands and offices on both sides of the Channel. Considerable severance conditions for loss of office were not unknown then. Geoffrey had been known to say that in any case he much preferred hunting to praying. He became Archdeacon of Rouen, Treasurer of York and received two castles in Anjou. On 6 January 1182 he announced his resignation of Lincoln at Marlborough. Unfortunately Geoffrey had a stutter and was thus a most indistinct speaker, and twice during the recitation of resignation Archbishop Richard had to ask him what he was saying and was in considerable doubt as to whether he had actually resigned. Walter Map had to interpret, during which he made a local joke – 'He is speaking the French of Marlborough'. This is a reference to a local tradition that whoever drank from a certain well in Marlborough would speak bad French for the rest of their lives.

In the spring of 1182, Henry was obliged to go across to France as he thought that he ought to try and bring some semblance of order to the chaotic situation. He decided to bide his time. He was quite happy to stay and watch his three sons quarrel, thinking that, at least, it kept them out of mischief and from plotting against him.

Later in 1182 after the tournament season, young Henry and legitimate Geoffrey turned on Poitou, expecting some rich pickings from the endless strife in that county to the detriment of Richard's interests.

The elder king now had to give succour to his daughter Matilda and his son-in-law, Henry the Lion of Bavaria, who had been expelled by Barbarossa of Germany after being defeated decisively in Cologne. The party also included their three children, who were Henry's first grandchildren and to whom, like all grandfathers, he was devoted.

Young Henry continued to argue with his father, still demanding complete authority in his kingdom in England. At one stage he stormed off in a huff to Paris where Philip, ever the opportunist, stirred him up to the latter's advantage. He then demanded to have Normandy and Anjou. When these were refused he threatened to take the Cross. All these were refused so he threatened to commit suicide. His father endeavoured to mollify and bribe him. He was given a larger allowance, the castle in Argentan and a year's pay for his soldiers. But he had to agree on oath to do what the King wanted and to make no further demands. Young Henry conformed to all this.

The Christmas season was intended to be spent in some amity and accord at Caen. The castle of William the Conqueror had been refurbished and Henry reminded his sons that they were to attend at the seat of the founding father of their dynasty. He was most anxious to try and persuade them to stand together and present a united front to the world and their enemies. To this end he also summoned all his vassals in Normandy who were to renew their homage. Over a thousand knights congregated upon the castle for this festival and the entertainment was to be the most lavish that anyone could remember. The two Henrys, Richard and Geoffrey of Brittany were all gathered together, probably with all their wives and most of the Bavarian family. But there was immediate discord. Margaret was to be the leading lady in the court.

Young Henry arrived in a rage without William Marshal in attendance. He was not speaking to his wife and it soon transpired that William had been accused of casting longing looks at Margaret in the Poitevin tradition of courtly love. William appeared hotfoot, demanding an apology. He challenged all those who had accused him to meet him in combat. If he won, he asked for no reward other than the restoration of his honour. If he lost, he demanded to be hanged for his crime. Such was the Marshal's reputation and prowess, there were no takers. William then departed on a pilgrimage to Cologne.

Things went from bad to worse. One of the guests, a well-born and noble troubadour from Poitiers, Bertran de Born, took the opportunity to make mischief. He taunted young Henry as being a lord of little land, a prince of cravens and a crowned king who lived upon the dole. He wished that Geoffrey of Brittany was the Duke of Normandy as he would know how to exercise his power. He tried to flirt outrageously with the elder Henry's daughter Matilda, Duchess of Saxony, and sang songs of love to her praising her fresh and lovely beauty, her grace and her stimulating talk. Matilda was not amused. Then this ungrateful guest criticised Henry's hospitality as being far worse than that offered in any secondary baronial fortress. Bertran had been a snake in the grass for many years and had been much encouraged by Eleanor in her court at Poitiers. He had been a thoroughly pestilential influence on young Henry, who had always been weak in his relationships. It is surprising that he managed to continue to be welcomed so often.

Having put most of the Plantagenets in fearful rages with each other, he sat back and watched with malevolent amusement. Young Henry flew to his father demanding support against his insufferable brother Richard who had just built a castle at Clairvaux on land within Angevin territory and outside his duchy of Aquitaine. Richard had been his usual brutal self in subjugating a number of treacherous and dissident barons on his borders whose primary allegiances were due to his father and

254

elder brother. Young Henry demanded redress from Richard. After his recent promises on oath and generosity from his father he expected that Richard would be brought to heel. The elder Henry was becoming bored by all these tantrums and told his son that Richard had permission from him to restore order in these border areas. The young king then threatened to support his vassals and attack Richard.

'Then do so, I will not hinder you', said his father dismissively.

Once again young Henry threatened to resign all his useless honours, go on a crusade and serve under a foreign prince who would appreciate him more. He then resorted to the tactic which was always successful. He burst into tears.

His father gave way and summoned Richard and Geoffrey to do homage to young Henry. Geoffrey was quite easy about this – after all, he had done it recently and if it kept everyone happy he would do it again. Richard was furious. He had only recently done homage to Philip II and he was not in any subordinate position to his elder brother.

'After all,' he said, 'we both come from the same father and mother and have the same blood in our veins. Henry has his father's lands, I am due my mother's lands and that is all that there is to it.' With that he stalked out and refused to have anything to do with young Henry.

Christmas at Caen was not a success and was prematurely brought to a close.

Early in January 1183, Henry summoned them all to Le Mans and tried to broker a deal between them. Young Henry admitted that he had encouraged the border barons to rebel. He swore yet again to obey his father in everything and subject to Clairvaux being ceded to the elder Henry and an oath of fealty to him from Richard he would be reconciled to Richard. Richard gave similar undertakings which were hedged with so many qualifications and was so ungracious that young Henry refused to accept them. Neither of them had really done what was asked of them. They parted with even more ill will and rancour.

It was only a matter of time before hostilities began. Geoffrey came to the support of his elder brother and they massed a large army and began to prepare for war. The elder Henry moved to Limoges to keep a wary eye on matters but there were two skirmishes in which the King's life was in danger. Young Henry swore that these were mere accidents and should not have occurred but his father was not convinced. Henry stopped his son's allowance and his money quickly ran out. The young king was reinforced by William Marshal and this pair were reconciled. Then they moved south and first of all pillaged the shrine of Rocamadour, stealing the great and much venerated sword of Roland and looting as many monasteries as they could find in order to replenish their depleted funds.

The weather became intolerably hot and young Henry fell seriously ill with dysentery and a fever. He tried to get back to Limoges but his strength ebbed remarkably quickly. He reached Martel where he had to remain. The Bishop of Agen was summoned and the young Henry made a final confession of all his sins. The bishop went quickly to Limoges to fetch Henry.

However, Henry suspected a trap. His son's army consisted of many who were only there to obtain prominent positions in the young king's government once the elder king was dead. Henry sent his son his physician, some money and, as a token of his affection, a sapphire ring, once the property of Henry I. He hoped that, upon recovery, they would be reconciled.

On 11 June young Henry knew that he was nigh unto death. He asked to be clothed in a hair shirt and covered with a crusader's cloak and then to be placed upon a bed of ashes with a stone pillow. His mind was rambling and he was disturbed that he had not fulfilled his vow to go on a crusade. William Marshal tried to calm him and promised to go in his stead.

Henry begged William to intercede with his father to release his mother who had been for so long in captivity. He besought his father to look after Margaret, his wife. He instructed that all his possessions, saving the sapphire ring, be given to the poor. A monk who attended for the last rites asked why this alone was to be excepted.

'My father gave it to me as a pledge of forgiveness and I want my Judge to know this,' he said. He died later in the evening and they were not able to remove the ring from his finger.

* * *

Eleanor was now in the castle at Sarum. That day of 11 June had been hot and sultry. She and her guardian, Ralph FitzStephen, both agreed that they needed some air and exercise so they had

256

spent the day riding over to Stonehenge. On their way they stopped at the convent of Amesbury Abbey where the abbess gave them refreshment. They viewed the mysterious stones and wondered about their origins, then wended their way back to Eleanor's place of custody. They noticed the clouds had begun to gather in the west and they both felt that they were in for a thunderstorm.

When they reached Sarum Castle, Eleanor began to feel unwell and Amaria, her maid, suggested that she retire early, which she did. She had a restless night and fell at last into an uneasy and fitful sleep. She had a nightmare in which she saw young Henry lying as if on a couch but with his hands folded in prayer and resembling a tomb effigy. On his finger she saw the sapphire ring, of which she could not possibly have been aware. Above his face hovered two crowns, one being the crown that he wore at his coronation and the other a circlet of dazzling light with no beginning and no ending. She woke in a sweat, with a soaking coverlet as the storm broke, the heavens opened and the thunder rolled and cracked round about. It was late in the evening of 11 June.

Within a few days, a messenger from Henry came hotfoot from Southampton where he had just landed. Thomas Agnell, Archdeacon of Wells, brought the dire tidings. She told him that she had been expecting him and already knew what he was about to tell her. She recounted her dream and asked him if her interpretation was correct.

'My dearly loved son has been received into eternal bliss as exemplified by the brightness of the eternal crown. As the Gospel says, "Eye hath not seen, nor ear heard, neither have entered into the heart of Man, the things which God hath prepared for them that love Him." My son is at last at rest.'

The archdeacon was astounded at her dream and her interpretation and composure. She was however far more distressed than she allowed those around her to see although, of all her children, the young king was least close to her.

* * *

Those at the deathbed were terrified about how to break the news to Henry, who was eventually told by the monk dispatched to him. Henry was found near Limoges and the monk too was

257

told that the King knew what the bearer had to say. The King had excessive paroxysms of grief, so much so that those about feared for him.

The burial arrangements became bizarre. The young king's eyes, brain and entrails were buried at Grandmont, a monastery only just pillaged by him. His body was meant to be carried to Rouen Cathedral, the place that he had chosen for sumptuous interment, but, *en route*, the citizens of Le Mans seized the body and demanded that it should be buried there, which was duly done. The people of Rouen threatened to raze Le Mans to the ground unless the body was surrendered to them. Henry intervened and the body was disinterred and finally reburied at Rouen where it is to this day.

It is difficult to be sympathetic to the young king. He had everything in life that he needed but he was utterly weak, idle and incapable of keeping any of his promises. He was the most dearly loved of all the sons of Henry. He had been brought up in England and had the best of tutors but was much distressed by his removal from the Becket household at the impressionable age of seven. His father was determined that young Henry's upbringing should follow the same lines as his own by Earl Robert. This had achieved so much success that all had acclaimed the stature and potential of their future King. But history is littered with the failures of fathers who try to cast their sons in their own mould.

The trauma of the marriage of young Henry's parents would have left its mark on him, though these problems were not unusual in those days. But the young king would have played one parent's influence against the other. There is no doubt that he became thoroughly spoilt and developed no interest in the matter of ruling a huge kingdom of immense complexity.

Henry had no common interests with his father. He had no passion for hunting, no intellectual pursuits such as music or chess. He had no enquiring mind into other people's interests. He had no concept of justice and law, two things to which his father was dedicated and which had stabilised the country after the horrors of the previous reign. He was embittered by having no authority or responsibility and was a classic case of not understanding that rights are always earned after duties have been undertaken. Perhaps a good example of his failure to grasp the problem was when he was so extraordinarily rude and boorish to his father at his coronation.

He was very good-looking and had much charm and was able to get his own way far too often for his own good. His only passion was jousting and this would certainly breed a degree of confidence and bravery. To this end he was indebted to William Marshal, a leading exponent in that field of activity. But the hangers-on were a bad influence, an idle and disruptive lot with far too much time on their hands so that they could all get up to mischief. Young Henry was profligate and incapable of living within his means. He was always in debt and having to be dug out by his father.

What is quite extraordinary is the part that William Marshal played in all this. One would think that he would have been responsible for so much that went wrong and taken much of the blame but he was a man of probity, honour and sense. Perhaps the King continued to hope that William's influence would ultimately prevail and that young Henry would settle down.

Young Henry died at the age of twenty-eight. He had been married since he was a child to Margaret and they had one son in 1177 who only survived for three days. Perhaps she had had some miscarriages and became barren. After young Henry's death Margaret married King Bela of Hungary but it is not known whether she had any children by him. Perhaps young Henry was infertile. This aspect of his life is also puzzling. There is no record that he was promiscuous as his brother Richard or his mother Eleanor were. His Aquitainean forbears all had innumerable mistresses. His father did not set a good example either. It is possible that he was homosexual; he was certainly a pretty boy and his company was mostly *louche* young men, but history does not comment on this.

Young Henry was dominated by his powerful father who transparently did not trust him. The King was not the best of delegators. This lack of trust, this disinterest in work and this lack of seriousness led to the frequent rows between them. The young king was always comparing himself with his two younger brothers who had independence and authority in their territories and were able to control their own financial affairs without endlessly having to go to father to beg for more money.

Henry could never refuse his son anything and endlessly bribed

259

him to conform. The young king was always swearing allegiance and cooperation, but no sooner had he done so than he reneged with alacrity.

There is therefore no doubt that this lightweight and temperamental young man was going to continue to cause problems and would have been a disastrous successor to the Plantagenet throne. It is brutal to say so but his premature death was a blessing in disguise. The chroniclers of the time were more trenchant: 'The sons who rise up against their fathers to whom they owe everything are worthy only to be disinherited'.

William Marshal fulfilled the young king's vow to go on the Crusade on his master's behalf.

* * *

The succession was now clearly destined to fall to Duke Richard of Aquitaine who stood to inherit not only his mother's possessions but also Normandy, Maine and Anjou. Henry realised that the balance of power was now much too much in favour of Richard. Richard was a totally different man to deal with – he was an experienced warrior and well used to governing his mother's territories and did not tolerate any interference from any quarter. He was operating from a base of immense power. Henry was conscious that Geoffrey had a relatively secondary position and his youngest, John, a youth of seventeen now, was portionless. John now began to become known as 'Lackland' – a soubriquet which was to dog him for the rest of his life. Henry was also beginning to slow up and was not able to carry out his punishing schedule of travels throughout the realm as he had done in the past.

The three sons were summoned to Angers for a redistribution of the empire. Geoffrey seemed to be given a back seat at this meeting. Henry proposed that Richard renounce Aquitaine and Poitou to John and that he should inherit England instead of young Henry. Richard was furious. The last thing that he wanted was to exchange his complete independence for being his father's lackey in a country that he hardly knew. He knew all too well how his elder brother had suffered under this regime and was not going to put his head into the same noose. He left Angers in high dudgeon and from the safety of Poitou told his father that his ideas were totally unacceptable.

260

There is some doubt as to what happened next. Eleanor may have been brought to Windsor, although some sources suggest that she immediately came to Normandy. The three sons also came and there was a family conclave. Eleanor was now sixty-two and as formidable as ever. Age had not dimmed her faculties and her bodily strength was not diminished at all. It would be nice to think that her luxuriant tresses had become silvered or grey, but we do not know. She must have been showing some signs of ageing.

The bond of suffering that Henry and Eleanor had undergone following the death of their eldest son may have helped their personal relationship and given them some common ground at this time. But Eleanor was not going to concede the major decisions and she still knew where her support lay. She was aware that John had now emerged as Henry's favourite. She was still the arbiter of the future of Aquitaine and she was not going to see her own favourite being deposed just like that. Neither the French king, Philip, nor the new Archbishop of Canterbury, Baldwin, would have countenanced such a redistribution. Not least in all this, the rumours of the position of Alice, Philip's sister, were most important. Henry was still supposed to be negotiating for this poor girl either to marry him (after, of course, he got his divorce from Eleanor) or even John. The original swain, Richard, was now out of the equation. It was becoming Byzantine in complexity. Eleanor stood firm and resolutely refused to renounce her inheritance in Aquitaine to anyone other than Richard. The only concession that Henry was able to negotiate was that Richard restored his Aquitainean territories to his mother.

Later in that year of 1183, Henry arranged for Eleanor to visit Aquitaine to consolidate her hold on those lands. Whether she was escorted by Henry or not is not known. It would seem to have been unwise to let her go on her own as she was still a most valuable prize. There may have been some kind of parole conditions imposed. It seems that Eleanor returned to England before Easter, which she spent at Berkhampstead. In June Eleanor was moved first to Woodstock and then to Winchester where her daughter Matilda and her husband Henry the Lion of Saxony joined the party. Matilda produced a son which she called William and Eleanor was present at this confinement. Afterwards

261

Eleanor returned to Berkhampstead accompanied by her Saxon family where they spent the rest of the summer in Becket's old palace. Princess Alice was meantime being kept at Winchester. There was little love lost between Eleanor and the supposed paramour of her husband.

Philip of France now began to demand a solution to the Princess Alice problem as well as other matters which were irking him. On 6 December 1183, the two kings met under the elm tree at Gisors. Philip was a much more forceful character than his father and was quite determined to get the better of these Angevins who controlled so much more of France than he did.

Henry went straight into the attack which disconcerted the French camp. Vexin, the key to the defence of Normandy, which had been acquired by no less than a ruse by Henry when he married off young Henry to Margaret when they were still mere children, was claimed back by Philip as the returnable dower of Margaret. Henry reiterated his historical claim to this area and magnanimously offered an annual endowment as a compensation. Henry well knew that possession was nine tenths of the law and Vexin was in a key strategic position to defend Rouen. The Alice question was more difficult. Henry was most reluctant to see Richard married to her as this would repeat the problems that he had had with young Henry, who was always going off to Paris with his wife and then plotting with Philip. Henry avoided the unspoken rumour that he was consorting with Alice himself and suddenly changed his tactics by promising that Richard should marry Alice forthwith, and failing that she would marry John. Henry ignored the reluctance of Richard to wed his father's supposed cast-off mistress. The John suggestion brought a new aspect into the negotiations. Finally Henry paid homage to Philip for all his French possessions. He had managed to avoid doing this at Montmirail and again at the coronation of Philip. Thus Henry recovered his control over all his Angevin territories and now his sons were answerable directly to him and not to Philip. Thus these tortuous and complex negotiations all emerged to the advantage of Henry who had outmanoeuvred the French, at any rate for the time being.

The Christmas arrangements for 1183 are not recorded for any of the family.

On 10 June 1184 Henry returned to England. It would be interesting to speculate that the King went to join Alice at Winchester, but a substantial payment of fifty-five pounds, seventeen shillings was made available 'for the purchase of clothes, hoods and cloaks for Bellebelle for the King's use'. It is unlikely that these were really for Henry and there is strong evidence that Bellebelle became the King's paramour. It is not recorded whether this all occurred at Winchester, but if it did Alice would not have been best pleased. This mention of Bellebelle is isolated here but commentators refer to her as sharing Henry's bed for some years. There is no record of any illegitimate children by her. We do not know what Henry did during the summer of 1184 which is unusual as he still kept a very busy schedule of activities. Perhaps he relaxed on the hunting field and spent his evenings in dalliance with this young lady of questionable morals with the intriguingly flirtatious name.

Henry's quarrelsome sons returned to hostilities. Geoffrey and John joined forces and raided Poitou. In retaliation Richard plundered Brittany. This was simply not good enough, so in the autumn Henry summoned the three of them to Westminster to try and restore some harmony. On 30 November Eleanor joined the party. It has been said earlier that this meeting took place in 1183. The subjects under discussion were the same. It could be that this was a repeat meeting to try again to negotiate a settlement. The new Archbishop of Canterbury was also present and the format of the conclave was the same. Henry made his three sons renounce their hostilities and swear peace each to the other. He then made them give each other the kiss of peace. So far so good. Henry then asked Eleanor to ratify the assignment of Aquitaine to John. Eleanor again refused and in this she was supported by Baldwin and the attendant lords. It was again made clear that Philip of France, as overlord, would never agree. Henry had to climb down.

Henry now sent legitimate Geoffrey back to Normandy to take over control of that duchy. This immediately created the climate of opinion that Geoffrey's succession was the favoured option of the King. Henry's tactics of playing one son off against the others were dangerous: he was pursuing a policy of divide and rule. In this he assumed that his sons would never combine against him.

Meantime Constance, Geoffrey's wife, produced a daughter named Eleanor in honour of the Queen.

There was a family Christmas at Windsor which was the first time that, with the surprising exception of Geoffrey, they had all been together for many years. The well-known film and play called *The Lion in Winter* must have been set in this year. The theme is hardly jolly and there is no doubt that the tensions between them all lacerated more feelings than the season of goodwill intended.

In January Richard returned to his beloved Poitiers. Eleanor was transferred to Winchester with her Saxon family. Alice and Bellebelle were presumably parked elsewhere, perhaps with Henry commuting between them, although he certainly made a brief visit in the winter to the north of England. Perhaps he needed to see his illegitimate son, Morgan, and the cooperative knight Ralph Bloet and his winsome wife, Nesta – Morgan's mother.

During the early part of 1185, Heraclius, Patriarch of Jerusalem, arrived in England with alarming news of the disasters in the Holy Land. Heraclius was second only to the Pope in Christendom and he had to be listened to with all seriousness. Henry and his barons met him in Reading. The king in Jerusalem, Baldwin V, was but a child of five and a half, a first cousin once removed of Henry. Henry's grandfather, Fulk of Anjou, had married as his second wife, Melisande, the queen of Jerusalem, and Baldwin was the great-grandson of this union.

Heraclius offered Henry the kingdom of Jerusalem. Only he had the strength, the experience and the robustness to restore the flagging forces of the Christians. Only he could combat the all-powerful, well-organised and brilliantly led Saracen armies under the command of Saladin. Little did Henry realise the irony that Saladin was the son of his Queen Eleanor or, in other words, his stepson. The interplay of the family relationships was not only tortuous but almost incestuous.

This prospect was flattering and almost tempting. But Henry had never been attracted by the crusading zeal of others. In the Second Crusade Louis had nearly lost his throne and his wife, and was a party to military disasters. The lack of cohesion and the quarrelling factions within the Christian ranks caused many problems. The German emperor also emerged at that time with

264

his reputation much tarnished. Henry, although he was reluctant to admit it, was too old for all this campaigning in the hot and disease-ridden Holy Land. Ten years ago he could have coped, but the solution now lay with the next generation. In Henry's view the whole problem was a can of worms.

Heraclius was persuasive: he fell to his knees and amidst tears and lamentations begged Henry to come and come quickly. He brought presents such as the keys of the Tower of David and the Holy Sepulchre and the banner of the Holy Cross. The assembly sensed that Henry was wavering, but the King had always avoided such commitments and was now searching in his heart for the best way to escape with honour. He was also fearful because his kingdom was fraught with dissension between his sons and his departure could have appalling consequences. The Truce of God imposed on all those who took the Cross in theory allowed crusaders to depart without any fear of attack in their homelands, but these safety rules were regularly bent with dexterity by those left behind.

Henry drew back from the brink. He promised to provide money, soldiers and every support, but not his presence. Gerald Cambrensis leapt to the support of the patriarch but he misread his King's strong feelings and was sharply rebuffed. Heraclius then begged for one of Henry's sons to be sent so that the Angevin presence would restore the shattered morale in Palestine. John immediately responded and begged to be sent on this brilliant mission but his father refused. Heraclius sadly returned to Jerusalem where he soon died of a broken heart.

Henry now had to address the outstanding problem of John Lackland who was smarting from not being allowed to take the Cross. On 31 March Henry knighted John at Windsor and made him king of Ireland. The Pope had sent a golden crown adorned with peacock's feathers for the enthronement. On 15 April Lincoln Cathedral was devastated by a mighty earthquake which was heard and felt throughout the kingdom. The next day Henry returned to Normandy with the intention of controlling Richard who had reverted to his customary pillaging and raping in Poitou. Towards the end of April Eleanor and the Saxon family came to Normandy. Richard was now instructed to surrender Poitou to his mother which he agreed to do. This was an extraordinary volte-face for Eleanor and her favourite son as she had always resisted any encroachment upon Richard's rule in Aquitaine. Richard now moved to Normandy and remained in his father's shadow for the moment. Eleanor was still constrained in her freedom and was not able to take up the reins in Poitiers although from time to time she issued edicts in her own name. In effect Henry assumed direct rule there, partially shared with Richard. Henry seemed to be determined to show who was master, but was now tending to treat Richard in the same bullying way that he had earlier dealt with young Henry, with such disastrous results.

Henry the Lion and Matilda, his wife and Henry's daughter, were permitted to return in safety to Germany during this year but they left three of their children to be brought up in Normandy. Geoffrey and Constance of Brittany had a second daughter, Matilda, during this year, who lived only for a short time.

On 25 April John set sail for his new kingdom with an entourage of young men who were to be the nucleus of his court. His rule started badly and went from worse to worse. His court was irresponsible and insulted all the local kings and nobles. The petty kings were summoned to render homage and John with his cronies laughed and sneered at them and pulled their beards contemptuously. He confiscated lands arbitrarily and reallocated them to his followers, to the fury of the Irish. His idea of administration and justice were palpably inept and his military prowess ridiculous. The Irish kings and the local Norman nobles collaborated and demanded that John be withdrawn by the end of 1185, or rebellion would take place. Henry agreed and the Pope's crown was never used. Henry then appointed John de Courcy, a valiant and experienced soldier in Irish affairs, as viceroy of Ireland, and he was soon able to restore some semblance of good order. Later de Courcy was created Earl of Ulster.

During the early part of 1186 Henry and Eleanor were together in Normandy. There was a further inconclusive meeting between Henry and Philip of France and again Henry promised a solution to the Princess Alice problem. The King reinforced a number of his castles in Aquitaine, and Richard was deputed to deal with Raymond of Toulouse who was rattling his sabre.

On 27 April Henry and Eleanor sailed together back to Southampton and they spent most of the summer together at

Winchester, but probably not in close harmony since Ralph FitzStephen was replaced as the Queen's custodian by Henry Berneval. Eleanor was now sixty-four, but was still a most attractive woman and had not lost any of her zest for a full life. Her closeness to Ralph was not only a cause for concern over her safety but she could well have been enjoying his company too much and there is no reason to suppose that her libido had lessened. For Ralph's own sake and for Henry's peace of mind a new custodian was considered to be better for all.

The erstwhile favourite son, Geoffrey of Brittany, now spent most of the summer in Paris plotting with Philip of France. The Angevin princes continued to underestimate the wiles of the French king whose strategy continued to be directed at undermining their family. Events now moved rapidly and have always been obscure. Some say that Geoffrey caught a sudden fever from which he died. Others say that he took part in a jousting match during which he was unhorsed and trampled to death. He died on 18 August and was buried in Notre-Dame Cathedral in Paris. Philip was so upset that he had to be forcibly prevented from throwing himself onto the coffin and into the open grave.

It seems quite extraordinary that such widely different reasons are given for Geoffrey's death. He seems to have been the least loved and least attractive of the sons, although his death was bitterly regretted by the French. He was probably the cleverest and most intelligent of them all but he had a very nasty streak in his character and was two-faced. He was short, dark haired and unprepossessing in visage but had great charm when he wished to impress or to try and get his own way. He was brave and a skilled jouster but inspired little loyalty or affection. Generally he was as slippery as an eel and would sell his grandmother for two groats. His family did not seem to grieve much over his death. His widow, Constance, was pregnant at the time and gave birth to a son six months later, who was called Arthur.

The see of Lincoln had not had a resident bishop for nigh on twenty years. Geoffrey Plantagenet had been bishop from 1173 to 1183 but had not been ordained as a priest and therefore had never been enthroned. This huge diocese was suffering from neglect and the cathedral was now in ruins after the earthquake. A man of great ability, authority and saintliness was needed to tackle these problems. As so often happens Henry chose a man who fitted all these criteria and whose company the King always enjoyed: Hugh of Avallon, of the obscure friary at Witham in Somerset. At first Hugh refused as he had no ambitions whatsoever. Henry persuaded the prior of the Grande Chartreuse that it was Hugh's duty to God and the Church to accept this translation. Hugh, dutiful monk that he was, obeyed but stipulated that he should make a retreat of one month each year in solitude at Witham. The monks of Lincoln had been divided for many years, every one considering that they had the qualities for the bishopric, but they were persuaded that Hugh was of sufficient stature to succeed and almost immediately were unanimous in confirming his election. On the day after his enthronement, he retired to his manor at Stow, some eight miles from Lincoln, where a huge swan, never before seen, made his appearance and became so tame with Hugh that it was regarded as a miracle. Whenever Hugh was at Stow, only he fed this bird and it would nuzzle the bishop's hand and hiss gently into his ear as if talking privately to him. Whenever Hugh was due to return to Stow, the swan became intensely animated and excited during the previous four days or so and welcomed the bishop with an astonishing warmth when he arrived back at the manor. The new bishop fought for the rights of the foresters to hunt without restraint in the surrounding woods and persuaded the King to support him. Henry seldom refused any request made by Hugh.

Henry and John spent Christmas together at Guildford Castle. In February 1187 they returned to Normandy and, with Richard, prepared for a further round of hostilities with Philip. These were inconclusive and an unsatisfactory truce was signed. Richard then departed for Paris in high dudgeon and became bosom friends with the French king to the consternation of all. The two young men were inseparable: they ate together, shared the same dishes and were in each other's company day and night. This gave rise to the rumours that they were enjoying a homosexual affair of much intensity, so much so that they shared the same bed at night. It is generally considered unlikely that their relationship was anything other than platonic and political. At that time most people slept on the floor and it was therefore quite usual for those of rank to share a bed. Chroniclers of the time make no mention of anything untoward, and they were never slow to pass on gossip.

Henry was perturbed though, and delayed his return to England to see how affairs developed. There is no doubt that the wily Philip persuaded Richard that his inheritance was very far from secure and the two of them agreed to join forces after the expiry of the uneasy truce.

For some years Walter Map, rector of Westbury and a much respected friend of the King, had been engaged in continuous contention with the abbot and monks of Flaxley. This had all started when the abbot had persuaded certain Westbury parishioners to leave property to the Abbey despite an agreement between Map and the abbot that the Abbey would avoid this. Things had not improved so Map produced a catalogue of abuses perpetrated by the Abbey. The vitriol expanded to include not only the whole Cistercian order but also other orders and even the Pope and the whole Church hierarchy. His accusations alleged venality, drunkenness, greed, corruption, debauchery, immorality and indolence. It became an obsession with him, and he produced a pamphlet, *De Nugis Curialem*, about an imaginary 'Bishop Goliath' who epitomised all these vices. Map was not only an excellent scholar but a satirist with considerable wit and humour. But this publication was too near the knuckle for many and notice began to be taken. Things came to a head in 1187 and became known as the Flaxley Scandal. The main Cistercian house at Cîteaux was obliged to investigate and report. The Flaxley abbot, Waleran, was made to resign and was replaced in 1188. Several other abbots were also replaced and there was a general tightening up of discipline. Henry was embarrassed by this episode involving his favourite hunting lodge but it did not affect his friendship with Map.

On 6 April 1187 Henry's old friend and supporter, Humphrey Bohun, died. Humphrey had married Milo's daughter, Margery, and had inherited Milo's earldom of Hereford. Humphrey had been Lord High Constable of England. It was the beginning of the passing of an era.

*　*　*

Events in the Holy Land were moving rapidly towards a flashpoint. The sad little king of Jerusalem, Baldwin V, had died in 1186. His mother, Sybilla, after some devious chicanery, was elected queen and immediately married Guy de Lusignan whom she crowned king. The Christian ranks were now at loggerheads although they had at last got a king of some authority.

A truce with the Saracens was about to expire and Saladin began manoeuvring his army. He crossed the River Jordan on 1 July and took Tiberias. The Christian plans were indecisive and disagreements regarding tactics and the deployment and use of reinforcements were aired endlessly. King Guy was inclined to accept the last speaker's view, and vacillated.

On 2 July the Christian camp was well sited at Sephoria with ample water and excellent pasturage for animals. Saladin was unable to extract any advantage whatsoever and he decided to wait and see what would happen. The two armies were of equal size and armament. But further dissension rent the ranks of the crusaders. There were those who wanted to force the infidels into premature action against their excellent position. There were those who wanted to retake Tiberias, avenge their precipitate withdrawal and relieve the small garrison still holding out there. Accusations of honour and cowardice were bandied about. The hotheads won the day.

On 3 July, a hot and airless day, the Christians left their safe haven in three echelons to march over the barren hills. There was no water anywhere and horses and men began to suffer agonies of thirst. Saladin's scouts harried the columns with fast and furious forays into their flanks, shooting volleys of arrows and then wheeling and returning to the safety of the overlooking hilltops. By the afternoon the Christians had reached a plateau above Hattin. Ahead was a rocky hill with twin summits on either side called the Horns of Hattin. On the other side was a village, and beyond that a lake – and water. The echelon commanders told Guy that their men were so exhausted that they could not march another step. Other counsel pressed for a final push towards the lake. Guy compromised and called a halt by a well which would go some way towards assuaging their thirst. The well was dry.

Saladin could not believe his luck. He now had the Christian army at his mercy. From his knowledge of the terrain he had camped around the few wells with water in the vicinity and he ensured that his men conserved and used their meagre water supplies carefully. He was sure that the Christians had not taken similar care to look after their men's needs. He made his dispositions carefully and instructed his archers to use their arrows with intelligence.

'Do not,' he said, 'shoot at the armoured Christian cavalry. Your arrows will bounce off and you will have wasted your shot. Aim for the horse. An unhorsed Christian knight in armour will be at our mercy.'

The exhausted crusaders spent a miserable and sleepless night in agonies of thirst. All around them they could hear the chants and prayers of the Muslims exulting in their advantage. Just before dawn the Saracens set fire to the tinder-dry scrub and the hot acrid smoke poured into the Christian camp to compound their plight. Then Saladin's army circled the camp and the trap was set and sprung. At daybreak the attack started. The crusader army was in a dreadful state of disarray. Some tried to break through to get to the water so near yet so far. Most fell from weakness and many begged to be put out of their misery. Their mouths were swollen and their feebleness was pathetic. The cavalry fought with incredible bravery but were no match for the fresh Muslim horsemen. A few managed to break out and escape to Tripoli. The Bishop of Acre had been killed and the Holy Cross carried by him was now in Saracen hands. Guy and his household troops fought with outstanding bravery and courage so that even the infidels could only admire and pay tribute. Finally the red tent, Guy's headquarters, was toppled and only then did Saladin know that he had won the most decisive victory of his career.

Saladin greeted his prisoners with courtesy and manners. Most of them had to be carried to his tent and many were too weak to surrender their arms. Saladin gave his own cup of iced rosewater to King Guy who drank and then passed it on to Reynald of Chatillon, one of his corps commanders. Saladin said to Guy, through an interpreter, 'Tell the King that he gave that man drink, not I.' By the laws of Arab hospitality, to give food or drink to a captive means that his life is then safe.

Saladin reminded Reynald of his appalling crimes, which were unforgivable, and that he, Saladin, had sworn not only to bring him to justice but also to execute him personally. Reynald answered with truculence. Saladin took a sword and beheaded him on the spot. Guy was in terror that it was his turn next but Saladin reassured the King that he was safe and that he had not

271

offended against the laws of honour and behaviour. 'A king does not kill a king,' said Saladin.

Saladin treated all his prisoners with courtesy save the Templars and Knights Hospitallers, who were executed. The ordinary soldiers were sold into slavery and those of higher status could be ransomed. Guy was kept in captivity as a hostage.

Saladin then moved on to take Acre on 10 July, which surrendered abjectly without any resistance. The small garrison holding out in Tiberias also surrendered under the command of the Countess of Tripoli. She was released to rejoin her husband. During August Saladin mopped up Galilee and took Sidon, but Tyre was too heavily fortified and reinforced so he withdrew towards his main prizes.

In September Guy was told that he could have his liberty if he persuaded the garrison at Ascalon to surrender which they did, and this was followed by the surrender of Gaza. But it was not until the spring of the following year that Guy was finally released. Saladin now marched towards Jerusalem, the city from which he had sworn to expel the crusaders.

On 20 September he encamped before the Holy City and began his attack firstly upon the north and north-west walls, which were well defended. He then moved to the Mount of Olives and began to mine from that direction with more success. By 29 September a huge breach had been made and the assault began ferociously. The Christians were hampered by large numbers of refugees, mainly women and children, and had very few knights of experience and quality. On 2 October the garrison laid down their arms and Saladin entered in triumph, in fulfilment of his vow eighty-eight years after the Muslims had been ejected.

Saladin reminded Balian, the Christian commander and the Patriarch how, in 1099, the crusaders had raped, pillaged and looted without mercy. The indiscriminate slaughter of the Muslims by the crusaders at that time had never been forgotten or forgiven and it was with the greatest difficulty that Saladin controlled his victorious forces, many of whom were bent on revenge. He now set an example of restraint and control: all the defeated Christians were treated with humanity and respect and his troops were made to behave impeccably in the best tradition of Arab hospitality. Perhaps it was not all quite as perfect as it sounds, but it was certainly far better than the earlier Christian victory followed by those consequent appalling atrocities.

So it was that Saladin, the son of Ayub and Eleanor, fulfilled the expectations forecast for him by his illustrious parents when he had been conceived outside the walls of Antioch during the Second Crusade. This victory was to be the apogee of Saladin's career.

* * *

The news of the disasters in the Holy Land sent shockwaves throughout Christendom and the Pope immediately proclaimed a new crusade. On the very day that this was received at Tours, Richard took the Cross and vowed to dedicate his life to liberating Jerusalem from the infidel. He had not consulted Henry, who flew into one of his rages and retired to his chamber in solitude for four days. Richard agreed to delay his departure until his father gave irrevocable guarantees that his succession as Angevin heir was assured. Henry most unwisely refused to agree which merely confirmed Richard's view that John was to become the favoured son.

Henry did not stop his machinations and was determined to turn Richard from his avowed commitment. A number of simultaneous rebellions broke out in Aquitaine, probably encouraged by Henry. On 22 January 1188, Henry and Philip met yet again under the elm tree at Gisors. This time instead of quarrelling they both took the Cross and swore to maintain a truce whilst they campaigned in Palestine. It does not seem that this truce would be effective or honoured before they were to depart on the crusade. Meantime Henry returned to England on 30 January to initiate a tax to finance the crusade, which was called the 'Saladin tithe'.

During the summer Henry made his last visit to Flaxley together with Geoffrey Plantagenet to meet the new Abbot, Alan, who had replaced the deposed and venal Waleran. The King was reassured that Flaxley was now in good and godly hands. They had some most enjoyable hunting together and Henry saw and rewarded William the Hermit, now very old, who had been such a loyal servant and friend to both him and Rosamond, and who had facilitated their travels across the Severn between Frampton and Flaxley for so many years. William was to be clothed and fed and all his needs catered for for the rest of his life, and he was to be housed in the Abbey. Geoffrey noticed that his father was considerably less agile than he had been and was most concerned. He was obviously suffering greatly from a number of complaints.

The punitive Saladin tithe was beginning to bite on both sides of the Channel with much wailing and lamentation from both Jews and Christians. The funding of this crusade was to be formidable. The stringent rules for behaviour were drawn up and there were to be no Amazons or womenfolk in attendance. There were to be no released prisoners to make up the numbers and strict discipline would be imposed. Meantime all classes were to renounce luxuries and eschew meat and fish on certain days and not to have more than two courses at any meal.

In June Henry went to visit Eleanor, now at Winchester, and tightened her security as he suspected that she was up to her old tricks and plotting against him. The news from France was not good and any doubts about the timing of the Truce of God were made very clear. So he assembled a large force of English and Welsh soldiers and in the following month returned to Normandy as Philip was again on the rampage, besieging Berry fortress. In another twist of circumstances, Richard, having fallen out with Philip, relieved Berry. Henry now marched against his adversary with fearful intent.

On 16 August the two kings again met under the, by now, spreading elm tree at Gisors. Craftily Henry had encamped on the shady side leaving the French to occupy the sun scorched open fields. Once again the two kings had endless rows lasting several days over Alice and her dowry of Vexin, all to no purpose. Henry complained about the breaking of the truce and reiterated his time hallowed right to the Vexin. The still unwed and now twenty-eight years old, poor Alice was shuttled back and forth as a pawn in this endless game. She had been held in Henry's court for twenty years.

Tempers began to fray amongst the soldiers. The French were tormented in their discomfort and taunted the edgy and short-tempered Welsh levies who responded by letting fly with an arrow which wounded an arrogant Frenchman. This was a gross violation of the tradition of immunity during parley. The French charged the English who retreated into the local castle. The

French attacked the ancient and hallowed elm tree and brought it crashing to the ground to the horror of both sides. It was a bad omen for the future.

War was now inevitable. Henry, in spite of his infirmities, was always most dangerous when forced into a corner. He attacked and virtually destroyed Mantes and spread a trail of destruction far and wide. Philip was under pressure to seek another truce and there was an inconclusive meeting at Chatillon in October. Just as it seemed that Henry held all the cards, Richard deserted him for Philip. The two kings met at Bonmoulins in November, to try once again to bridge the chasm between them. To the surprise of Henry, Richard and Philip arrived together in close harmony. Henry demanded an explanation, and Richard replied speciously and with far too much readiness that funnily enough they had run into each other as they approached the conference place and it would have been discourteous for them to have deliberately avoided each other. The original closeness and cordiality between Philip and Richard, followed by an abrupt parting of the ways, may indicate that this happy resumption of sharing everything so intimately was significant

The parley began with the same tedious repetitions concerning their differences when there was an astonishing development. Richard knelt in front of Philip and, in front of his father, rendered virtually unconditional homage. The meeting broke up uneasily but not until a truce was hammered out which was to last until Easter.

Henry withdrew to recuperate at Saumur and dispatched Geoffrey Plantagenet to secure and fortify his border castles against both Philip and Richard. William Marshal had rejoined Henry after his vow to take the Cross on behalf of the young king had been fulfilled. Marshal was sent to Richard to try and bring him back into the fold. Richard remained adamant and was summoning his supporters to join his standard in the following year. Delegates from the Pope tried to break the impasse for until it was resolved the new crusade could not proceed. Henry and Geoffrey spent Christmas at Saumur but too many of the King's nobles were keeping their distance as they were not anxious to commit themselves to the losing side at this critical time. Richard and Philip spent Christmas in close accord in Paris, which was ominous.

The new year of 1189 opened quietly. Henry moved to Le

Mans and was trying to recover his strength, nursing his suppurating leg wound which had flared up again. Pope Urban had died, broken in heart by the turn of events in the Holy Land and the inability of his leading Christian kings to resolve their differences. The new Pope, Clement, sent a powerful delegation to break the log-jam. The senior cardinal legate was given short shrift by Philip and Richard who both jostled him and told him to mind his own business. They accused him of having been bribed by English gold.

In June of 1189, the eldest daughter of Henry and Eleanor, Matilda of Saxony, died aged thirty-four.

The attack by the French began in June. Henry could only rely on John, Geoffrey Plantagenet, William Longspee and the stalwart William Marshal. The King's party ventured into the Maine. Everywhere they went they found their strongholds taken by Philip and Richard. They were being continuously harried and then had to retire to Le Mans where they barricaded themselves into this loyal city, the birthplace of Henry. The defences were strengthened and they awaited the attack. The French forces invested the city and Richard knew all the tracks and paths and all the weak parts of the defences.

Henry ordered that a suburb be fired to clear lines of fire and remove cover from attacking forces. The wind changed and the flames and smoke blew back towards the castle, setting even that on fire. The French broke through and the King's party had to flee for their safety. Henry was in mental agony and turmoil at having to abandon this city so dear to him and could only be persuaded to leave by the unanimity of his advisers. Normandy was still safe and loyal and they sped towards Fresnay, although progress was much hampered by Henry's increasing infirmity. They paused only to destroy bridges and block other approach roads.

Richard led the vanguard of the pursuit of the King, his father. Lightly armed and at full gallop they were intent on implementing the final *coup de grâce*. William Marshal fell back to guard the rear and to delay the pursuers to the best of his ability. He turned with his lance levelled and met Richard well in the front of the armed party.

'By God's legs, Marshal, do not kill me! I wear no hauberk,' shouted Richard.

'May the Devil kill you, for I will not!' cried William, and he thrust his lance into Richard's horse, killing it and unseating the King's son. This delayed the advance party sufficiently for Henry to evade any immediate confrontation.

That night the King's party rested at Fresnay. Henry was in a very poor way by now and was unable to undress. Geoffrey Plantagenet put his own cloak over his father for comfort. During that night John disappeared.

The next fortnight saw a determined effort to reinforce the King's army. Both William Marshal and Geoffrey travelled extensively throughout Normandy and achieved a modicum of success. Henry's retreat to Chinon was secured but there was now no doubt that he was a dying man and many were not willing to support a defeated king against his powerful successor, now on the rampage. His stronghold of Tours now fell – a further bitter blow and a shock for morale. Henry could hardly walk and was suffering from suppurating abscesses.

The Archbishop of Reims negotiated a meeting between them all at Columbieres (now Villandry). Philip summoned Henry to appear before him and heard that the King was now so weak that he was not able to attend. Richard sneeringly told Philip that his father was up to his old tricks again. With anger in his heart at this jibe, Henry dragged himself to the parley on 4 July. Geoffrey begged to be excused as he did not wish to see his father's final humiliation.

Philip was genuinely shocked at Henry's appearance and offered him a seat and a cloak. Henry refused and insisted on keeping on his horse. Philip presented his Draconian terms. Henry was to pay homage for all his Continental possessions, agree to make Richard his successor on both sides of the Channel and instruct his barons to swear fealty to Richard to this end. He was to forgive all those who had fought for Richard and to go on crusade by Lent 1190. He was to surrender Alice at once and to arrange Richard's marriage to her immediately after Richard returned from his own crusade. He was to pay an indemnity of 20,000 marks and surrender three castles in Anjou and the Vexin. Finally he was to give the kiss of peace to Richard.

A clap of thunder rent the air – then a second, even louder. Was this an omen for the victor or the vanquished? Henry had to be steadied on his horse or else he would have fallen. There was to be no negotiation. These were the terms. Henry dejectedly whispered his agreement, only asking for the list of those who had deserted him.

When Richard approached for the kiss of peace, his father said quietly and bitterly to him, 'May God not let me die, until I have avenged myself on you as you deserve.'

He was carried back to Chinon on a litter in a terrible state of despair.

On 5 July the list was brought and the messenger said, in distress, 'Sire, the first name on this list is Count John, your son.'

This was the worst blow of all to the dying King. 'Is it true that John, whom I loved beyond all my sons and for whose gain I have suffered all this misery, has forsaken me? It is enough, no need to read the others. I care no more for myself or for aught in this world. Shame, shame on a conquered king.'

Henry lapsed into a coma with some moments of lucidity, comforted by his bastard son, the chancellor, Geoffrey, to whom he said, 'You of all my sons have shown yourself a son of natural affection.' He removed the Plantagenet signet ring with the inscribed leopard and gave it to Geoffrey. He then expressed the wish that Geoffrey be appointed Archbishop of York. This thus fulfilled Rosamond's promise to Eleanor that their own beloved son could not now be eligible to succeed to the throne.

On 6 July Henry died, still in the arms of his oldest and favourite son.

Those around the King then initiated the final degradation by stripping the body of all his effects and clothes, leaving this great man naked in death. William Marshal restored some dignity by covering the body with a gold embroidered cloak and finding a ring and sceptre. Richard was sent for and hastened to see his father's body in death. He knelt for a brief (too brief, some say) prayer. As he rose with an equivocal expression – was it joy or sorrow, grief or pleasure? – gushes of blood poured from the dead king's nostril as if in anger at his son's presence and did not cease until Richard had departed.

Weeping and lamenting, Richard accompanied Henry's body to Fontevraud where it was buried with due and fitting solemnity in the nun's choir. A magnificent tomb and effigy was built in due course in his honour.

* * *

Henry was fifty-six when he died and had reigned for thirty-five years. He will be remembered as the founder of English common law. He was passionately enthusiastic in matters of justice and fairness and set a system in place to enforce these. He had admirable administrators, starting with Becket and ending with his bastard son by Rosamond, Geoffrey. The phrase that we all know, 'from time immemorial' dates from 1190, the year after his death, and is a landmark in our system of law. He had inherited a complex arrangement of Anglo-Saxon systems melded onto the Norman arrangements and a multiplicity of courts. He coordinated all these into a single workable system which brought out the best of each. It was only the exemptions that the clergy were historically entitled to that nearly proved to be a stumbling block. And he was so near to solving this when Becket fell out with him.

He was instrumental in establishing the time-honoured trial by jury involving justice being agreed by a peer group of twelve men good and true. This system has stood the test of time to this day which is a remarkable achievement.

By giving a fair and just structure to England, Henry stabilised the country after the previous reign's disasters. The result was a thriving economy which encouraged the emergence of a strong mercantile class.

Henry's energy was prodigious but as he got older he simply could not maintain his hectic schedule. He realised that he needed to be seen and heard and his method of appearing suddenly and unexpectedly kept his officers on their toes.

He was a brilliant field commander and even as late as 1188 was as near as defeating the French forces as he could be. But he was not addicted to war for its own sake, unlike Richard. He preferred the diplomatic solution if he could get it.

He had an extraordinarily wide and catholic choice of associates and friends and he was good at choosing his advisers. Becket was perhaps the most brilliant choice and if this had been maintained as it had been intended what then would have been the course of history? Gerald and Map were stimulating and eccentric. Hugh of Avallon was outstandingly remarkable. Ranulf de Glanville and Geoffrey Plantagenet were brilliant administrators. His early friendships from his schooldays in Bristol and inspired by his uncle Robert of Gloucester gave him a powerful support base in the West Country. Humphrey de Bohun, the de Braose family, the de Clares and the Cliffords were all intensely loyal.

Henry was very abstemious but, like all the Planagenets, he had a very energetic lifestyle and a healthy appetite and so became very corpulent as

279

he grew older and this created some of his health problems, which were exacerbated by his rages.

His marriage with Eleanor was masterly in concept. It combined two huge territories and gave him the largest power base in Europe. But it was too disparate to become homogeneous and his personal method of direct rule could not possibly be effective over such an area. As soon as a fire was put out at one end, it flared up somewhere else.

His personal relationships with his sons were his undoing. He simply could not trust them. Eleanor was a key in all this; she was disruptive with them all and there is no doubt that she was jealous of Rosamond's benign and gentle influence. Henry's well-documented and uncontrollable rages were legendary and could not have helped his health especially in his later years when he probably underwent a personality change as he felt himself becoming more isolated.

But he did maintain affection and his love affair with Rosamond was a huge stabilising factor with not only his legitimate sons but also his two illegitimate sons. The Rosamond and Henry story is one of the greatest and most poignant in history. When Rosamond died this family cement began to crumble.

All in all, Henry was a truly great king, who established the Plantagenet dynasty which ruled England for over 300 years and from whose bloodline the present royal family is directly descended.

13

In July 1189 William Marshal and Richard met at a critical meeting in the crypt at Fontevraud. Two weeks previously William had had the opportunity to kill the heir and had instead unhorsed him unceremoniously.

The new King spoke first. 'Marshal,' he said, 'recently you tried to kill me, but my arm turned aside your lance.'

'I had no intention of killing you, nor did I try, although you were at my mercy, sire. It would have been as easy for me to drive my lance at you, but I chose to drive it at your horse and saved your life. My loyalty was to my King, as it always will be. I did not desire your death and never will. I did not do wrong, nor do I repent.' These were brave words and Richard knew them to be true; loyalty was something that he would desperately need in the ensuing reign. William would be as true to him as he had been to his father and to the young king.

'Marshal,' he replied, 'I pardon you and hold no enmity. Go forth to England now and look after my lands and affairs till I come. See to it that my mother, the good Queen Eleanor, is released at once and that due honour is accorded to her. You have my full authority as my marshal. Tomorrow I bury my father with all due ceremony as befits his greatness and genius.'

William, the one time penniless nephew of the great Patrick, the inheritor of the rank of marshal, the crusader who had fulfilled his vow as proxy to the young king, now needed to retire and found a family and a home. He was wealthy, immensely respected and a true champion of all knightly chivalry and honour.

He paused. 'Sire,' he said, 'I crave a boon. Your late father promised that he would give in marriage to me his ward Isabel de Clare, the Countess of Pembroke, the daughter of the famous Strongbow, Richard de Clare. I am hoping that you will honour the late King's wish and as you are now this good lady's guardian, you can now confirm that this marriage may proceed.'

Richard had already promised this lady's hand to another of his close associates, but he immediately recognised William's claim and readily agreed. Nor did Richard forget that the de Clares were related to the Cliffords and he was not unmindful of the fondness and respect that he had always had for Rosamond and the part that she had played in his father's wider family. Nor had he forgotten that Strongbow's mother had been a concubine of his great-grandfather, Henry I.

William only deviated for personal reasons on his speedy journey back to England. His new and young bride was not only very beautiful but exceedingly wealthy. William was thirty-five now and although still very strong and fit, his face was beginning to become lined and his hair had become grizzled. He much hoped that his bride would be happy, and he needed to see her and reassure himself that she was as keen and willing as he was. She responded with much enthusiasm and they became a devoted couple to the joy of all that knew them.

William now sped to Winchester to release Eleanor and to appoint her regent for her favourite son until he was able to come and claim his kingdom in person. To his pleasure he found that the sad news of Henry's death had preceeded his arrival and Eleanor's gaoler, Henry Berneval, had without demur unlocked the gates of her prison. From far and wide her erstwhile nobles and subjects, led by Ranulf de Glanville, had flocked to see her and to render homage. Eleanor was now sixty-eight and by the standards of the times could be regarded as an old woman. But she had worn extraordinarily well. Her luxuriant hair was as thick as ever and only just beginning to grey. Her brain was as needle sharp as before and she held herself with undiminished regal authority. She had looked after herself in captivity, had exercised well and had kept herself fully informed. She was ready for action and she was quite determined that her son should inherit and enjoy both ends of his kingdom.

As soon as William had delivered Richard's instructions, she moved at once to Westminster with the justiciar and the Archbishop of Canterbury, accompanied by William, to decree that all should present themselves for homage and to swear fealty to the new king. She then made a royal progress throughout southern England to impose Richard's authority and demand support, which was more than willingly given. She had not forgotten the one-time stripling who had rescued her in Aquitaine those many years ago and to whom she had entrusted the custody and training of the young king. She now instructed William to wed his bride at once so that he could resume his rightful duties after his well-deserved honeymoon. She rewarded some whose estates and liberties had become forfeit to Henry and encouraged a new generation of able young men to join her administration. This generosity was to stand the new king in good stead and to foster some badly needed loyalty at this critical time. She sent messengers in her name throughout the realm to endorse the authority of Richard and especially to pray for the soul of her late husband, the great and just King Henry. She righted many wrongs and loosened harsh laws which were unduly oppressive. But it was not all sweetness and light; she expelled a papal legate who had presumed to land without her permission. The only injustice that remained in force was the continued restraint placed upon that poor royal pawn Princess Alice who was kept under strict confinement at Winchester. Alice was now twenty-nine and still unwed, and Eleanor was not promulgating any match for her with Richard.

* * *

We now return to Richard in France after the departure of William. The relationship between the new king and his senior half-brother, Geoffrey Plantagenet, was complex. Geoffrey was five years older and the eldest surviving son of Henry. Richard's influences in his later childhood and young teens had been mainly in Aquitaine and the two boys had drifted apart. Richard was jealous of Geoffrey's military ability and success and many thought that the elder half-brother was more than a match in warfare compared with the Coeur de Lion. Henry had certainly given very considerable thought to legitimising Geoffrey by marrying Rosamond in the mid-1170s and this had always rankled with the legitimate sons, especially Richard. Geoffrey had been the closest of them all to their father and had been consistently loyal and supportive. He was a brilliant administrator and chancellor and the most like the old king in that he had inherited the temper, looks and frenetic energy. He had been disgusted by the treachery of Richard during the final months of his father's life, so much so that he had refused to attend that awful last meeting at Columbieres during which Henry had been humiliated. In the fluid inheritances of that time, Geoffrey was certainly a contender for the throne and Richard knew it. Richard was also aware of the promise made by Rosamond to his mother, Eleanor, at Woodstock twenty years before which had so nearly been fulfilled when Geoffrey was elected Bishop of Lincoln and which his father had then so craftily aborted.

Geoffrey was asked to make funeral arrangements for their father and the two brothers met four days later. Richard was clear about his strategy and mindful both of their father's wishes and their own friendship and shared memories from long ago. Richard demanded that Geoffrey resign his chancellorship immediately in return for which the York chapter would endorse Geoffrey's elevation to the archbishopric with the concomitant commitment that Geoffrey should be ordained a priest. This achieved a complex plan whereby Henry's last wish was honoured and Geoffrey was promoted to the second senior position in the English Church but would be disbarred from the throne. Rosamond's promise was fulfilled and Eleanor would be relieved at the removal of this threat to Richard's inheritance. But Richard and Geoffrey's friendship, already soured, was never to survive and this unusual ecclesiastical elevation was to be beset by a multitude of rows in the future. Eleanor had mixed feelings over Geoffrey's elevation as she did not like him or trust him. However, providing he was ordained very soon and did not drag his feet as he had done before, she would accept the solution with reluctance.

The York chapter meeting endorsed Geoffrey's election by a majority on 10 August. Hugh de Puiset, Bishop of Durham, an old adversary of Geoffrey's could not be present and he bitterly resented the election. It was during the rebellion of 1174 at the time when Geoffrey so brilliantly coordinated the defeat of Henry's northern invaders that the two fell out when Hugh virtually refused the king's armies passage through his bishopric. The second objector was Hubert Walter, Dean of York, who had had his eye on this preferment and was outmanoeuvred, to his fury. This was but the start of a running battle in York.

Initially Richard had more problems in getting support in France than Eleanor had had in England. During July Richard obtained Henry's treasury at Chinon and on 29 July he was invested as Duke of Normandy. On 31 July this was ratified by Philip of France and Richard reiterated his promise to marry Alice on his return from the crusade. He now felt secure enough to go across the Channel to claim his English throne. On 13 August he sailed from Barfleur to Portsmouth where he received an ecstatic welcome. Next he went to Winchester to secure the English treasury there and was greeted enthusiastically by Eleanor. There is no mention as to whether he passed any time with Alice.

On the same day, 13 August, Prince John landed at Dover and with almost indecent haste went to Gloucester where on 29 August he married his half-second cousin, sometimes called Hawise and sometimes Isabella, who was the granddaughter of Robert, Earl of Gloucester. It is puzzling that this marriage was permitted as it was well within the prohibited consanguinity rules. But Hawise was an extremely wealthy woman and this would have had considerable attractions for John Lackland. Richard also gave his brother six English counties and Mortain in Normandy which increased John's wealth, stature and standing immeasurably. This was intended to show the world that John was to be the King's heir. Prince John may have lacked land but he certainly did not lack wealth. Both Richard and his mother were present at the wedding but after the ceremony the speed of movement of the Plantagenets astonished all those who were at Gloucester.

Three days later, on 1 September, Richard and Eleanor rode in state to St Paul's in London where they were duly acclaimed and two days later Richard was anointed King in Westminster Abbey by the Archbishop of Canterbury in the most lavish ceremony ever witnessed in England. It is said however that he crowned himself by taking the crown off the altar and placing it upon his head with the words, 'I receive this in token that it comes from God himself.' Eleanor and John were present together with a vast host of nobles, clergy and sheriffs. The feasting lasted for three days and wine flowed like water. Richard distributed generous amounts of money and largesse to all those present but only in accordance with their rank and status.

The festivities were only marred by one unfortunate incident. On the eve of his coronation Richard had issued an order forbidding the attendance of any Jew at the ceremony. During the ensuing feasting, several Jewish leaders appeared and were roughly, even brutally, handled and expelled from the scene. There were even some who were killed. On the eve of a new crusade, feelings were running high against them and the rioting spread to the city. The Jews were a vital part of the social and mercantile structure and they were the only source of lending or, as it was more pejoratively described, usury. Their rates of interest were generally considered to be excessive and most citizens feared them and resented their easily gotten wealth. The King needed them and, for reasons of borrowing for his expensive requirements, had granted them his protection.

Henry had left a full treasury but even this huge source of riches was going to be inadequate for the crusade. Richard spent the next few months in England extracting every penny he could lay his hands on. 'If I could find a buyer, I would sell London itself,' he said. Abbot Samson, the great Abbot of St Edmundsbury, offered to buy the royal manor of Mildenhall for 500 marks and was told that he could have it for double that amount, an excessive price.

The rows in the York chapter began to simmer more dangerously. Those who had opposed the election of Geoffrey Plantagenet appealed against his appointment and Richard told his half-brother to get himself ordained at once. On 23 September the newly consecrated Bishop John of Southwell ordained Geoffrey and Archbishop Baldwin of Canterbury then claimed upon totally spurious grounds that this ceremony could only be performed by the Archbishop of Canterbury and that Geoffrey's priesting was therefore invalid. In retaliation Geoffrey overruled the election of some new members of the chapter and was unwise enough to invert a gold bowl over his head, saying jocularly that his head would easily fit a crown such as this seemed to be. In retaliation the York chapter confiscated all Geoffrey's lay estates. This was too good an opportunity for Richard to miss. He returned them to Geoffrey upon payment of a 3,000-pound fine!

After Richard's coronation he sped down to Flaxley to recall the many happy childhood days that he spent there with

Rosamond and especially with his contemporary who now accompanied him, William Longspee. These two half-brothers were always close and had much in common. They spent a few days hunting and, in particular, inspecting the iron works and armoury which were vital for the impending crusade. He also investigated the systems of supply of charcoal and ore from the Forest of Dean so that the furnaces could be kept at full blast. They both ordered new swords and other equipment.

The new abbot did not lose the opportunity to ask that the tirades from Walter Map could be curbed and Richard supported the Abbey in this. The King was most anxious to encourage the monks in giving their wholehearted support not only in their agricultural successes but also in their more warlike armament production, which would be of such importance in releasing the Holy Land from the yoke of the infidel and to recover control of that soil upon which the Saviour had once walked. One of Richard's attributes was his powers of persuasion combined with his diplomatic abilities.

The King issued a grant to the Abbey granting them extensive rights for firewood and a waiver against vexatious insults with the right of direct appeal to the King or his chief justiciar. This seemed to be directly pointed towards Map and gave valuable protection for many years to come, reinforcing the importance attached to the Flaxley activities. Later in 1189 Richard gave a further charter giving the Abbey an extraordinary set of privileges of 'sac', 'sol', 'quit of tol', 'theam' and 'infangenethef'. Sac gave royal discretion in the case of suits against the monks. Sol was a privilege only the King could grant, but what it meant is not now clear. Quit of tol provided freedom from tolls when crossing the Severn. Theam gave extensive powers to the Abbey in cross-examining persons suspected of having stolen property including livestock; it seems probable that this would include some licence for brutal interrogation. Infangenethef gave Flaxley the right of jurisdiction over any apprehension of a thief caught on their property.

These were all invaluable concessions and of immense financial benefit to the Abbey. Their granting is all the more significant when one recalls the longstanding connection between Henry and Flaxley. It reinforced Richard's own love and early memories of happy days spent at Flaxley when he was a child.

287

On one of their visits there, William was displeased to find that Roger, the son of their wet nurse Hikenai, was staying in the Abbey guest house. It had been many years since these two had seen each other and they had never got on. Roger told William that he thought that Hikenai had been badly treated by the family. Roger was still as vituperative as he had ever been and reminded William that his mother's part in the bringing up of Rosamond's two sons had not been rewarded as he considered appropriate. William was furious and recalled that Hikenai had been given a life tenancy in a small property from the de Morville family as an ample reward which more than adequately looked after the needs of the two of them. He asked kindly after Hikenai who had been good and kind to the two brothers and had herself been utterly loyal to their mother, unlike Roger who had so disgracefully betrayed the secret of the maze to the Queen. He was glad to hear that Roger's mother was still hale and hearty, though showing her age.

William told Richard about this unfortunate meeting. The King well remembered Roger and told William to stand no nonsense from this odious and disreputable fellow. He promised his backing after Hikenai's death in any legal dispute that might arise.

Richard came down several times during the autumn with his last visit in December when he found the place so cold he gave yet another grant for rights to gather firewood yet further afield. The boundaries of the extent of these confines are still identifiable.

The Abbey celebrated the favours granted to them by having a simple service of dedication in that month. Mass was celebrated in the presence of Richard and his entourage. A sword, lance, helmet and battleaxe, all cast at Flaxley and embossed with the King's emblem, were laid upon the altar, given to the King as from God, duly blessed and then handed back for him to use in the Holy Land. William Longspee's accoutrements were blessed at the same time.

Richard then left Flaxley for the last time, and rode to Gloucester where he was welcomed by huge crowds. As they made their way from there the two half-brothers talked about Geoffrey.

'He really is getting more and more like papa,' said the King.

'It worries me. His tempers are just like our father's were. It makes him most unstable.'

William replied, 'I am afraid that he has a really deep resentment over the last few days of papa's life. He sees himself more and more as the successor of all that drove our father forward. But never fear, he does not want to be king. Your problem is how to use his abundant abilities. He is his own worst enemy.'

They then probed between them Prince John's proclivities with the fair sex. John was known to have a roving eye and nobles were wiser to keep their wives well out of sight from his hot and fumbling hands. He was also prone to bed women of the baser sort. On the whole he did not broadcast his mistresses but there were some who were beginning to excite interest.

'William, what do you know of the wench, Clementia, called by some "Queen" Clementia?'

William laughed. 'He has just had a daughter by her called Joan. I doubt whether his bride, our cousin Hawise, will be best pleased when she finds out.'

'What is she like? The usual, I suppose. Below the salt sort of wench?'

'You have it in one. She's got tolerable looks, lusty and very beddable. John enjoys himself and, sadly, encourages her to give herself airs which is immensely tedious to all around him. But that's life, I'm afraid.'

Richard grunted and both proceeded on their way to Oxford, to the place of Richard's birth, to spend time with Eleanor.

Richard appointed early in the New Year his own justiciar and another chancellor to replace his half-brother who had resigned some months earlier. He could not have made a worse choice for justiciar from Geoffrey's point of view and it was undoubtedly a deliberate slight. The new man was none other than Hugh de Puiset, Bishop of Durham, who had always been in intense enmity both with his father and his half-brother. With Richard's impending departure on crusade he needed to balance the power so he appointed an odious man, William Longchamp, as chancellor. The scene was now set for many problems to emerge in the near future as neither of these men was going to cooperate in any way with the other.

Geoffrey meantime had been sent to Scotland to escort the Scottish King to Canterbury to swear homage to Richard whilst the latter was absent on crusade. On Geoffrey's journey south he was embroiled in another bad-tempered escapade. On the eve of Epiphany he gave notice that he would celebrate vespers in York Minster with all his cathedral chapter in attendance. Those canons who were in support of him made due and solemn procession into the cathedral to find that the dissenting canons had already lit the candles and the service was in full flow with a vast congregation from the city in attendance. Geoffrey's temper flared and he ordered the choir to cease. He then intoned the service on his own, with due accompaniment from his own supporters. The leader of the dissidents, the cathedral treasurer, then extinguished the candles, as they were his sole responsibility. None of the canons were brave enough to relight them so Geoffrey finished the service in the dark. The next day the two factions met in the cathedral again with a large concourse of citizens wishing to witness the outcome of this astonishing scene from the previous evening. Geoffrey demanded an apology which the treasurer refused to give. The latter then endeavoured to incite the citizens to riot against their new archbishop. Unfortunately for this person the citizens turned against him and nearly killed him but for the prompt action by Geoffrey. Geoffrey was now in full control and was on the brink of obtaining total support from his chapter. But the archbishop overreacted and overplayed his hand. He excommunicated both the treasurer and another canon and closed the minster for all services. The citizens reacted most angrily at this and refused to pay their rents and other dues for the archbishopric. Hugh de Puiset then intervened giving full support to the citizens and forbade any future payments.

Richard continued to take every opportunity to harry his half-brother but he still needed him to become archbishop sooner rather than later. He banished him from England for three years and put pressure upon the Pope to ratify his elevation as soon as possible to end the disgraceful chapter disputes.

Richard crossed the Channel on 12 December and spent Christmas at Bures near the Norman border. Eleanor was remarkably active and is noted as having visited Sarum, Windsor, Canterbury, Winchester and another undisclosed location in Hampshire. The main thrust of these activities was undoubtedly to raise funds for Richard's crusading expenses and all offices of employment had to be redeemed with the payment of large sums. De Puiset, the ageing Bishop of Durham, who had had to pay for his appointment as justiciar, was now obliged to buy the earldom of Northumberland with the King's quip 'Out of an old bishop I have made a new earl.'

Other prelates were pressured into buying estates, which were exceedingly profitable investments in their own right. Nobles were able to purchase immunity from having to embark upon the crusade and the lemons were all duly squeezed to good effect.

Eleanor was perturbed about the succession problem. Richard was now thirty-five, unmarried, with no legitimate heir and an unattractive and unwanted potential bride who was no longer in the first flush of youth and who might well be infertile. The perils of mortality for those on crusades were dire. Those in the running for the succession were Arthur of Brittany, an infant of but three with a mother for whom Eleanor had very little time or sympathy. There was Geoffrey whom they were about to see off as archbishop, but who had about as much tact as an enraged rhinoceros and who left a trail of fury and confusion wherever he went. Finally there was John and Eleanor did not much trust him out of her sight. However, she now began to eye Berengaria as a suitable consort for Richard. This princess was the nubile daughter of Sancho the Wise, King of Navarre. She was comely rather than beautiful, but most accomplished. Berengaria was moreover a southerner and this appealed to Eleanor much more than the French contender who had, in the modern terminology, reached her sell-by date. The Navarrene princess was the elder of two sisters and Richard had met her and dallied with her some years earlier in the court of Poitiers and had been impressed with her qualities. Eleanor decided to make a visit to Navarre and negotiate a suitable match as soon as she could.

On 2 February 1190, Eleanor sailed from England and joined Richard at Bures bringing with her John, Geoffrey and Alice, the latter being immediately placed into custody at Rouen. A family conclave was summoned at Nonancourt in March and the arrangements for the English interregnum during Richard's absence on his crusade were finalised. Longchamp, now Bishop of Ely as well as chancellor, and de Puiset were to be jointly responsible for the country. John was banished from England for three years and Geoffrey's similar banishment was endorsed.

Eleanor was later to persuade Richard to mitigate John's terms, allowing him to return at will and this latitude they both were soon to regret. Philip and Richard then met and agreed that they would both depart together for Palestine in July.

Meanwhile a tide of anti-Semitism swept England culminating in the slaughter of 150 Jews who were sheltering in Clifford's Tower in York. Longchamp was instructed to speed north to punish those responsible and to his pleasure found that most of the guilty parties were cronies of de Puiset and had undoubtedly been encouraged by the latter to wreak vengeance upon the Jewish fraternity. Longchamp seized his co-ruler to be and cast him ignominiously into prison thus leaving himself with sole responsibility for England, and he assumed the position of justiciar as well. He was then appointed papal legate for England by the Pope and began to behave with an intolerable regal tyranny and arrogance to all. The hounding of the Jews spread to Lincoln, Stamford, Norwich and Bury St Edmunds and the slaughter of their leading citizens became widespread and most serious – so much so that later there were many long-term repercussions.

Richard made all suitable arrangements for continuity of rule during his absence in Aquitaine and reminded all his vassals of the conditions for the Truce of God which had to be maintained whilst he was on his crusade. Eleanor seems to have enjoyed the relaxation of her first summer break in her native land for a great number of years and she stayed most of the time in Chinon and made a grant to Fontevraud for the repose of Henry's soul.

Richard then met Philip at Gisors to finalise their joint departure arrangements in early July. The French King did not miss the opportunity to remind Richard of his obligation to marry Alice forthwith. Richard was aware of his mother's intended machinations and tried with indifferent success to pacify Philip in that they had jointly proclaimed that absolutely no women would be allowed to follow this crusade in view of the problems that ensued during the Second Crusade. Philip demanded the return of all Alice's dowry lands and Richard became duly evasive and considered that all this was now inopportune since his own safe return to Alice was vital to their future together. The two kings were becoming less enchanted with each other's company which augured badly for their joint venture which lay ahead, although they formally agreed that they were to be equal partners in this vital enterprise for Christendom.

On 30 June Richard's naval flotillas set sail from Dover to make their way to Marseille. The two kings' armies met at Vezelay in early July and all commented on how much more professional and competent these forces seemed. There were no hangers-on, no Amazons, no prisoners on parole and no sponging camp followers. Philip was however becoming even less enthusiastic over the venture as his wife, Queen Isabella of Hainault, had just died and her territories were open to a very disputed succession. And he was more than aware that his cousin Richard's military prowess, experience and reputation were far superior to his own and he was becoming consumed with jealousy.

Richard was in the prime of his life. He was tending towards corpulence, a Plantagenet failing, but was tall, powerful, well built and with a commanding presence to whom all paid attention. Philip was small, unprepossessing and insignificant albeit that he was wily and very intelligent.

The two armies marched together as far as Lyon where the two kings realised that there were insuperable problems in provisioning these huge numbers so their paths diverted. Philip was prone to seasickness so opted for the overland route. His troops made their way south to Genoa whilst Richard's forces marched via Tours to Marseille to join the English fleets which were now expected to round the Iberian peninsula. Both armies were showered with food, wine and blessings accompanied by copious tears and embraces from the ecstatic well-wishers bidding them *bon voyage* and success against the infamous infidel.

Richard's ships had been delayed by headwinds and had not yet arrived at Marseille. Richard was unwilling to wait any longer as he had problems to attend to in Sicily and did not want Philip to get there first. He commandeered a number of local vessels and set off at once. Despite his pressing wish to get on, he made a leisurely trip down the Italian coast calling at Naples, Amalfi and Sorrento, admiring the gently billowing smoke from the summit of Vesuvius. His delays allowed Philip to get to Messina two days before he did on 14 September, but Richard had not wished to arrive without the comforting presence and support of his own men.

Richard's sister Joanna had married King William of Sicily in

1174 and she had had mixed pleasures in her husband's court which adopted too many aspects of the life of the harem. William had recently died without any issue and the kingdom was in disarray. His legitimate successor was the German Prince Henry, a nephew of Frederick Barbarossa. But Henry was in Germany and too far away to claim his inheritance and anyway he was immersed in his own problems there. Tancred, a bastard nephew of William's, seized the throne and the huge wealth of his uncle which included the most valuable and vast dowries of Joanna which he was intending to enjoy without let or hindrance. Richard naturally had other ideas. But Philip had got to Sicily first and had been welcomed at Messina. He was well ensconced in the palace of Tancred and Richard was reminded with firmness that there was not room for both of them there. He was graciously allowed to camp outside the city walls. Tancred had prudently removed Joanna to the comparative safety of Palermo.

Richard demanded the immediate release of his sister whom he had not seen for fifteen years and who had been only eleven years old when she was sent to Sicily. Richard certainly would not now have recognised her, but she was a most important pawn in his game. Tancred decided that discretion was the better part of valour and that he would be unwise to cross swords with Richard, so he graciously allowed Joanna to join her brother at Messina and sent with her her bed, furniture and a tolerable sum for her expenses. Tancred conveniently forgot to include her revenues and her late husband's considerable legacy.

Joanna's arrival at Messina was joyously welcomed not only by Richard but also by Philip, whose eyes lit up when he saw the beauteous and accomplished Plantagenet princess. The souring relationship between the two kings showed a marked improvement.

* * *

Alison Weir's book Eleanor of Aquitaine *refers to Philip as being still a married man and so he should not have been quite so obviously smitten. But Amy Kelly (*Eleanor of Aquitaine and the Four Kings*) writes that Philip had recently lost his queen before the crusaders departed from France in which case Philip would have been permitted to be thinking of a new consort.*

* * *

294

But these castings of sheep's eyes from Philip were not intended to be part of Richard's plans. He was still in comparative discomfort outside Messina, so he seized a priory in Calabria in which to house them both in more style and this placed the straits between the seasick prone French king and Joanna and thus cooled the ardour of the lovesick Philip.

Richard now needed to play for time as he was waiting to hear of news from Eleanor, whom he was expecting to appear with his new intended bride. In those times communications could be sparse although vital letters were often able to get through. For the time being, however, Richard was in the dark although he was fully aware of what Eleanor was intending to do. Before she arrived he would have to negotiate an extremely tense unscrambling of his betrothal to Alice and this would undoubtedly cause a diplomatic storm of the first order. In any case the onset of winter and the storms to which the Mediterranean was prone made any later departure for Palestine impossible.

Philip was not going to pass the winter in idleness so he began to make mischief with Tancred and was also edgy about Richard's manoeuvres. His spies were not unaware of what was going on, and what they reported confirmed his worst fears.

* * *

As winter approached, Eleanor, despite her age of sixty nine, departed for Navarre and crossed the Pyrenees with her retinue and was given a royal welcome by King Sancho VI. His two daughters were paraded for inspection and Eleanor was delighted with both but chose the elder for Richard. Berengaria was now twenty-five, and no chicken, but had many suitable attributes not least that she was pliable and dutiful and more than willing to play second fiddle to her powerful mother-in-law to be. Berengaria was chosen for one purpose alone which was to produce a legitimate heir for Richard. As far as the diplomatic niceties were concerned it was an excellent move to have a friendly country protecting the southern flank of Aquitaine and the trading opportunities were mutually advantageous. For Sancho the prospect of his daughter's union with the all-powerful Plantagenets was alluring.

A magnificent feast celebrated the visit and both parties were particularly careful not to link this with any formal betrothal as

Richard had given many solemn undertakings to Philip about Alice. The French King always had friends who kept him informed of what was happening. The glamour and amazing beauty of Eleanor captivated all those who saw her in Navarre and despite her age she was indefatigable in all the ceremonies and dominated the social gatherings that she attended.

Eleanor and Berengaria now made the long and dangerous journey in midwinter back through France and Italy to join Richard in Calabria accompanied by a suitably large retinue provided by Sancho. Their route was uncertain but they must have taken the shortest and most obvious way. They are said to have gone through Montpellier, across the southern part of France, then over the Alps and into Lombardy. By Advent they had reached Rome and here they rested awhile and sent news of their progress to Richard through a trusted emissary. The exceptional rigours of Eleanor's journeys over the past few months entitled her to a rest to recoup her energies for the final phase of her master plan. And perhaps Berengaria needed to look her best for the ordeal that she was about to undergo and to fulfil her destiny in the scheme of things. Richard too had his part to play – he could hardly bring Berengaria to Messina and tell Philip that 'here was his fiancée' when he had already got one of twenty years' standing. Richard had already made his plans.

In February 1191 Richard underwent a penance and purification in Messina, perhaps with the intention of cleansing his past sins as a prelude for his impending marriage or possibly with the intention of arriving in the Holy Land duly shriven. He publicly confessed to 'sins against nature and the foulness of his past life'. He received an absolution and a ritual thrashing.

Tancred had been duly flattered and bribed by a suitable betrothal between Richard's infant nephew, Arthur of Brittany, and Tancred's small daughter, combined with a more tangible and immediate gift of the legendary King Arthur's sword, Excalibur, recently unearthed at Glastonbury, indubitably of spurious provenance. Philip was becoming increasingly aware that he was now being sidelined. He reiterated his demands that Richard should fulfil his contractual obligation to marry Alice forthwith or return the dowry in Plantagenet hands. Richard replied that since his father had grossly violated poor Alice's virginity the union would now be impossible to fulfil. The King of England reiterated the calumny that his father and Alice had produced a son as a result of their liaison and this Philip was in no position to refute. Richard expressed his utmost sorrow at this development and said he realised how sad it must be for Philip but 'the Church could not, under any circumstances, sanctify this union. Two of the leading princes in Christendom could not offend Holy Law so capriciously – the more especially as they were both embarking upon a crusade against the Infidel. An example such as this would not be acceptable.'

The mortified King of France now had no option but to concede defeat and in high dudgeon set sail for Palestine only hours before the arrival in Messina of Eleanor and Berengaria. He was partially mollified by the payment of a quit-claim of 10,000 marks and the promise of the return of Alice's dowry after they had both returned from the crusade.

Eleanor was delighted that Richard and Berengaria found much in common and the auguries for their future together were propitious. The dowager Queen was not keen to tarry – there was much that needed her attention back at home and she had been away far too long. She had intensive discussions with Richard and briefed him about what was happening with John, who was throwing his weight about quite intolerably. It was probably during this time that she made a rare error of judgement in negotiating the reversal of Richard's banishment of John from England. Her reasons were sound but her youngest son was more intractable than she realised. Archbishop elect, Geoffrey, was continuing to create disarray within the province of York and had tried to imprison Longchamp, the acting regent and chancellor. Richard authorised Walter Coutances, Archbishop of Rouen, to have an overriding mandate in England.

It would not be appropriate for Richard and Berengaria to marry during Lent, nor was it sensible for Richard to stay any longer in Sicily. Before leaving, Eleanor considered it politic and seemly that Richard and Berengaria should leave separately so she suggested a suitable chaperone would be Joanna, Richard's widowed sister. It was fortunate that these two ladies were developing a close and cordial rapport.

The night before Eleanor was scheduling her return, she suggested to Richard that they should have a few hours together in complete privacy. She told him that she had never talked about her experiences in Palestine during the Second Crusade with her first husband, Louis VII of France, and that Richard might be interested and learn something which could stand him in good stead when he arrived. She told him of her Uncle Raymond of Antioch and his sure grasp of the political infighting both in the Christian and the Saracen camps, and how decisions were taken for all the wrong reasons. The weakness of Louis and his inability to pursue the right military strategy led to disaster after disaster.

'Raymond was adamant that the crusader's best strategy was to attack through the soft underbelly of the Saracen position in Aleppo and to exploit their internal divisions. Instead the Christians chose to go for Damascus and spent most of the time quarrelling over who should rule that city when they captured it. Damascus was, perhaps surprisingly to us, quite friendly and cooperative with the Christians in Palestine. Tactically the crusaders made every mistake in the book and only succeeded in uniting the infidels in opposition. Raymond was so firm in his objectives that he and I went on a reconnaissance into the environs of Aleppo. We were accompanied and escorted by two senior Kurdish warriors who wanted to work with us.'

The King was intrigued to see that his mother was enlivened by her recollections. Her eyes became alight and sparkled as they not done since she held court in her Poitevin, nigh on twenty years before. He also realised what a beauty she must have been in those days of her youth and how men must have fallen for her. He knew of some of the rumours that had dogged her during the Second Crusade.

'Their leader, a Kurd, was the famous Ayub. Brave, fearless, resourceful, such a man of action. Wise, humane, just and God-fearing. So much more Christian in precept than so many Christians. Oh how I wish that he was leading us then! We would have recovered all that we had set out to do.'

'Was he handsome too, mama dear?'

Eleanor paused, thought for a moment or two, sighed. 'Oh yes,' she said. 'Yes he was.'

Richard waited and wondered if there was more that she wished to say.

'He had a little son, a lovely little lad. I, er, met him once or twice. He was the apple of his eye. Ayub once told me that I would produce a son like him. He would be brave, fearless, handsome and a great ruler. You are that son, Richard. You are in the mould that he and I expected.' The Queen put her arms around her son and hugged him hard. It was years since she had done this. Her eyes were welling with tears.

'And Ayub's son?'

'The great Saladin, the man who is leading the Saracens and with whom you will be engaging in mortal combat. He has been brought up as the true son of his father, in his image. You are each worthy of your upbringing, and your families.'

'How do you know all this, mama?'

'You would not know as it was all before your time. That great man, once your father's friend and counsellor and always my friend, Thomas Becket, had a Saracen mother, Rohesia, who came from Acre and fell in love with Thomas' father during the First Crusade. She escaped to London, married him and became a Christian. She was related to Ayub, always kept in touch and told me how Saladin grew up into the man that he now is. Respect him and behave to him as you would to a brother.'

Richard gave a half smile. He had not always treated his brothers as well as he perhaps ought to have done but a foster brother might be different. He began to look forward to his venture.

Eleanor put her hand into her kirtle and pulled out a jewelled dagger. It was the same that she had so nearly used against Rosamond. 'Ayub gave this to me as a present after we had returned to Antioch. It is very precious to me but I would like you to give it from me to Saladin and tell him that it came from his father. I am sure that you will be able to engineer an opportunity. I am certain that you will become close although you are on opposite sides.'

Eleanor paused and said very slowly and carefully, 'There is no truth in the stories about Raymond and me. It was convenient to some to spread such base lies. Raymond was my uncle and a very honourable man.' She embraced her son and wished him God-speed.

So it was that three days after her arrival, on 2 April, Eleanor departed from Sicily and arrived in Rome in time for the consecration of the new Pope, Celestine III, an old friend. She took the opportunity to press for the authorisation of Geoffrey's elevation to the see of York. She also took him into her confidence about Richard's betrothal and affairs in England, Aquitaine and

Normandy. Eleanor was developing a sure touch as a matriarch and there was no one to gainsay her in view of her long experience in so many roles spreading over half a century. She drew funds to replenish her treasury which had been depleted during her extensive travels and left Rome in the early summer to reach Rouen in July where she was not reassured by what she found.

* * *

Richard of Devizes, although describing Eleanor as a matchless woman, beautiful and chaste, adds the cryptic comment: 'Many know what I wish none of us had known. The same queen, in the time of her former husband, went to Jerusalem. Let none speak more thereof; I know well. Be silent.'

* * *

On 10 April Richard and Berengaria sailed in separate vessels towards Cyprus. Berengaria's vessel became separated from the main crusader fleet and then sank on the coast of Cyprus whereupon the tyrannical ruler, Isaac Comnenus, seized his opportunity by refusing to let her land or obtain fresh water. He then threatened to hold her to ransom. Richard wasted no time in appropriating the island and, more importantly, the treasury, and imprisoned Comnenus for his impertinence. The Cypriot begged the angry Richard not to be put in irons to which the King readily and, seemingly unexpectedly, agreed.

'My dear Isaac, one king does not put another king into irons. It would be discourteous and unseemly.'

Richard arranged for fetters to be cast in silver from the bullion in Comnenus's own treasury. He then personally undid the iron chains and refastened the silver handcuffs himself and Comnenus was immediately aware that Richard's promises were not always as they seemed.

Richard and Berengaria were married at Limassol on 12 May and at the same time the bride was crowned Queen of England. There followed three days of merriment, albeit that Roger of Devizes opined that the Queen was still a virgin and that her recently-wed husband was spending more time than he should closeted privately with the nubile child daughter of Comnenus, to whom he had kindly offered to give his protection. The King's recent penance in Sicily was conveniently forgotten and his tastes were wider than Berengaria had hitherto realised. Richard took also under his wing a little, dark Arab boy, one Tariq, who had been in the Cypriot King's household. This little lad had been captured in Palestine and had become a slave. He doted upon Richard and would do anything asked of him. He begged to be taken back to the Holy Land and perhaps, if his lord and master was willing, to be released.

Ignoring the agreement that no ladies should accompany the crusaders, Richard took his new wife and sister on his final stage of progress to the Holy Land, departing on 5 June and arriving at Acre three days later to find the dispirited besiegers of that city under the King of Jerusalem and Philip of France in a demoralised state.

The King of Jerusalem was none other than that Guy de Lusignan who had so nearly captured Eleanor and had been thwarted by that young and spirited knight, William Marshal, now a veteran in Richard's council. Guy had lost that battle of Hittin by being completely outmanoevred by Saladin. He badly needed the port of Acre to ease his supply problems and had invested it with his forces. The wily Saladin had then surrounded the besiegers and for two years they had engaged in a cat and mouse campaign. Saladin had many difficulties in keeping his forces up to strength as dissensions within the infidel ranks and harvesting commitments reduced the numbers that he was able to deploy. The crusaders suffered from disease and lack of supplies and badly needed the reinforcements that were so tardy in coming from Europe.

With the arrival of Philip some hopes had been raised and it would have suited the French King to have forced the surrender before the English King's arrival. Philip's military expertise, such as it was, inclined more towards siege warfare, so he constructed some siege engines and catapults, but he lacked the thrust to follow this inititiative through and bombard the walls of Acre. The French were dispirited and fell prey to disease and disaffection and Philip succumbed to a malaise. Many feared for his life. The siege continued on its inconclusive course and the reinforcements were completely ineffectual.

Upon Richard's arrival, he took immediate command to the mortification and fury of both Philip and Leopold, the Austrian Emperor, although he himself soon contracted a malarial fever

301

which caused concern to all. However, the supplies and highly professional reinforcements uplifted the army's spirits.

One evening, whilst Richard was sweating on his couch, Tariq came to him and told him that an emissary had asked to see him privately with a message from Saladin. Richard readily agreed and arranged for an escort to accompany Tariq and the messenger. A tall cloaked man appeared and after making sure that they were alone and not seen or overheard threw off his cloak. A beautifully apparisoned man of commanding presence and bearing stood before the King of England. Richard was immensely intrigued and asked what message he had from his master. The man held out his hand and raised him from his couch.

'My master, the emir, sends you salaams and greetings and says that he is grieved that you are suffering from the sickness that bedevils so many on both sides. He has instructed me, his humble and unworthy emissary, to bring you gifts of fruit and food together with some herbal medicines which he hopes will restore you speedily to full health.'

The King replied, 'Please give my own deep and sincere greetings to your much respected and famous sultan and master. May I know to whom I have the pleasure of speaking?'

The messenger smiled and embraced Richard. 'You have surely realised that it is me, Jusuf S'alia-eh-Din ibn Ayub, your humble adversary and friend at your service. I have heard so much of your prowess and fame and now today, at last, we meet. Tomorrow we shall be foes but will always treat with each other in the traditions of our respective backgrounds.'

It was quite extraordinary how alike they looked, each tall, each powerfully built (albeit that Saladin was more lithe and wiry), each with an authority and presence. They looked into each other's faces.

'My mother...' Richard began.

'The famous and beauteous Queen Eleanor. My father spoke often of her with affection and respect. I have been brought up in the light of her influence. I feel that I know her so well and wish that I had met her within my own living memory. Is she well?'

'My mother has a huge affection for your great and revered father, Ayub. She was given a dagger by him which I have here. She would dearly love you to have it in her memory and that of your father.' Richard handed the dagger over to his visitor, who was much affected by this unexpected gift.

'I shall treasure this as it has been treasured both by my father and your mother. It will be forever an heirloom in my family.'

Richard then asked Saladin to take with him the little boy, Tariq, who so ardently wished to return to his people.

The two clasped each other and Saladin rerobed and slipped into the night with his new servant. As the emir left, Richard had an inspired thought, but for the moment he let it continue to germinate in his mind. It could be the key to a solution in the crusaders' strategy.

* * *

Alison Weir's book Eleanor of Aquitaine *makes the bizarre statement that, upon Richard's arrival in Acre, Saladin sent him gifts of fruit and food. In return, Richard chivalrously responded by sending the emir a black slave. Alison does not give any source for this assertion and it would be incomprehensible unless the two leaders had a closer relationship than is generally acknowledged. If, as this book contends, they were half-brothers, then Saladin's gifts are entirely understandable. At this stage Richard was still unaware of this. Runciman's book* The Kingdom of Acre *does however say that some overtures were made between the two leaders to meet.*

* * *

During the ensuing four weeks Richard made his dispositions for a final assault, having made a careful reconnaissance. He moved his powerful siege engines to critical parts of the walled city. When he was ready a fearsome bombardment began on 12 July with huge stones battering the walls at their weakest points. These were unable to withstand this onslaught and began to crumble allowing the massed crusader army to breach the defences and swarm into the beleaguered city. The Saracen forces were weakened after their long siege and were in no condition to resist the Christian forces whose morale and fighting spirit had been so uplifted by Richard's presence and his fresh troops.

Richard as always was in the vanguard of the assault fighting ferociously and forever encouraging the troops to greater success and glory. Acre capitulated and 3,000 prisoners were taken, along with their arms and equipment. To Richard's fury, Leopold of

Austria, whose own contribution was negligible and conduct indifferent and whose troops had played a derisory part, had seized the deserted palace and flown his own flag from the highest point, claiming occupation. Richard's men in some fury tore down the Emperor's flag and flung it into the muddy moat before ejecting that monarch to secondary quarters. Richard claimed the royal quarters for himself and for his wife and sister. Eleanor's wise counsel that the Second Crusade had been bedevilled by internal dissension and that Richard should try and keep the leaders in accord was forgotten. Leopold was furious and never forgave Richard with long-term, serious and prejudicial effect. Meanwhile Philip, who was suffering very badly from malaria, was making plans to return to France.

Saladin withdrew his outer siege and deployed his troops to harry the Christians in their next move, which he correctly interpreted as an advance along the coast towards Jerusalem.

Richard demanded a surrender from the emir which was robustly refused. His conditions were savage. He demanded the release of 1,500 Christian prisoners held by Saladin and the return of the True Cross. Saladin was given a week to agree. Quite apart from the conditions, a problem of logistics was exercising Richard's mind. He was having to feed the Saracens from very scanty reserves. His army had to guard the prisoners and he could ill-afford to spare valuable fighting soldiers for this duty. Many prisoners were sick and diseased and the risk of infection to his own men was considerable. Saladin was well aware of this and he too did not want the released prisoners consuming his own supplies and infecting his own fighting men with their diseases. The Christian prisoners that he held were well away from the fighting zone and Richard would not have any immediate benefit in reinforcement. It was a cat and mouse position.

Richard remembered the massacre of the Templars and Hospitallers carried out by Saladin after the battle of Hittin. The deadline passed and Richard ordered the execution of all his prisoners including women and children. His decision was a hard one, never to be forgiven or forgotten in Palestine. For centuries afterwards Muslim mothers would threaten their wayward children with punishment from '*Malik Ric*' (Evil Richard). Both Saladin and Richard had had to take tough decisions but these were part and parcel of warfare in those days.

On 22 July the French King threw in the sponge and announced that he was returning to France immediately, owing to his sickness. He feared for his life. But his hidden agenda was to disrupt the tenuous truce between France and the English King's domains and to encourage Prince John to destabilise Richard's kingdom. Count Philip of Flanders had already died, leaving no heir, and Philip considered that the future was outside any crusade stand-off agreement. Philip's Parthian shot was to remind Richard that they had undertaken to share all successes on this crusade equally, and hence he was entitled to half of Cyprus. Richard's response was to demand half of Flanders, which more than ever concentrated Philip's mind to return to France as soon as he could! Richard considered himself well rid of Philip and hoped that his formidable mother could contain any problems until his return. Philip departed from Acre on 31 July denigrating Richard to all and sundry.

Richard then marched towards Jaffa to consolidate his position there and to prepare himself for his attack upon Jerusalem. Saladin's tactics were to track the crusaders, harry them and swoop upon any laggards *en route*. His light and most mobile cavalry was ideal for these probing raids and the lumbering Christians found that they were no match in intermittent skirmishes of this nature. Richard paused at Caesarea and craftily enticed Saladin to commit himself to a more serious attack. His vanguard reached the plain of Arsuf not far from Ascalon and seemed to provide an ideal target being well in advance of the main troops. Saladin fell for the honey trap and sprang his men onto the rearguard.

On 7 September Richard and his main cavalry took a vantage point from where they could see the development of the battle. Saladin sent in his crack foot soldiers recruited mainly from the Nubian tribes from the Sudan, and his wiry and very mobile Bedouin bowmen. The advance was signalled by fanfares of discordant trumpets, bugles, drums and kettledrums accompanied by chants and fearsome noises, all intended to strike terror into their opponents. The Christian foot soldiers responded fearlessly and with determined valour. Their armour and heavier weapons stood them in good stead but the weight and fluid mobility of the attack was daunting and not much quarter was given or taken by either side. Richard waited until he considered that the moment was right and the Saracens were beginning to tire. The fury of the attack by the fresh heavy cavalry was overriding and the infidels were overwhelmed, suffering catastrophic losses. The battle turned into a rout and Saladin himself only just avoided capture. Both sides were now exhausted and retired to regroup. Richard again succumbed to malaria.

The crusaders were nevertheless able to capture Jaffa which allowed them a suitable place for respite, although several of their leaders were in dire straits from sickness and exhaustion. Archbishop Baldwin of Canterbury and many other leaders had already died and others abandoned the Holy Cross commitments to return home leaving the Christian forces much depleted with many in poor health and condition.

Saladin positioned himself at Ramlah and reduced Ascalon to rubble to deny this valuable base to Richard. Richard might well have been able to seize Jerusalem as both sides were so depleted in strength, although the English King had the balance of power. Richard wisely decided that he would not be able to hold Jerusalem for long with Saladin's reinforcements due imminently. His own fragile supply lines of communications back to Jaffa were also precariously open to attack.

Richard did however push on into the hills towards Jerusalem but, with the onset of winter bringing wind and incessant rains, he was unable to achieve his intended goal. He got as far as Beit-Nuba, only twelve miles from Jerusalem, which from his advance posts, could just be seen in the distance on a clear day. Richard covered his face with his shield as he did not wish to see Jerusalem until he was able to enter in triumph.

*　*　*

In France, Eleanor's problems were beginning to escalate. On 24 June 1191 she arrived at Rouen from Bourges. Richard's nominee, Walter of Coutances, had in the meantime arrived in England and found utter confusion. The chancellor, Longchamp of Ely, had been at loggerheads with John Lackland and was exploiting the perfidy of that prince who was spreading alarm and despondency by saying that Richard would never return from his crusade. Unfortunately, at that moment, Richard's nomination for any succession was Prince Arthur, his four-year-old nephew from Brittany – a choice fraught with difficulty from every side and one that Longchamp was not slow to exploit to John's increasing fury.

Coutances trod a delicate path between the two protagonists. After all, Richard might not return and John was, despite all his character defects, very much more likely to succeed, especially if Eleanor threw her support behind him. It would never do to antagonise a future king even with the present king's mandate.

By the end of July, Coutances had managed to separate the pair. John had surrendered some castles that he had seized and Longchamp promised to support John in any potential succession. The truce was uneasy but better than before.

Meanwhile, in accordance with Eleanor's agreement with the Pope, Geoffrey Plantagenet was consecrated Archbishop of York at Tours. Despite his banishment from England, he returned with the intention of being enthroned at York as soon as he could. In any event his half-brother, John, had already returned with dire results for the country. Geoffrey landed at Dover but Longchamp (both in his capacity as Bishop of Ely and as chancellor) was determined to obstruct the Archbishop. Longchamp's sister controlled Dover Castle and she demanded that Geoffrey swear allegiance to both King Richard and her brother. Geoffrey refused as he had already sworn his loyalty to the King and he certainly was not going to kowtow to the obnoxious Longchamp, his subordinate bishop. He escaped to seek sanctuary but was arrested and dragged ignominiously through the mud back to Dover where he was thrown into a dungeon and nearly starved. The people of Kent were appalled and a real fear arose whereby another archbishop could be murdered, so soon after the Becket episode. Geoffrey was becoming a champion of the people.

Longchamp protested his innocence and was ordered to command the Archbishop's release at once. Bishop Hugh of Lincoln excommunicated all those responsible at Dover and Longchamp fled to the safety of Windsor. John exploited the crisis by summoning a council in October which included Geoffrey. This meeting proposed that Longchamp be deposed from his chancellorship, a procedure totally in accordance with the views of Coutances. Thereupon John marched to London where the council decision was ratified and Coutances' mandate from King Richard was confirmed, the latter now formally assuming his position as head of the council of regency.

Longchamp was required to surrender all his estates and property and was firstly confined to the Tower of London and then transferred to Dover. This move was somewhat bizarre in that his sister was responsible for that stronghold and had behaved reprehensibly over Archbishop Geoffrey's arrival. Not surprisingly Longchamp escaped and, disguising himself as a woman, persuaded a boatman to take him across the Channel. An amorous fisherman tried to seduce this seemingly nubile female and the chancellor's disguise was penetrated. John was highly amused and permitted the displaced chancellor to cross the water and go to Rouen to get him out of England.

Meanwhile, also in October, the French King arrived in Rome on his return journey from Palestine and briefed the pontiff on his treatment by the English King. He suggested that there was a plot to poison him and that he had been continuously and unexpectedly sick during his entire stay. He reiterated his fury at the cavalier treatment of his sister, Alice, so shabbily handled by both Henry and Richard. He was duly released of his crusader vows. The Pope, Celestine, listened carefully, having already heard Eleanor's side of the story. Philip concluded his return journey by calling on Henry, the Holy Roman Emperor, and Leopold of Austria's treatment by Richard lost nothing in the telling. Traps were being laid and were only waiting to be sprung.

Longchamp was not contrite and went to Eleanor claiming that only Richard could deprive him of his office, an assertion which the Queen ignored as he was nothing but a disruptive influence. Longchamp then had a meeting with two cardinals in Paris who had been instructed by the Pope to heal the rift between him and Coutances. Eleanor was well aware that the French King had stirred all this up and when the prelates sought to enter Normandy to mediate with her they were refused entry upon Eleanor's authority. They retired in high dudgeon and threatened the Queen with excommunication, which she also ignored. They settled by excommunicating the seneschal at the border crossing and put Normandy under an interdict.

To reinforce insult by further injury, Longchamp excommunicated the whole council which included the only archbishop now in the English Church – Archbishop Baldwin of Canterbury having died on the crusade. Only Eleanor and John were now excluded.

On 2 November Geoffrey was enthroned with immense solemnity and pageantry in York and was riding high in general estimation. His old protagonist Hugh de Puiset, Bishop of Durham, was pointedly absent and refused to give any explanation or excuse. Geoffrey was congenitally unable to let matters simmer down and promptly excommunicated the errant, and by now very aged, bishop who had been so obstructive in Henry's reign. The Dean (Walter) and some of the canons of York had always opposed Geoffrey's election. Geoffrey's goodwill started to evaporate as the feuding escalated.

Prince John, showing a rare bout of common sense and responsibility, spent much of the autumn travelling throughout the kingdom making himself accessible to all and dispensing justice. Although Richard had only shown himself to his subjects for a few weeks, John's largesse and *bonhomie* went some way towards reconciling the country to him. However his nobles and knights had a delicate balancing act as they knew his inherent unpredictability. But he could be their next king and they had to keep their options open. During these travels, he deviated to Flaxley where, like his father he much relished the hunting.

Meanwhile Eleanor's spies kept her informed and her unease increased to cause her much concern. She ordered the strengthening of all the Norman and Angevin defences. She had her Christmas court at Bonneville-sur-Touques near Deauville and refined her planning for the New Year. Eleanor, now sixty-nine, had had a punishing year with an immense programme of travel but there was no sign that her energies or abilities were flagging.

* * *

With the onset of autumn and inclement weather both armies were in need of rest and reorganisation. Saladin disbanded half his men for the duration of the winter, following vigorous representations from his field commanders. There was a need for attention to harvests and nomadic cattle affairs. The crusaders had had a gruelling time in an unsympathetic climate and their marching and fighting in their heavy equipment and clothing was debilitating. Soldiers and knights were allowed to filter back to the fleshpots of Jaffa and Acre and were reluctant to return to duties at the front. Neither side was in any position to mount an offensive and would have been hard pressed to resist any serious raid or attack. King Guy was sent to Acre to order the Christian forces back to the front but was ignored. Richard himself went and left William Longspee to continue these persuasions.

* * *

It is difficult to establish what William Longspee was doing during the early 1190s. The Dictionary of National Biography *and other sources refer to his career from the mid-1190s. He was in his mid-thirties and a virtual contemporary of Richard's and at the height of his military career. Unlike his brother Geoffrey, he was intensely loyal to both Richard and John and became a valued member of their administrations and, in due course, was suitably rewarded. It is reasonable to assume that he joined Richard on the crusade, although he does not feature specifically in any of the contemporary reports of that campaign.*

* * *

Both Saladin and Richard were in poor health and needed to recuperate and rest. It seemed propitious to explore areas for a sensible compromise although there were obvious wide gaps between the minimum demands from both sides. Richard deputed his leading Arabist, Humphrey of Toron, and Saladin's brother, Saphadin, also known as el-Adil, to meet and negotiate with a view to finding common ground for a truce or armistice. Both legates were extremely able and talented with considerable diplomatic skills. They met at Lydda. Richard's opening ploy was the ceding of Jerusalem with the whole territory west of the Jordan, together with the return of the Holy Cross. Saladin's reply was that the Holy City was holy to the Muslims too. He needed concessions from the crusaders. At this stage both sides were more than willing to talk and there was optimism that a compromise could be reached. However, much more negotiation would be needed.

One evening Richard and his half-brother were chatting in the King's tent and the King was clearing his mind over certain ideas that he had been considering for some weeks and encouraging William to react. They heard a discreet cough outside the flap. It was the small Arab servant, Tariq. The lad had a message from Saladin that the four of them – Richard, William, Saladin and Saphadin – should have a private meeting with no advisers present to try and ease the logjam in negotiations. This was immediately agreed.

On 20 October a historic parley took place near Lydda.

After the customary salutations and courtesies had been exchanged, Richard opened the proceedings with his proposals.

'Why cannot we move to an acceptable *modus vivendi*? We are battering each other. One of us obtains an advantage, the other responds and we are both back where we started. We want the Holy City. Jerusalem is sacrosanct to you. You and we both regard Jesus as an integral part of our faith. Jesus is our saviour and a major prophet in your religion. We want the Holy Cross, and it is holy to you as your prophet (and our saviour) was crucified on it. You have it and will not release it without something in return. I make this suggestion. I have a dearly loved sister, Joanna who was lately widowed and was the Queen of Sicily. Would you consider, Saladin, emir, great leader of the Saracens, taking my sister as your wife? This would be a marriage made in heaven. You will keep Jerusalem jointly with my sister and Christians would have full access. You will keep Palestine, my sister will keep all the northern coastal cities down to and including Ascalon. Our jointly revered Holy Cross would be restored to Jerusalem. You have more Christian attributes than many crusaders. It would be a dramatic diplomatic solution, which the world would admire.'

'This is a most extraordinarily historic occasion,' replied the emir, seizing Richard's hand and smiling as he looked at each in turn. 'Our respective sides will never credit what you have been saying. You have produced a masterly solution, but we have one insuperable problem. The four of us standing here have a unique relationship which no one in the world will understand, believe or credit.' Saladin paused, the others waited. Something quite incredible was about to be said. 'We four here have a common bond which the world will never understand and is quite unique. You, Richard and William, share a father of immense distinction and ability and one whom my father, Ayub, would have admired and approved of. Adil and I share a father whom your mother loved and revered. But I, Joseph S'alia-eh-Din and el-Adil do not share a mother, we are half-brothers as you are. My mother, Richard, is your mother, the great and incomparable Queen Eleanor. We are not to be brothers-in-law, we are brothers. So it would not be possible for me to marry Joanna, as she is my half-sister.'

The bombshell sank into the two Normans. The four of them

clasped each other in brotherly love. Richard rapidly recovered himself. 'Then would Adil consider being the bridegroom? There is no blood bond between them.'

'I would gladly consent and,' he glanced towards el-Adil, who nodded, 'it has our blessing. We both have problems in delivery. We, as you well know, are outlaws in our own land. We are the distrusted Kurds and have to fight for every honour and advancement. Our people quarrel amongst ourselves perhaps more than the crusaders.'

Richard laughed. 'You think that you have problems. I am King of the outlying English, a remote island to the mainstream Europe. For my major possessions in France, I am a vassal to the French King and have to pay homage to him, much as I resent that little upstart. For spiritual guidance I owe subservience to the Pope who demands allegiance from all in Christendom. We are surely more quarrelsome than your colleagues!'

'We have so much common cause between us. Your god is our god and we both worship him, and as you have reminded us we both have Jesus Christ in our common heritage. As the psalmist, your psalmist, our psalmist too, says, "Jerusalem is built as a city; that is at unity in itself – O pray for the peace of Jerusalem: they shall prosper that love thee, peace be within thy walls". Also we have a further common bond between us. Your great Archbishop and saint, Thomas Becket, was a kinsman of mine. As a child, I was much under the influence of my much-loved grandmother – she it was who inculcated many of what you would call Christian virtues and behaviour into my upbringing. She was close to and very fond of Rohesia, Becket's mother. She it was who kept in touch through her and Becket with your lovely mother. Thus it is, dear Richard, that I know and admire you so much.'

Eleanor's words on that last evening together in Sicily now came back to Richard with greater poignancy and understanding. 'I shall found, at once, a hospice in Acre in memory of St Thomas, in whose martyrdom my father had such a terrible part to play. This place will tend the sick and the wounded of both our peoples without prejudice. It will be under the authority of the Knight's Hospitallers whose origins were dedicated to such charitable activity. On my return to London, I shall cause a church to be built there as a tribute to both my friend Becket and his mother, Rohesia, your own kinswoman.'

Turning to William Longspee, he added, 'Please see that this is done as soon as you can. Both places will be called St Thomas Acon. St Thomas of Acre. Both will be in honour of his roots.'

Saladin clasped his brother's arm again with emotion. 'I appreciate this inspirational idea and we shall, whatever happens in the future, respect your foundation and what it stands for.'

The four of them parted with many protestations of friendship and the hope of future accord and cooperation. They swore that the meeting and its revelations would never be divulged to the world as the consequences could have been catastrophic.

Richard and William returned to their camp and Longspee congratulated his brother on his stroke of genius and masterly and diplomatic handling of the meeting.

* * *

This explains the most curious naming of both the hospice in Acre and the church in the City of London. This reinforces the hitherto seemingly unrelated connection between Becket and Acre. Tariq Ali's book refers to Saladin's upbringing by his grandmother – he makes no mention whatsoever of his mother.

* * *

Joanna, however, threw an appalling tantrum, displaying the legendary Angevin temper in no small way. Under no circumstances was she prepared to marry an infidel, nor was she willing to live in Jerusalem with a man who was used to harem conditions; after all she had already had one husband in Sicily, albeit a Christian who saw nothing wrong with a multitude of liaisons in his pseudo-harem complex.

On 8 November, Adil hosted a banquet at Lydda, graced by a bevy of belly-dancers present for the pleasure and edification of the English King. Richard counter-proposed that Saphadin should become a Christian, hoping thereby to remove one major obstacle. This Saphadin refused to concede albeit with much courtesy and the happy feast broke up with much cordiality and expressions of hope that all was not lost. Richard was sure that the Pope would assuage his sister's reservations by issuing a suitably worded edict. The feast culminated with Richard dubbing Saphadin a knight, although he persisted in refusing the customary baptism.

The next day, the Saracens were offered all Palestine with an equal share of Jerusalem. Richard then offered his niece, the young Eleanor of Brittany, who was his ward and over whom he had complete control.

Saladin was having difficulties with his council, who were most reluctant to continue negotiations on these lines. There was, on both sides, an immense caucus of distrust although the principal parties were committed to an honourable and just solution. Saphadin kept the negotiations in play during the approaching winter season but inevitably the main parties were beginning to draw apart.

There were odd moments of drama. Richard was nearly captured by a Saracen raiding party whilst out hawking and escaped when one of his companions claimed to be the king and was apprehended. Saladin was most amused at this foray's claims for a large hostage reward. The loyal knight was released without any compensation. As winter set in, raids and skirmishes continued but were of no real importance.

Richard spent Christmas at Latrun with Berengaria, Joanna and King Guy. The English King had never made a full recovery from his earlier fevers and was now much enfeebled, which caused considerable concern within the command of the crusaders.

14

1192–1194

In the winter of 1191/1192, or probably during the early months of 1192, Bishop Hugh of Lincoln, whose consecration as bishop owed much to the patronage of Henry II, behaved in a most uncharacteristic, ungrateful and almost spiteful manner. He was making a pastoral visit to Oxford, then within his diocese, and decided to call on Godstow nunnery. He was enraged to find within that priory church the elaborate and much embellished tomb of Rosamond in a prominent position, being lovingly tended by the nuns. He demanded to know who this seemingly illustrious person was and on being told that she was the much loved companion of the late King, he retorted that this woman was nothing more than a harlot and that her conduct was an appalling example to other women who must abstain from illicit and adulterous intercourse. Under no circumstances could the Church tolerate this exhibition and encourage such behaviour in others. He ordered that the body be removed from within the sacred ground of the sanctified building and reburied outside in a common cemetery.

In 1220 this good bishop was to be canonised and was, in most things that he did, much loved and revered. This act was not only uncharacteristic but also unsaintly, uncharitable and ungrateful to the memory of Henry, who had such a high opinion of Hugh and much enjoyed not only his company but also the most Christian life that he led. It is possible that Hugh resented his new archbishop. He had always been forthright and uncompromising in his views. The nuns were most upset and well remembered the good life and works done by Rosamond. They were conscious of the extensive benefactions accruing to the nunnery in Rosamond's memory, but the bishop's orders had to be implemented. Immediately after the departure of his examining chaplain, a messenger was sent to Archbishop Geoffrey, who was most distressed at this desecration of his mother's tomb. He had, whenever he was near Woodstock or Oxford, always come to celebrate a Mass there.

He told Prince John, who was also distressed for he too had many happy memories of Rosamond, and they agreed that Richard would wish them to make substantial and practical amends in her honour. The authority of Hugh could not be overridden without more distasteful and unseemly reinterments. It was also sad that Godstow was the resting place of Rosamond's dearly loved mother, Margaret. The nuns were instructed to transfer the body into the chapter house and to bury mother and daughter in the same vault with a suitably elaborate tomb and an appropriate inscription in her memory. The body had putrified so her bones were enclosed in lead with sweet smelling herbs, spices and perfumes encased in a leather pouch. The tomb above the vault was of superb and intricate workmanship consisting of flying birds, leaping fishes, cavorting animals and conflicts of mythical heroes. This work of art was much admired in the years to come.

John made an additional grant to the holy virgins of Godstow nunnery that their Masses should include prayers for 'the souls of my father King Henry and of the Lady Rosamond there interred'.

* * *

The expense of building the new tomb was borne by Rosamond's sons and the two half-brothers. The tomb was seen in 1350 by one Higden. It was still in perfect order according to a report by Leland of 1542. The inscription (which obviously cannot have been the original) then read:

TOMBA ROSAMUNDAE

Hic jacet in tumba rosa mundi, non rosa mundae;
Non redolent, sed olet, quae redolere solet.

Here lies the rose of the world, not a clean rose;
She no longer smells rosy, so hold your nose.

*When the tomb was broken open shortly after the dissolution of Godstow
nunnery a very sweet smell emerged.*

*   *   *

It is significant that so few people realised that neither King
Richard nor Saladin were fit men during the time of the Third
Crusade. Richard was continually suffering from intermittent
bouts of malaria and dysentery whilst Saladin was under the
weather from a number of undisclosed maladies. It was generally
considered that the latter had lost much of his incisiveness and
single-minded resolve, but it must be remembered that he had
had to contend with almost as many dissidents amongst the
Saracens' leading commanders as Richard had. This led to a continual urge by both field commanders to find a peaceful solution,
but they were continuously thwarted by the warlords in the background.

On 3 January 1192 Richard gathered his forces at Beit Nuba,
twelve miles from Jerusalam. There was much enthusiasm to
make a final push for the Holy City now at last in sight and there
were only very limited defences before them. These overseas
crusaders, who had come specifically on this crusade, smelt
success in the wind despite the torrential rain, mud and lack of
essential supplies and foodstuffs. Those other crusaders, who had
been the occupying army in Palestine for so long, begged the
rampant Richard and his commanders to display caution. They
pointed out that it was impossible to defend with Saladin's rear-
guards encamped in some comfort in the hills nearby in the hin-
terland with his reinforcements expected at any moment. They
also reminded Richard with some asperity that once many of the
crusaders had achieved what they had come for, recaptured
Jerusalem and prayed at the Holy Sepulchre, they would return
home. The remaining crusaders would be left in an impossible
position. Richard very reluctantly but sensibly agreed and the
crusaders retired to their own winter quarters.

After the unusually wet and windy winter, the spring of 1192
saw a resumption of manoeuvring and fighting between both
sides. Richard rebuilt the devastated fortress of Ascalon and
made it a key point in his defences. Reinforcements had arrived
although the Pisan and Genoese contingents were far more interested in fighting each other than dealing with the infidels.

Richard was much involved in diplomatic moves to restore some semblance of accord within the resident crusader ranks but Conrad of Montferrat was continuing to be obstructive and uncooperative. Conrad was the one commander who had emerged with his reputation intact after the disaster of Hattin five years earlier. However, when the sloth and sybaritic lifestyle enjoyed during the winter had been shaken off, both the Christians and the Saracens began to rattle their sabres with intent.

One of Richard's envoys to el-Adil was shocked to see one of Conrad's knights and his escort in far too friendly discussions with his hosts, enjoying hawking and jousting with them. Treachery seemed to be in the air. El-Adil continued to keep his lines of communication open with Richard with much dexterity, and doubtless Conrad felt that a prejudicial deal was being negotiated to his disadvantage.

The crusaders intercepted a large caravan of supplies and arms destined for Jerusalem. The French contingent seized what they plundered and kept it all for their own use, whereas the English passed all their booty to the Hospitallers and Templars for the general good of the crusading cause. These irritations were not conducive to harmony and goodwill although, to be fair to the French, Philip had returned to France with most of his treasury thus depriving his forces of funds.

An envoy from England brought disturbing news about the activities of John and Longchamp implored the King to return as soon as possible. It was becoming more and more vital for an honourable truce to be negotiated. The crown of Jerusalem issue needed resolving before any other settlement could be reached. As so often happened in the kingdom of Jerusalem young daughters succeeded to that throne and suitable and potentially able husbands had to be found for them to act as king consort. Thus Guy de Lusignan had married the Queen Sibylla in 1180 but she had died without issue from him ten years later and Guy had refused to abdicate. Richard summoned a council and starkly presented his ultimatum as he had to return home and they must decide on their own king – Richard's candidate being his old adversary, Guy de Lusignan. The tabled choice was Guy or Conrad and to Richard's intense surprise there was a virtual unanimity for Conrad, a decision duly accepted and endorsed democratically and wholeheartedly by Richard. Conrad had married Isabelle, the heiress to the throne in Jerusalem, in somewhat bizarre circumstances in 1190. (Conrad almost certainly had not one but two earlier wives still living, but they were both in far off countries and apparently would not have intervened! Isabelle was also inconveniently married to a young lordling that she rather liked, but who was somewhat effeminate. Isabelle's mother had a few well chosen words and that young man was put out to grass).

Conrad agreed to come, at last, to Ascalon but stayed for a few more days in Tyre to join in that city's celebrations. On 28 April he intended to have a celebratory dinner with his young wife, Isabelle. Finding that she had not completed her toilet, and was in fact still in her bath, he went to see his old friend, the Bishop of Beauvais, who lived nearby, to have some refreshment. The bishop had already dined, but offered to have some small snacks prepared. Conrad declined and returned home, hoping that by then his wife would be appropriately bedecked and ready to receive him. *En route* two men waylaid and murdered him. They were Assassins from the mountains whose leader bore a grudge against Conrad; there were some who claimed that Saladin was behind this, others claimed that Richard was the instigator. Be that as it may, Conrad's death was dire news as he would have pulled the kingdom of Jerusalem into some coherence and direction.

Henry, the Count of Champagne, who had fought with distinction so far and was not only a cousin of Philip of France but also a nephew of Richard, was now a prime candidate. Richard moved with alacrity. The solution was simple. Henry should marry Isabelle. Henry was young, gallant and popular and Isabelle was amenable. Within two days the betrothal was announced and within the week they were married. Luckily the reluctant bridegroom fell completely in love with the lovely princess.

The dispossessed King Guy was palmed off with the kingdom of Cyprus and had to buy that country from the Greek inhabitants, including, incidentally, an overrider for Richard, which was only partially settled.

On 14 May Richard retook the fort at Darum which had been strengthened and then lost the previous year. Five thousand Saracen prisoners were captured and a few unfortunates were barbarously butchered. Richard still had to learn something from his brother, Saladin, about the honourable treatment of captives.

In June the crusaders again took up advanced positions at Latrun and Beit Nuba in preparation for a grand assault on the Holy City. Outposts got as far as Emmaus. Once more the walls and towers of Jerusalem were within sight. The Syrian Bishop of Lydda produced a portion of the True Cross that he had acquired. The Greek Abbot of Mar, Elias, showed Richard the place where he had secreted another piece which was dug up and given to the King. These were real acquisitions to compensate for the relic now reinstated by Saladin in the Holy Sepulchre and were to be the nearest they were ever to get to this precious object.

On 20 June Richard surprised a major Muslim supply caravan near Hebron and seized huge quantities of food, equipment, arms and animals. Saladin was now on the verge of retreat, his situation worsened by the flight of not only his own Kurdish followers but also a number of experienced and vital Turkish troops. The French were enthusiastic about pressing on, but seasoned campaigners knew of the lack of water and the insuperable difficulties in holding open lines of communication in this hostile countryside.

Richard's health was deteriorating and the news from England was going from bad to worse. A truce was becoming more and more urgent. Henry of Champagne nearly wrecked the delicate balance by sending an arrogant message to Saladin in his new-found authority as King of Jerusalem. In July, the crusaders reached the evocative site of Emmaus where the arisen, but unrecognised, Christ partook of supper with strangers. Again Richard shielded his eyes from the sight of Jerusalem, the city which he had still not fulfilled his vow to God to deliver. Richard now knew that this vow would not be fulfilled.

A withdrawal to Jaffa was undertaken to the sound of jeers from the French. Negotiations were resumed. Saladin offered to cede the coast of Palestine and the right of Christian worship in Jerusalem without molestation, but insisted upon Ascalon being dismantled. He would regard Henry as his son. Richard baulked at the Ascalon clause and Saladin counter-offered by substituting Lydda. Richard moved to Acre before leaving Palestine without a signed treaty.

On 31 July Saladin took Jaffa in a daring swoop and his troops went berserk to such an extent that the emir ordered the Christians to contain themselves within their citadel until he could restore order. Richard immediately counter-attacked from the sea with inspired ferocity and swept through the citadel catching the Saracens completely unprepared and repulsing them with ignominy. Further negotiations were nearly concluded but were aborted, again due to the disagreement over the slighting of the fortifications of Ascalon.

Saladin was now aware of the size of Richard's force, and on 5 August attacked early in the morning hoping to catch the crusaders before they were ready. Luckily a wakeful Genoese heard the neighing of horses and saw steel glinting in the early morning sunlight and raised the alarm. Richard brilliantly deployed his men in pairs behind stakes driven into the ground, and, with spears angled into the ground, impaled the light Saracen cavalry and repulsed them seven times. The enemy horses began to tire and Richard then released shower after shower of arrows from his bowmen and led a charge on horseback. Richard's horse was cut from under him and the great Saladin, lost in wonder and admiration, sent Richard two further steeds for him to mount and continue his amazing fight. By evening Saladin admitted defeat and withdrew to safety.

By now Richard was seriously ill as indeed was el-Adil. Saladin sent fruit and snow from the mountains to cool Richard's drinks and to comfort the King on his sickbed. On 9 August a truce was agreed, and was signed on 2 September with the terms not materially different. Christians were to be allowed to enter Jerusalem unmolested providing they were unarmed and Muslims similarly were to have freedom of movement. Ascalon was not negotiable and was to be demolished. The Archbishop of Tyre threatened to excommunicate any who availed themselves of this concession as it was contrary to their crusader vows. This truce was to last from the ensuing Easter for three years, three months, three weeks and three hours and it was wisely said that 'a threefold rope is hard to break'.

The Third Crusade was now over.

Passports were issued for those who wished to make their pilgrimage, but Richard declined the opportunity and refused permission for any French to make the journey. The most notable person to go was Hubert Walter, recently the obstructive Dean of York and a thorn in the flesh of Geoffrey Plantagenet. He was now the Bishop of Salisbury and was received and welcomed by Saladin most graciously. As a gesture of goodwill the emir asked Hubert if he had any request to make and he asked for two priests and two deacons to be allowed to officiate at Jerusalem, Bethlehem and Nazareth. This was granted and, in due course, they performed their duties freely. The Byzantine Emperor heard of this and asked for reinstatement of the Orthodox rites, which was refused. The Queen of Georgia asked to buy the True Cross for 200,000 dinars, and this was also refused.

On 29 September Joanna and Berengaria sailed from Acre and reached France before winter set in. Richard left Acre on 9 October but his voyage was beset with problems from the start. Bad weather and damage to his vessel caused him to stop at Corfu, and fearing capture he immediately pressed on up the Adriatic. With four companions he hired a boat which was wrecked at Aquilea where he landed and hoped to continue his return overland.

* * *

The machinations of the French King began to escalate. During the third week of January 1192, Philip attacked Gisors but owing to Eleanor's foresight in reinforcing the Norman defences the assault failed. He then demanded of Eleanor the return of his much-wronged sister Alice and her dowry but Eleanor had no mandate for this and refused. Next Philip turned his attention to suborning John. He suggested that if John were to marry Alice and surrender Gisors he could enjoy all Richard's Continental possessions without let or hindrance. The fact that John was already married was an obstacle easily overcome, if for no other reason on the grounds of consanguinity. The proposition was attractive to John, but fortunately Eleanor got wind of it in time.

Eleanor landed at Portsmouth on 11 February just as John was ready to sail from Southampton with an army of mercenaries. She implored him to abandon his nefarious scheme and made it plain that she had enough cards up her sleeve to make him think twice. Having made John think hard and long, Eleanor reinforced her threats with dynamic action. She summoned councils at

Windsor, London, Oxford and Winchester and swore her own loyalty to Richard and made every noble proclaim a fresh oath of fealty to the King. She had the support and encouragement of Walter of Coutances and obtained authority to confiscate all John's estates in England if he failed to conform to these decisions (despite his sobriquet, John had vast estates in England by this time). John retired in high dudgeon to the royal castle at Wallingford to sulk.

Meanwhile the French nobles were refusing to break the Truce of God which allowed all disputes for crusaders to remain in suspended animation, thus neutralising Philip's nefarious schemes.

Eleanor, despite the wintry weather, now took upon herself an arduous programme of travel throughout the country to see how matters stood. She paid particular attention to the diocese of Ely which had been much neglected by the ambitious Longchamp and was suffering under an interdict. She found much misery, neglect and deprivation and these problems she addressed. Although much has been made of the absence of the sacraments amongst the peasantry, she was appalled at their inability to bury their dead who lay putrifying in the fields. The husbandry under the control and organisation of the bishop's agents was neglected with the result that there was much hunger and starvation prevalent. Walter of Coutances was instructed to negotiate the lifting of the interdict and permit Longchamp to return and resume his pastoral duties only.

Meanwhile Longchamp was also bribing John to allow him to return and in March the bishop was invited back, only in his diocesan capacity. Longchamp then appeared at a council meeting demanding access in his role as chancellor which was summarily rejected.

Eleanor then started negotiations to lift the interdict in Normandy and asked the excommunicated Bishop de Puiset of Durham to go to France and persuade the Roman cardinals to repeal their decision. De Puiset was agreeable but pointed out that he had no status until his own excommunication imposed by Archbishop Geoffrey was lifted. Eleanor summoned Geoffrey to London who appeared in a ceremonial procession of clergy preceded by his archiepiscopal cross, which was entirely against protocol since he was not permitted to do this outside his own archdiocese. Upon remonstration, he replied that what he had done was completely in order since he was the sole archbishop in the country as the Canterbury see was vacant. He then refused any cooperation with the Queen or de Puiset and continued to insist that the latter should make a vow of obedience prior to any revocation of excommunication.

Eleanor threatened her stepson with the confiscation of all his estates in the diocese of York and some inconclusive fudging took place. Coutances managed to persuade de Puiset to swallow his pride and make a visit to France and open negotiations, which were finally concluded when Eleanor made a direct appeal to her old friend the Pope.

Geoffrey was continuing to go out of his way to antagonise not only his enemies but also his friends, who were becoming more and more disillusioned with his aggressive arrogance. He had never got over the disloyalty shown to his father by so many during the last years of Henry's reign and his power base as chancellor had been undermined when the old King died. His immense organisational abilities, his military prowess and his clear mind were being unfulfilled. There were many who claimed that he was a better military commander than the great Lionheart. He simply had not come to terms with the new regime as the great William Marshal had done. But his father's dying wish had been respected and the second most senior position in the English Church had been given to him. On the 'what might have been' scenario, the see of Canterbury could have been made available and within a very short time the throne would again have become vacant with a problematic succession. The Norman tradition of encouraging the king's bastards into positions of trust and use was there for the asking. Both Henry I and Henry II had achieved much success in exploiting these factors. Neither Robert of Gloucester nor William Longspee had any aspirations for the throne and this had (and was to have) much value to England. It is possible that Geoffrey never gave up his hope for the throne and never understood that the Plantagenets had to put him out of contention, and that the archbishopric did exactly this. Also, of course, of all Henry's sons, Geoffrey inherited that violent and uncontrollable temper, without the ability to mend bridges immediately afterwards and he bore grudges and developed intense hatreds. Geoffrey was going through an impossible patch and it was not likely to get better. In point of fact it got worse.

After his abortive trip to London, Geoffrey returned to York and excommunicated more of his canons for contumacy – opposing lawful authority with contempt. The canons' response was to close the minster, forbid the ringing of bells, strip the altars, lock up the archbishop's stall and block up his personal and private door into the cathedral from his palace. Then they left him to his own devices. This left Geoffrey with no support whatsoever from his chapter as well as a rapidly diminishing esteem from those who had been his friends. A frightful void in the spiritual well-being and administration of the archdiocese now occurred.

The council were in a quandary. Longchamp was still trying to be active as a discredited chancellor and still held Richard's commission. Coutances had countermanded this with Eleanor's support, but Richard was far away and probably unlikely to return, in which case John would become the new king and those who had opposed him might not expect to survive for very long. John was not noted for leniency. The councillors knew that Longchamp had offered John a bribe to reinstate him, so they went to him to try and stop this. John, never slow to exploit a situation, was entirely agreeable, but the councillors' bribe had to be larger than Longchamp's. John said: 'You see, I am in need of money. To the wise a word is sufficient.'

John now went off on another extended tour of the kingdom but this time with less sense of responsibility. He needed to bolster his own support, should he need to call for it. He obtained personal oaths of loyalty and raided as much as he could from exchequer funds. It was at this time that John's friend, the Sheriff of Nottingham, that ogre of so many legends, was trampling on the freemen of Sherwood Forest and Robin Hood and his band of merry men were robbing the rich to feed the poor in the name of good King Richard.

Eleanor once more became alarmed and dispatched her emissary, John, the Archdeacon of Lisieux, to Richard to warn him that all was not well at home and that the sooner he came back the better. She was only just keeping the lid on the kettle.

On 3 April a combined ultimatum was given to Longchamp and he accepted banishment to France, a move which relieved some tensions. Philip suffered an unexpected reverse in the south of Aquitaine when he mounted a surprise attack. It was not all bad news but the kingdom continued to simmer dangerously.

From this point there is a lack of knowledge of what was happening in England. Eleanor was active in keeping an eye on her youngest son. John was aware that he could lose much of his considerable estates in England if he stepped out of line. Richard's return was the key and the King's health was suspect. Isabella, John's wife, was not producing him the heir that any Plantagenet needed, but she had enough money to keep him in some sort of control. There was transparently little that they had in common and they did not cohabit with any enthusiasm. John's sexual proclivities were producing an adequate supply of male bastards, most of whom were born before the turn of the century, so there was nothing wrong with his libido and there was probably no constructive activity to take his mind off bedsport. The nobles were not very happy about his roving eye, but luckily his tastes were not always confined to those of high birth. Those who were from his class were caught in a Catch 22 situation. If they objected to his laying of their wives they had to come terms with the probable disfavour of their future king. John alternated with bursts of frenetic energy followed by extensive periods of lechery and indolence.

Eustace de Vesci had married the very beautiful Margaret, a natural daughter of King William of Scotland, upon whom John set his sights. Seated one day next to Eustace, the Prince evolved a tortuous scheme to ensnare this good lady. He saw that de Vesci had a valuable ring set in gold on his finger. He told Eustace that he had another stone which he would like to set in a similar fashion and borrowed the ring to have a copy made. John sent the ring to Margaret in Eustace's name asking her to meet him urgently and privately for their mutual pleasure. Margaret fell for this ruse, but fortunately Eustace met her whilst she was speeding on her way to the tryst. Eustace realised what was happening and arranged for a common woman, duly and appropriately apparelled, to entertain John seemingly to his delight. The substitution worked but unfortunately Eustace unwisely boasted of his trick to the enragement of John and he then had to flee the realm for his safety. He was accompanied by several others of the nobility whose wives had been ravished. On his way north he despoiled as many of John's castles as he could.

* * *

326

Other conquests of John included Matilda, the daughter of FitzWalter and the wife of Geoffrey de Mandeville. An interesting sidelight on this escapade was that this self same Geoffrey subsequently married Isabella, after she was divorced by John, no doubt as some compensation. He had a son, Richard of Dover by an unidentified sister of William, Earl of Warenne who had five sisters, four of whom had married well. This Richard became a captain in the army. Another lady, one Hawise, gave birth to John's son (called Oliver) who had land in Kent and was active in repelling the French invasion in the next decade. It is probable that Hawise was a Tracy and it is extraordinary how this family seems to have had such close interconnections with the Plantagenets. One of Henry I's concubines was a Tracy, another Tracy was a murderer of Becket and John had a son by yet another in this later generation.

Unlike his only known bastard daughter, Joan, whose mother was caustically known in court circles as 'Queen' Clementia because of her airs and graces, who achieved some prominence in the next decade after John ascended the throne, the bastard sons were all relatively obscure. John had probably at least twelve mistresses and except for those mentioned above their names are not recorded. Bastard John became a clerk at Lincoln. Richard became a custodian at Wallingford Castle in 1216. Eudo, named Fitzroy, is mentioned briefly in 1240, as is Ivo. One Henry had lands in Cornwall and seems to have married a minor heiress. Geoffrey died on active service in 1205 at Poitou. There was another Richard and finally Osbert Giffard, but there are no Giffard daughters mentioned in documents who could have been Osbert's mother. There is one other 'doubtful' bastard daughter called Isabel la Blanche, another family that has not been traced and there is no record of this girl's subsequent fate.

It would be an interesting speculation as to whether John tried to seduce the formidable Maud de St Valerie, who was not only a cousin of the fair Rosamond but also the wife of William de Braose. In 1185 William had murdered all the unarmed and unsuspecting Welsh chieftains who had been invited to a Christmas feast at Abergavenny, a crime never to be forgotten in south Wales. Maud's reputation being such as it was it is my view that she played a major part in that episode. John was later to treat Maud with outstanding cruelty and brutality and it could hardly have been because of any part that she might have played in the massacre. It could almost certainly be because she had rejected his lecherous advances.

It is interesting that many of the above noble families whose wives *and daughters were ravished by John were active in making that Prince, when he became King, implement the Magna Carta some twenty years later.*

Although there is no doubt that John's sexual depredations were spread over many years, he would have been especially active in the early years of the 1190s. He certainly had six bastard sons as well as one bastard daughter. He had two more probable sons and a possible daughter. Most of them became adult and active towards the end of the first decade of the 1200s so would have been born between 1190 and 1195. It is not considered likely that he sired many bastards after he came to the throne in 1199. It is generally thought that he used Flaxley Abbey extensively during this time, not only for sport but also as a discreet place to bring those he wished to seduce.

The details of Eleanor's movements in 1192 are not known although she spent all the time in England. She had had a punishing schedule during the previous year, travelling extensively from the southern confines of Aquitaine, through southern France and down the Italian peninsula to Sicily, and then all the way back to Rouen, all at the age of sixty-nine.

Now she had her impossible youngest son plotting, creating merry hell in England and quite prepared to trade much of the Angevin possessions with the devious French king for all that he could get. Eleanor kept as close a watch as she could on all that was happening and was longing for her favourite Richard to return and put his stamp of authority on it all.

*   *   *

Eleanor spent Christmas at Westminster and spoke to many of the crusaders who were now flooding back about the news from the Holy Land. They all waxed lyrical about the brave deeds of the Lionheart. But where was he now? Rumours spread from France that Philip and John were plotting to have him assassinated. Eleanor continued to give instructions to reinforce her defences against any attack. Meanwhile Berengaria and Joanna had arrived in Rome where they stayed for Christmas. They were advised to stay there for the time being as the conditions for travel were appalling, and there was a fear that they too could be captured and held as hostages.

During the first week of January 1193, Walter Coutances brought the dire news that Richard had been captured in Austria and was now the prisoner of his arch enemy Leopold, he whose ensign had been torn down from the citadel at Acre. Coutances had his spies in the French court and managed to intercept and copy a letter from the Emperor Henry of Germany to Philip. John saw an opportunity and fled forthwith to Paris claiming that he was the only heir to Richard and to offer his homage to Philip for his Angevin possessions. He also promised to marry the unfortunate Alice and would divorce his barren cousin Isabella of Gloucester immediately. He told the King that his wife was well within the forbidden grounds of consanguinity and reminded him that his dearly loved mother, Eleanor, had had to be divorced from Philip's father for exactly the same reasons. Philip was not unaware that John had very limited support from his French nobles but was anxious to recover Gisors and the Vexin.

Eleanor immediately assumed control of the government in England and was ably supported by Walter Coutances and the aged but still very sagacious Hugh de Puiset of Durham. She obtained support for her justice and wisdom throughout the country despite the bribes and unfulfilled promises made by John to several dissident barons during the previous year. She was also aware of John's proclivities with the wives and daughters of so many of the loyal nobility which had weakened his standing at this critical moment. She now awaited developments.

* * *

There is much conflicting thought regarding what happened to Richard after he was wrecked at Corfu. My source work is by Ralph of Coggeshall and derived from one of his companions, the chaplain Anselm. Amy Kelly and Alison Weir both refer to this work but give two largely irreconcilable versions, although there are some areas of common ground. I shall endeavour to give my own account but realise that the truth will never be known.

Kelly says that Richard set off for Brindisi but never arrived, having deviated to Marseille. He had a stormy passage, taking six weeks to get this far and, on putting in to friendly Pisa, was warned that Marseille and every other neighbouring port was barred to him. He gave some thought to going via Gibraltar and through the Bay of Biscay but the prospect of winter storms dissuaded him. It is also curious that he did not consider joining Berengaria and Joanna who were by now in Rome. However Richard then reversed his tracks and went back to the east coast of Italy and up the Adriatic. But the timings for this are transparently impossible. If Richard reached Corfu on or about 9 November and took six weeks to reach Pisa and then came back to land near Venice he could not possibly have been captured near Vienna on 21 December. Even if there are some misinterpretations of timings from the original sources, this journey is quite impossible.

The Alison Weir timings and story make more sense. Richard hired two Romanian pirate vessels to take him and a few companions up the Adriatic. These ships were driven ashore at Dubrovnik where he transferred to another galley which was duly wrecked at Istria, near Trieste. These decisions for his homeward route seem more and more bizarre. The obvious direction should have been towards Marseille on the western seaboard of Italy as in the Kelly story. The difficulties of weather and availability of vessels and the need to get home as soon as possible were obviously germane and the Truce of God would have given Richard some protection. His Romanian piratical crew and their moral standards must leave one aghast, but nevertheless this must have been the option that Richard exercised.

Both Kelly and Weir agree that Richard landed at Istria and then opted to take the overland route through what was transparently hostile territory with winter setting in. Here again there are differences in the alleged interpretations from Ralph of Coggeshall but they are relatively immaterial to the story as it evolves. Kelly says that Richard put himself at the mercy of the local Count Mainerd of Gortzn (which must be the present Graz between Klagenfurt and Vienna; it might be Gorizia, now in Italy to the south and in the foothills of the mountain pass into Austria) claiming that he was a merchant from the Holy Land called Hugo. Mainerd tumbled to this deception and allowed Richard freedom of passage but privately and unhelpfully alerted the next nobleman on this route, Frederick of Frisi. Frederick sent one of his trusted vassals, a Norman called Roger, who located the King. Richard invoked the Truce of God and their common Norman heritage and Roger allowed the King to proceed and gave him a fresh horse to continue his escape with a much reduced retinue. Frederick was not convinced by Roger's story and he apprehended the balance of Richard's entourage, but the delay enabled the King to escape and make good speed northwards.

Both these stories are full of gripping and stirring detail and make good yarns. In the next phase, Weir's story is again slightly different. Istria was in the territory of the friendly King Bela of Hungary who was helpful, although undoubtedly the Austrian spies in the court of

Bela were keeping their eyes and ears open. So Richard soon entered the lands of his arch enemy Leopold and he needed to travel through the Alpine passes until he reached the plains near Klagenfurt and Villach. Weir says that Count Mainerd was Leopold's vassal which increased Richard's danger. Leopold could not believe his good fortune when he discovered what Richard was intending to do and alerted Mainerd who closed all the local roads and captured most of Richard's entourage. The King, with three remaining companions, escaped and made for a village on the outskirts of Vienna, managing to evade the patrols on the roads. Once again the verve and horsemanship of the Plantagenets came to the fore as they covered over 200 miles from the coastal area, up the Alpine pass and thence to Vienna in three days in the middle of winter.

These two accounts have much in common. The involvement of Mainerd, the Hugo disguise, the arrest of most of Richard's entourage and the flight to Vienna are in both stories. There are differences as to whether Mianerd was helpful or obstructive, whether Bela gave a wayleave and whether Frederick and Roger had an involvement. But these details are not important. Richard's route was known and he was escaping capture by the skin of his teeth. His enemies were closing in.

* * *

Richard now had bad luck and suffered a recurrence of his malarial fever and could go no further. They had to stop and rest in a humble hovel. They needed food and supplies and the third person in their group was a young lad who could speak German. This lad was indiscreet and unwisely displayed more wealth and gold than was acceptable for so-called modest pilgrims or merchants. He was cross-examined by the locals, released and returned to the verminous tavern to try and rouse the bedridden King to escape at once, but Richard was too ill to make the effort.

Once again the lad had to return to the town for provisions and unwisely behaved imperiously and with too much hauteur, drawing unnecessary attention to himself. He had also carelessly thrust the King's gloves bearing the royal insignia into his belt. He was again arrested and tortured until he confessed all. On 21 December this affair was reported to Leopold who was holding his Christmas court in Vienna. Soldiers were dispatched to seize the King, who hearing much commotion donned a fresh disguise and took an unconvincing turn in the kitchen turning spatch-cocks on a spit.

Richard refused to yield to anyone other than the Emperor himself who, in his delight at this coup, hastened to the scene, arrested the King and initially treated him with honour and respect.

It is difficult to know why Richard wanted to put his head into the lion's mouth. Perhaps he was exploiting the surprise element, but his moves had been well tracked ever since he landed at Istria. More probably he considered that once he had reached the Danube, he could bribe his return journey by river with safety and ease. The Danube in its upper reaches is not too far from the Rhine so he could cross the stretch of country separating the two rivers and continue on another vessel. If his fever had not laid him low at the last hurdle he may well have been successful and the events of the next few years would have been completely different. History would then have credited him with a brilliantly executed dash across Europe.

The Austrian nation was generally regarded as brutal, barbaric and savage and the people there lived like wild beasts. Richard's prison conditions soon turned nastier. He was moved to a remote and formidable castle at Durnstein on the Danube, where he was kept in solitary confinement and guarded day and night by uncouth soldiers with drawn swords whilst Leopold considered his next move.

Leopold reported his coup to his overlord, Emperor Henry of Germany, who gleefully passed on the news of this Christmas present to Philip of France. Philip learnt this on 28 December, only seven days after the capture, a quite incredible feat of communication. Both Leopold and Henry realised the value of their prize, but there had to be some hard bargaining between them regarding the division of the spoils and how much ransom they could demand. For the time being, Leopold held the cards. They were also quite determined to humble this arrogant Plantagenet. Quite apart from Leopold's own anger at Richard's behaviour, Henry had his own personal scores to settle and was currently engaged in furious exchanges with the aged Pope in Rome. There was, for the time being, a rapport with the French King so the immediate future looked bleak for Richard and the German and Austrian made sure that no one knew where he was being imprisoned.

By the middle of February Henry and Leopold had agreed the ransom terms that they would demand and the division of the spoils between them. Henry the Lion, King of Saxony, who was married to another of Richard's sisters and was a loyal friend of the Plantagenets, started to make his views known to Henry of Germany, invoking amongst other things the Truce of God. Henry of Germany did not take kindly to this intervention and reminded his vassal in Saxony that Richard deserved the death penalty for his heinous crimes, especially those he had committed during the crusade, and that if Henry the Lion persisted any more he would carry out this threat. Obviously this was an empty threat since Richard's value lay in the ransom that he would fetch and a dead Richard would be worthless.

In the midst of all this, Leopold agreed to transfer Richard in the middle of February to the custody of Henry, and he was moved in stages via Ratisbon (Regensburg) and Wurzburg to Trifels Castle at Annweiler where he arrived in the middle of March.

* * *

On 3 March 1193 Saladin died. He had been a sick man throughout most of the previous year but had managed to disguise his indifferent health and infirmities from both his friends and his enemies. Much of his dynamism had evaporated but he was quite determined to conclude the fighting of the Third Crusade as soon as he could on honourable and sensible terms. Neither side was able to continue campaigning at the pace originally envisaged and he knew that both armies had to retire and lick their wounds. Once Richard had departed in October 1192, Saladin tidied up the administration of Palestine. His intense wish was to make his pilgrimage to Mecca before he was called to his Maker, but every week brought more matters which needed his attention. After years of campaigning, the accumulation of these important details needed his decisions and he was too meticulous to ignore them for personal or spiritual fulfilment. During the winter he found himself slowing down and had intense periods of weariness and forgetfulness. On 1 March he fell into a stupor and died two days later.

He could be ruthless and beheaded Reynald of Chatillon with his own hand because of his outrageous crimes against humanity. He had an immense courtesy and his word could always be trusted. He had a great respect for the Christian faith albeit that, in his view, its adherents were mistaken and would be consigned to perdition. Without his military genius the Saracens would never have achieved the cohesion that they needed to overcome the heavy armoury of the crusaders, and he exploited their own mobile tactics with consummate skill. His great problem was that he was a Kurdish outsider and never part of the inner councils. The Kurds were never able to get their just due and were never fully trusted. Saladin was buried in the great mosque of the Ommayads in Damascus. His closeness to Richard and his many kindnesses to him during the campaign are quite extraordinary.

* * *

Saladin's age at death is alleged to have been fifty-four, which would mean that he was born in 1139. But if he was the son of Eleanor he must have been born eight years later and I have promulgated theories about this discrepancy earlier in this book. Other sources give Saladin's date of birth as 1137 – all this indicates doubt about when he was born. There is another curious anomaly. Saladin's younger brother, el-Adil also died on 31 August 1218 supposedly aged seventy-five, thus making him born in 1143. This could therefore mean that my theory is incorrect. But Runciman's book on the Third Crusade quotes an Arabic source saying that el-Adil was only sixty-five *when he died. Therefore my theory continues to hold water and confirms that there was much obfuscation on dates and ages from contemporary sources.*

The letter from Henry of Germany to Philip of France which Walter of Coutances copied and sent to Eleanor was most revealing and explicit. The cordial salutations between Henry and Philip and the abundant joy between them are ominous. The letter refers to the guilt of Richard whose treason, treachery and accumulated mischief in the Land of Promise led to his arrest. It describes Richard's landing at Istria and the chase and seizing of followers by both Mainerd of Gortze and Frederick of Frisi.

* * *

No one in England or France knew where Richard was. Philip and Prince John were acting as if Richard was already dead. However Eleanor knew from the letter that Richard was still alive albeit a prisoner, and that he had an immense value to Henry and Leopold only whilst he was alive. She immediately made her plans. Richard had to be found and communication re-established both with his captors and the King. Savary, the Bishop of Bath and a cousin of the Emperor, was immediately sent to Henry's court. The abbots of Boxley and Robertsbridge were sent to Austria to locate Richard. The exiled and impossible Longchamp of Ely was ordered to use his undoubted diplomatic skills to negotiate with Henry – after all, Richard had appointed him as chancellor and the sooner Richard was back the more likely it was that Longchamp would be more gainfully employed. Hubert, erstwhile Dean of York, now Bishop of Salisbury, was *en route* back from the crusade and had reached Italy. He was diverted to go and reinforce the delegations converging on Germany. Walter Coutances's spies were active and every rumour was followed up.

It would be nice to think that that great legend of Blondel the troubadour contributed to the finding of Richard. The story goes that Blondel went from castle to castle in Austria singing the songs that he and Richard had composed and sung together, until he reached Durnstein where he heard the chorus re-echoed from a high up and remote window in the tower and knew that he had found the King. There was a famous minstrel of the time called Blondel le Nesle and this is a picturesque and piquant tale.

Longchamp persuaded Emperor Henry to move Richard to a more accessible location. The abbots of Boxley and Robertsbridge were able to meet the King in mid-March at Ochsenfurt near Wurzburg and were able to report that he was in good heart and spirits and had a healthy contempt for 'that gosling', the Emperor.

The Pope was horrified by the capture of Richard which entirely ignored the Truce of God. He excommunicated Leopold and threatened Philip with the same should he attack any part of Richard's French possessions.

Eleanor demanded new oaths of fealty from the nobility and clergy and with the wholehearted support of her council governed England with remarkable sense and balance. She was also anxious to keep a balance with her youngest son and avoided any confrontation despite much provocation.

In March Emperor Henry and Leopold finally agreed on the

terms of the ransom and the division between them. The amount demanded was 100,000 silver marks (which was twice the annual revenue of England) and the delivery of 200 hostages from among the leading English families and Norman nobility. In addition Richard had to help the Emperor overthrow Tancred of Sicily and restore Henry to that throne which was rightfully his by inheritance, and the King of Cyprus (a cousin of the Emperor and still bound by his silver chains) was to be released.

Eleanor now wrote the first of three letters to Pope Celestine III. All were remarkable and, indeed, unique in the archives of the time. The first, being of some 1,800 words, was astonishingly lengthy and impassioned and implored the pontiff to demand the release of her son. She referred to herself as 'the miserable ... the commiserated Queen of England, Duchess of Normandy, Countess of Anjou' and went on to say, 'I am defiled with torment, my flesh is wasted away and my bones cleave to my skin. My years pass away full of groans ... I wish that ... my body would die ... that my brain and my marrow be dissolved into tears ... that my bowels are torn away ... would that my eyes be condemned to blindness that I may no more see the woes of my people... O wretched me, yet pitied by no one ... two sons sleep in the dust ... Richard is in bonds ... his brother John depopulates the kingdom with the sword... The Prince of the Apostles still rules and reigns in the Apostolic See ... You father [must] draw the sword of Peter against these evildoers.' Her entreaties waxed more and more eloquent and she reminded the Pope of his promises made the previous year when she visited him. She prophesied that the seamless tunic of Christ would be rent again and the net of Peter broken, and ended her letter in despair.

* * *

It is almost certain that most of these letters were written by Eleanor's secretary, Peter of Blois, but some parts bear the imprint of a different style as well as some repetition, so the Queen could have inserted her own distinctive input. Her lamentations and distress are poignant.

* * *

The eighty-seven-year-old Pope did not reply as he knew that he had very little influence with Emperor Henry who would treat all his objections with contempt. Celestine was too old and too tired to enter into any more frays at his time of life. Emperor Henry was determined to expand his empire and his military might was far greater than anything the Pope could command. His treatment of bishops who displeased him was brutal and decisive and the threat of excommunication was immaterial to him.

Easter saw a number of seemingly unrelated activities. On 21 March Richard was brought before Emperor Henry and his council at Speyer to answer numerous charges regarding his crimes. Amongst those present were Bishops Hubert Walter of Salisbury, Savary of Bath and Longchamp of Ely and the two abbots who had located Richard earlier. The Emperor had a formidable prosecution team and presented the case with great skill. Richard relied entirely on his own dialectic. He explained with great charm and persuasiveness all that he had done for the greater good of the crusade and spoke with such candour and reason that all those present fell under his spell. They were convinced that it was not he who had wronged so many and that he was entirely innocent and blameless. But for him the infidel would have continued to rage rampant throughout the Middle East and the crusader cause would have been utterly lost. As it was he had negotiated an honourable and just peace to the benefit of all Christians. When Richard had finished speaking a ripple of applause rang round the hall, welling to an acclamation. Many were weeping, including Henry, who on coming down to the dock embraced Richard who had fallen on his knees as a sign of contrition. Henry gave him the kiss of peace, took his hand and escorted him back to the royal dais.

The influence and advice of Hubert Walter played an important and pivotal role in Richard's oratory and defence tactics. The King rewarded him with a letter of commendation that Walter should be elevated to the see of Canterbury as soon as possible. Walter was an able lawyer and a nephew of the former justiciar, Ranulf de Glanville, and the family were loyal servants to the Angevins.

After this extraordinary volte-face at Speyer, Richard's imprisonment conditions were much eased. He was in effect treated as an honoured guest and was able to receive visitors and conduct some of the business of his kingdom. He was allowed to go hunting and hawking, challenged his gaolers to wrestling matches and enjoyed getting them drunk. His health was much improved and he was in good physical shape at long last.

Philip of France was not unaware of this turn of events. He had, with some trepidation, realised that the German Emperor was considering the release of Richard without any consultation with him. The effusive letter (that which was copied by Coutances) from Henry to Philip just before Christmas had indicated that the two monarchs would act in accord in this affair and now events had seemingly changed. Philip, being the wily negotiator that he was, kept his options open and had a private meeting with the German Emperor but there are no minutes of what was said.

With Lent over, John returned to England in advance of a Continental mercenary army. He failed to persuade the King of Scotland to give him any support but achieved a modicum of success amongst the Welsh. He then went to London to try and browbeat the Queen and her council into agreeing that Richard would never return and even announced his death, which was not believed. The council was not intimidated. John retired to Windsor where he was besieged. His mercenaries were repulsed as soon as they landed. Eleanor's plans for reinforcing her defences and her vigilance had paid off.

On 12 April Philip invaded and seized Gisors through the treachery of the keeper. The French King laid waste through the Vexin and moved to Rouen where he demanded the release of his sister Alice and the surrender of the fortress. The commander, the Earl of Leicester, was made of sterner stuff than the castellan of Gisors and told Philip in no uncertain terms that he knew of no change of succession and had received no instructions from Queen Eleanor. He would, however, be pleased to offer the hospitality of the fortress to the King provided he entered alone and unarmed. Philip suspected that he would be taken as a counter-hostage for Richard and declined. Despite his aggressive approach and initial success, Philip destroyed his siege engines, emptied all casks of wine into the Seine and turned tail back to Paris.

Not having had any reaction from Pope Celestine, Eleanor now wrote the second of her letters to the Pope. This was much shorter, about half the length of the first, and began with the splendid phrase, 'Eleanor, by the wrath of God, Queen of

England'. She beseeched the Pope to be a man of action: 'Where is the passion of John against Herod? Go to Germany in person for the release of a great prince... Seize the sword of the spirit, which is the word of God much more firmly'. It was all splendidly stirring stuff. Eleanor, remembering what King Henry had threatened in the Becket saga, then rattled her own sabre and reminded the aged pontiff that 'the fateful moment is at hand ... when the bonds of Saint Peter shall be broken [and] Catholic unity broken'. Eleanor had only recently rebuffed two papal legates and was now openly and strongly hinting at a schism.

It seems that Longchamp brought the final ransom terms back to England some time in April with a letter from Richard giving instructions to raise the money and collect the hostages as soon as possible. Despite the King's authority behind Longchamp, London treated him with disdain and refused to revoke any of their restrictions on him. He was regarded as a mere messenger the purport of which was a mammoth assignment and Eleanor set about the Herculean task of collecting the ransom and collecting the hostages with her customary vigour and decisiveness.

Eleanor's instructions were Draconian. Every noble and every freeman had to give one quarter of their annual income; all clergy were to donate ten per cent; the poor were not to be excluded but had to give what they could. The abbeys and churches had to surrender all their gold, silver and treasure and every parish had to send their chalices. The Cistercian monks who eschewed wealth of any sort had to yield the profits from their annual wool trade. There were to be no exceptions. Those from the other side of the Channel were not excluded either.

Eleanor's agents, who were to be responsible for the collection and storage, were carefully chosen and had to be nobles or ecclesiastics of unquestioned honour and probity. The crypt of St Paul's Cathedral in London was selected as a safe and secure repository. The tax collection in England was more efficient than that on the Continent, but there were anomalies and evasions. Caen gave more than London. The Pope took pity on Berengaria and Joanna who were still in Rome and provided them with escort to reach Aquitaine with safety. Berengaria was most active in raising considerable sums there. The English were surprisingly cooperative, probably because the alternative to Richard was the venal John. John overtly gave every support to collecting the ransom but expropriated much of the levy from his own vast English territories for his advantage and seditious purposes.

Some time in April or May Longchamp was able to persuade Emperor Henry to move his captive to the more convenient and comfortable castle of Hagenau. Richard was able to set up a mini-court to deal more efficiently with the affairs of his kingdom and to encourage the collection of the huge ransom. He also wrote to the Old Man of the Mountains in Syria, the chief of the Assassins, asking him to exonerate him from any involvement in the murder of Conrad which was one of the key charges in the alleged crimes brought against him the previous month. Richard was allowed much freedom of action and enjoyed the sporting facilities available at Hagenau.

Emperor Henry was caught in a squeeze. He was rapidly running short of funds. His conflicts with many of his nobles and senior prelates were escalating and although he tried to ignore the Pope he was conscious that opinion was building up against him. He needed the ransom money sooner rather than later.

On 29 May the vacant see of Canterbury was considered following a letter from the King to the appropriate ecclesiastics involved in the selection process. Hubert Walter, currently Bishop of Salisbury and erstwhile Dean of York, was unanimously elected and Walter of Coutances gave the royal assent and confirmation. Geoffrey of York could not have been best pleased at this preferment of his arch enemy now to be his superior in God's earthly and spiritual hierarchy.

In June, following a meeting in Worms, Henry put pressure on Richard to increase the ransom from 100,000 marks to 150,000 and pressure was brought to increase the number of hostages. This latter stipulation was resisted as the crusade had decimated the ranks of the nobility. Part of this deal was to release Richard from any involvement in supporting Henry to recover his throne in Sicily. It was also due to the fact that Philip of France was suggesting that he and John could match the ransom and take over responsibility for the captive King. Richard's brother-in-law, Henry the Lion of Saxony, now intervened and Emperor Henry now needed his support against his own dissident subjects. Among other deals concluded was the marriage of the Lion's son with the Emperor's cousin which strengthened that alliance. The Old Man of the Mountains in Syria had also replied exonerating

340

Richard from any involvement in the assassination of Conrad. Richard's continued skill in diplomacy was beginning to pay dividends.

The first harvest of the ransom was totally insufficient so Eleanor sent agents into the field for a second effort and then a third, and slowly the treasure began to build up. Eleanor put pressure on Normandy and Aquitaine to increase their financial support. The choice for the hostages created many problems and it is not clear how this was solved. What is certain is that many noble houses were very uneasy over the supervision of the hostages being entrusted to Longchamp who was a noted homosexual, if not a paedophile. Some nobles would have been happier to provide daughters instead of sons.

Eleanor now wrote the third of her letters to the Pope in a far more conciliatory and apologetic tone. Celestine had obviously replied to her second letter although it may be doubtful if he ever saw her first missive.

During July Prince John moved across the Channel to France where he was nearer to his co-conspirator Philip of France. The French King now confused the issue. He had wished for some time to end his widowerhood and considered that an alliance with the Danish royal house could give immense advantages to his continuing warfare with the English King. The famous and intrepid sea captains from Denmark would be ideal to harass the shores and coasts of England. Ingeborg, the sister of the King of Denmark and a damsel of great beauty and innocence, was selected and she duly arrived in Paris in August with a suitable retinue. Within days she was wedded and crowned Queen of France and Philip's coup looked both propitious and masterly.

But Philip immediately had second thoughts as he realised that he had made a dynastic miscalculation. The German Emperor had an excellent and suitable cousin, one Constance, and a German alliance would be far more appropriate. The poor Ingeborg lasted but one day as wife and queen and was dismissed on the grounds of consanguinity and told to return to her brother. Ingeborg opted to enter a nunnery in France pending an appeal to Rome. It was also germane that Canute of Denmark had given no commitment to Philip to harry the English coast. Philip was duly excommunicated by the Pope for his behaviour.

Constance however was not enamoured of either Philip or the

French crown and with remarkable speed and the connivance of her mother married the son of Henry, the Lion of Saxony. Henry was, of course, Richard's brother-in-law, so once again the English King had outmanoeuvred Philip, this time in the diplomatic field.

The delays were beginning to irk Richard and his active mind and body were underemployed. It was during this summer that he turned his attention to his much vaunted, and by now neglected, abilities in the arts of poetry and ballads – these were inherited through his troubadour maternal grandfather Duke William IX of Aquitaine. He composed many worthy pieces, some railing against his many friends who were niggardly with their financial support to release him and one in particular set to music poignantly dedicated to his half-sister Marie, Countess of Champagne.

In October Emperor Henry arrived as a guest of honour in London where he was entertained lavishly and returned to Germany with two-thirds of the ransom money, gold and silver weighing no less than thirty-five tons as the first instalment. It was agreed that Richard would be released on 17 January 1194 when the balance of the ransom and the noble hostages were delivered. Events were beginning to move towards a successful conclusion for the Plantagenets.

On 5 November, Walter was enthroned as Archbishop of Canterbury by Richard, Bishop of London, assisted by the Bishop of Winchester and many others. By December Eleanor was poised to move to Germany with an impressive retinue of supporters and the balance of the ransom suitably and strongly escorted. The English were responsible for all the money and precious metals until they were duly and safely delivered to the German Emperor. Despite the bitter midwinter weather a safe crossing was made and on 6 January 1194 Eleanor arrived in Cologne, ready and willing to deliver her side of the bargain. The German Emperor now began to prevaricate, eventually advising the English Queen that the release date was to be indefinitely postponed without giving any reasons.

There was consternation amongst the English contingent as they were kept in suspense over this unwarranted delay, although tempered by the joy of the reunion between Eleanor and Richard after three and a half years apart. Emperor Henry then revealed his hand and very nasty news emerged. Philip and John had matched the ransom but required time to raise the money. They wanted Richard to remain in custody until September during which time they would be able to attack and subdue the English possessions and hence obtain the requisite funds. The added advantage for the German Emperor was that he could retain the whole ransom for himself without having to pass any part to Leopold of Austria. It was a diabolic intervention.

Emperor Henry now wanted time to evaluate his options and wished to exploit this development to his own advantage. First, he had committed himself under oath to accept Eleanor's ransom and this could not be lightly discarded. Secondly he had already received a substantial tranche and badly needed the balance as soon as possible to meet his considerable commitments, and September was nine months away. Thirdly he was fully aware that neither Philip nor John had any immediate resources to meet their counter-offer and a bird in the hand was worth two in the bush – he very much doubted that they could achieve what they had promised. But he had a powerful card in his hands and he was not prepared to let it go.

Henry needed English goodwill and support especially as he was heading towards a showdown with Philip. The Lion of Saxony was his vassal and he needed that additional support. The condition that he now offered on 2 February at Speyer was outrageous and humiliating. Richard would be released upon his acknowledgement that the Emperor would be overlord of England. Many of Henry's supporters were appalled at this development and his support was beginning to evaporate. Once again Richard deployed all his charm and persuasiveness to mitigate the disaster. Eleanor found a formula which would bridge the gap. She suggested that Richard should renounce his allegiance from the perfidious Capets and transfer his homage to and receive his kingdom back as a fief from the German Emperor. This formula was acclaimed and accepted subject to Walter of Coutances and certain others being held as hostages until they too could be ransomed for 10,000 marks. It was the best that Eleanor could achieve.

On 4 February Richard was formally released amidst copious tears of relief and the English contingent immediately departed to return to England. They paused only to celebrate a service of thanksgiving at Cologne Cathedral where the Archbishop paid the royal party the compliment of acting as precentor and took as his text 'Now I know truly that the Lord has sent his angel and has rescued me from the hand of Herod'.

Philip contacted John at once and warned him that 'the Devil is loosed'.

Richard and Eleanor now made good speed down the Rhine but cemented many alliances *en route*, mainly against the French interest. On 4 March they were met by an English ship in the Scheldt estuary and sailing by day thus avoided the French naval predators sent to harry them. Emperor Henry meanwhile was persuaded by Philip to rue the release that he had so lightly permitted and he sent pursuers to try and recapture Richard, but to no avail.

On 12 March Richard and Eleanor landed safely at Sandwich amidst much rejoicing. The royal party set off for Canterbury where they gave thanks for their safe return at the tomb of St Thomas. As Eleanor and Richard processed down from the high altar after the service, she took her son's arm and they deviated to the side chapel in the north transept. They stopped at the very spot where Becket had been murdered nearly a quarter of a century before by those faithful, ardent, albeit misguided aides of the King. Eleanor stopped and bowed her head as she prayed in silence. Her thoughts went back to those early days when they were all young and Henry and Thomas were active and so full of ideas and ideals. She was lost in a reverie and wondered how events might have been for all of them if Thomas had fulfilled the aspirations of the King when he had reluctantly accepted the archbishopric. She cast her mind back to that earth-moving evening which she had spent in Becket's rooms. And to that astonishing change in his character immediately afterwards.

Or was it as astonishing as all that? she asked herself as she clutched her son's arm. Would Henry and Thomas have achieved all that they had originally planned together? Would the Church and the kingdom have solved their seemingly irreconcilable differences? Was it really all her own fault? Only God knew. Richard stood still, awaiting his mother's next move. He could see that she was visibly shaking and trembling with emotion.

The next day the royal couple departed for Rochester where they were greeted by Hubert Walter, the new Archbishop, and a host of supporters all of whom were most relieved that their much loved King was, at long last, safely restored to them.

344

On 23 March Richard and his seventy-two-year-old mother entered London in state and attended a service of thanksgiving at St Paul's. Much now needed to be done urgently to re-establish Richard's authority and curb any remaining dissidents who had hitherto been consorting with his younger brother. Richard and Eleanor now visited St Albans and Bury St Edmunds and then obtained the unconditional surrender of Nottingham Castle. The Sheriff of Nottingham had been an ardent supporter of John.

On 30 March a council was convened in Nottingham primarily to reorder affairs in the kingdom but also to consider what had to be done with John. Geoffrey of York attended, as did his arch enemy, Hubert Walter. Walter immediately upset the prickly Geoffrey by preceding him with his episcopal cross, an insult to the Archbishop of York in whose province this meeting was being held. Richard, to whom the complaints were referred, chose to ignore them, primarily because Geoffrey was due to pay the King 3,000 marks for his licence as Sheriff of Yorkshire. The meeting eventually got under way and Eleanor counselled against any Draconian measures as this would drive her youngest son into the arms of Philip of France. Longchamp was reinstated as chancellor, thanks to his success in many of the negotiations over Richard's imprisonment. Walter of Coutances was now released following the final payment of his ransom.

An interesting visit was now made by Richard and Eleanor to Clipstone hunting lodge in Sherwood Forest. There are legends that Richard disguised himself as a prelate and allowed himself to be apprehended by Robin Hood. Richard then revealed himself to the joy of Robin and his men, whose support of the King had never wavered and who had done so much for the local populace so sorely oppressed by Guy de Gisborne, the wicked sheriff. Robin Hood was duly knighted by the King to the delight of all. There are many who question the whole authenticity of the story but this splendid episode is in character and thoroughly deserves to be true in its entirety.

Richard and Eleanor celebrated Easter at Nottingham and a second coronation was enacted at Winchester Cathedral on 17 April by the new Archbishop of Canterbury, partly to reinforce fealty to the King and partly to remind all present that loyalties extracted by John during Richard's long absence were no longer

345

valid. Again the awkward Geoffrey had threatened to appear at this ceremony preceded by his episcopal cross to remind Hubert of his gratuitous insult a fortnight earlier at Nottingham. Richard begged his half-brother not to do this and Geoffrey then typically and pointedly boycotted the ceremony.

Afterwards the two half-brothers had a brief meeting at Waltham when Geoffrey was preceded again by his episcopal cross just to continue to make his point. Subsequently, on 23 April, Richard and Eleanor went to Portsmouth preparatory to returning to France but their departure was delayed by bad weather. They landed at Barfleur on 12 May and neither of them was ever to return to England.

15

1194–1199

Richard and Eleanor landed at Barfleur during the second week of May 1194 where they were greeted with joy and acclamation. They went first to Bayeux, then to Caen and Lisieux.

The Queen now summoned John, who had been abandoned by Philip of France, to appear before them. John arrived with much trepidation and fear and wanted to see his mother first. Eleanor was anxious that the two brothers should be reconciled despite John's appalling behaviour during Richard's absence. At her age the last thing that she wanted was for her last two surviving sons to be at loggerheads and she was all too aware that Richard had no legitimate heir. She now had reservations about the ability of Berengaria and her son to consummate their marriage and fulfil their dynastic duties. It would also be a recipe for disaster for John to be driven back into the scheming clutches of the pernicious Capets. She understood the strategic issues all too clearly and used her considerable persuasiveness to bridge the gaps between Richard and John.

Upon entering Richard's presence, John made a full prostration, begged forgiveness and burst into tears. Richard raised him up and magnanimously gave him the kiss of peace saying, 'Think no more of it, John. You are but a child and were left to evil counsellors. Your advisers shall pay for this.'

He commanded that John should join them in their dinner. His words were a contemptuous way of treating a grown man of twenty-six years who had led a full if erratic life for many years, and it was surprising that John now seemed to pull himself together and behaved with sense and propriety during the rest of Richard's life. His life during this period was not particularly remarkable and little is now known of his activities for the next

347

few years. Richard, in due course, restored John's estates, which were very considerable.

Eleanor, after all her exertions during the past year in particular, now decided to go into semi-retirement at Fontevraud where she was able to enjoy a much quieter life and devote herself to charitable activities with surprising gusto and enthusiasm. There are a number of tantalising glimpses of her activities during the remainder of Richard's reign but she undoubtedly kept her finger on the pulse of all that went on. Eleanor recharged her batteries and kept herself in good fettle and trim as she had done during her lengthy captivity. She was clearly poised to leap into action should events demand it and she kept in close touch with her adored son to give him the necessary advice and counsel to keep the ship of State on an even keel. History would love to know more of the details of her involvement. Fontevraud Abbey was well situated between her extensive lands of Aquitaine and Normandy and she was well positioned to monitor all the traffic, both physical and intellectual, that passed through or nearby as it was the focal point for all visitors and travellers.

Richard now turned his attention to regaining all that had been lost during his absence and aggressively punishing the French King in every way possible. The following years saw a continuous scrapping and manoeuvring with brief periods of truce which were always short-lived. All this was costly and Richard was always demanding more and more funds from his kingdom. He was fortunate in that the economy was buoyant and Walter was an excellent and efficient administrator and tax collector in England.

After his return to the Continent Philip had the upper hand and the advantage of planning for his raids with well-deployed forces. But Richard was a far better commander and an inspirational leader and could anticipate and rebuff his enemy's moves to better effect. None of the fighting was large scale and consisted primarily of campaigns of attrition with the inevitable ebbs and flow of success and failure. Richard was fuelled with a righteous anger over Philip's blatant and deplorable abuse of the Truce of God during the crusade and his own subsequent imprisonment.

Within days of Richard's return, at Whitsun, he relieved Philip's siege of Verneuil causing the French to flee. In June

Philip countered by devastating Fontaine, a small castle garrisoned by twenty-four men only. Richard captured Montmirail and then subjugated Tours and besieged the powerful and well garrisoned castle of Loches which soon surrendered with ample supplies of booty. The Lionheart was on the rampage, seeking whom he may devour with an increasing vengeance.

Philip's manoeuvring brought his forces to an encampment near Vendome where he hoped to attack Touraine, but Richard moved more quickly and was about to pounce. Philip was fortunate enough to realise his danger in time, broke camp speedily and retreated in haste towards Freteval where Richard intercepted his baggage train with considerable treasure as well as capturing many prisoners of quality. Philip was lucky to escape to Chateaudun.

Switching to the south, Richard took Taillebourg, the lands of Geoffrey of Rancon and the county of Angouleme. Within thirty-seven days the Lionheart had roared and the sound was beginning to strike terror in the hearts of those who had flirted with the perfidious and devious Capets and their followers.

This pace could not be kept up and a truce was agreed in July at Le Mans between the two kings. Both sides needed time for their forces to return to their estates and recuperate. Funds needed to be replenished and affairs of state attended to.

Richard now reversed the ban on tournaments which his father had imposed. King Henry had realised that these were being abused and were counterproductive. Valuable lives had been lost and the young blades were far more interested in the profits of success than in the training that these games involved. But Richard now needed the training disciplines to return and to allow his military leaders to gain experience in jousting and fighting.

Richard's valuable ally and friend, Walter of Coutances, having, by now, been released from his position of hostage, reached London on 19 May 1194, where he preached at St Paul's and then departed to Normandy and his archbishopric at Rouen.

*　　*　　*

Meanwhile, in England, the insufferable Geoffrey Plantagenet returned to York in May 1194 and almost immediately antagonised the chapter. This was unwise as there were some whom he had appointed and who were friendly to him. But Hubert Walter, now chief justiciar of the realm as well as archbishop, was quite determined to teach Geoffrey a lesson that he would not forget in a hurry.

It all now might seem very petty and spiteful but Geoffrey was the late King's eldest son and the only one who had been loyal throughout. Henry II had moreover given very serious consideration to legitimising him and making him heir to the throne. Geoffrey had been an excellent chancellor and many thought that he was a better soldier than Richard. Only the year before he had patently demonstrated both his loyalty and his military prowess in reducing the Tickhill stronghold, which had been holding out and was a thorn in the flesh to the King's party in the north. Now that odious Walter, who had been so objectionable to him as Dean of York when Geoffrey was appointed as archbishop, was now pulling rank on him not only from the civil standpoint but also from the ecclesiastical aspect. Fangs were being bared.

It had all started some months earlier. The present dean, a nomination from Walter, was conveniently promoted to be Bishop of Exeter and this was gladly welcomed by Geoffrey. To strengthen his hand in the chapter he now proposed that a vague Plantagenet relation alleged to be his half-brother be elected, one Peter. It has to said that there is singularly little evidence that he was a blood relation, but he could have been a son by one of King Henry's later mistresses or, even more unlikely, by Hikenai. The King did not enthuse and suggested another. Neither candidate was immediately available. Geoffrey now put up Simon of Apulia whom the chapter endorsed. So far so good. Then Geoffrey fell out with Simon and annulled the appointment and yet another candidate was proposed. At this stage the canons, as well as the dispossessed Simon, were furious and were undoubtedly encouraged by Walter. Thus Geoffrey was back with a chapter who were unanimous in opposition to him.

In August 1194 Walter sent a delegation of justices to York to report upon all irregularities. They imprisoned Geoffrey's servants, threatened the archbishop with a trial and confiscated his estates, although they had not seen him or summoned him to give any evidence. There is no doubt that Geoffrey would not have cooperated even if they had as, in any case, it would have been far below his dignity to respond to such an outrageous demand. One of these justices was an up and coming lawyer, one William Brewer, who was clambering up the social and professional tree and who will reappear later on. Earlier Brewer had been appointed Sheriff of Devonshire and had accompanied Eleanor in her retinue to liberate Richard from his German captivity.

In September the Pope confirmed what had been done, so the first round went to Walter. Geoffrey promptly went to see his brother Richard and, ever aware of what the King always needed, proffered a bribe of 1,000 marks down and another 1,000 on restitution of everything. Richard agreed. Round two went to Geoffrey.

It is apposite to continue this ecclesiastical row and recount it in advance of the overall time sequence. In January 1195, papal commissioners met in York, were greeted with the King's order of restitution and were nonplussed. They then demanded that all parties come to Rome for a hearing on 1 June. Geoffrey, still in Normandy, asked for a respite, ostensibly on the grounds of ill-health but probably encouraged by Richard, and this was granted until 18 November. Still Geoffrey did not appear.

Then Geoffrey again put his foot in it. He exercised his authority as Richard's eldest brother and took it upon himself to castigate him at great length for his immoral lifestyle. Richard had been remarkably tolerant and supportive but this he was not going to accept. They had a blazing row and Richard then reversed his decision and deprived Geoffrey of his archiepiscopal property and sheriffdom. Third round to Walter.

Early in 1196, by now in despair, Geoffrey went to Rome where his case was heard and to everyone's intense surprise the verdict went his way and he was reinstated. Richard refused to accept this, probably because he was now unable to impound any fine for reinstating Geoffrey to his revenues. Geoffrey decided to stay in Rome until 1198. Round four thus went to Geoffrey. We shall return to this saga when the rest of this history has caught up with other events.

* * *

On 22 November 1194, Emperor Henry of Germany invaded Sicily to recover his kingdom there and was duly crowned in

351

Palermo. On 26 December, Emperor Leopold of Austria was badly injured in a hunting accident at Graz and had to have his foot amputated. This was generally ascribed to divine retribution.

Richard spent Christmas at Rouen but it is unlikely that his mother was present and is probable that she was at Fontevraud. She would not have approved of what she was likely to see and she was becoming more and more concerned over Richard's failure to produce a legitimate male heir. Berengaria's absence from the marriage bed was not going to solve this problem. Eleanor would have been unlikely to have kept her views to herself.

Bishop Hugh of Lincoln visited the King in the early part of 1195 and rebuked him for failing to be reunited with Berengaria and for his lecherous and faithless way of life. Richard responded by saying that his conscience was easy and ignored Hugh's strictures. During Lent Richard was accosted by a hermit whilst out hunting who castigated him for his outrageous sexual behaviour saying, 'Remember the destruction of Sodom and abstain from illicit acts for if you do not, God will punish you in a fitting manner.' Richard ignored him too. The King was undergoing rebukes from every quarter and he was plainly not best pleased.

Richard's behaviour must have become blatant and unacceptable to many of his court. But at Easter, Richard fell ill and his life was despaired of. He confessed his sins and was absolved. He repented and sent for Berengaria and seems now to have led a blameless life, but the resumption of conjugal relations failed to produce an heir. Whether this was the fault of Richard or whether Berengaria was barren cannot be known. Richard is known to have had only one male bastard, Philip of Cognac, who was by now adolescent, so seems not to have been too fertile and his Queen never produced any children at any time.

* * *

The reference to Sodom implies that the King was homosexual. This had been mooted earlier, especially during his closeness with Philip of France before he succeeded to the throne, and in relation to various other curious episodes in his life. Richard was generally regarded as a man with a voracious appetite for women. Stephen of Bourbon recounts that Richard lusted after a nun at Fontevraud and threatened to burn the abbey down unless this girl turned her lovely eyes towards him and submitted to his desires. The poor girl cut her eyes out with a knife and sent them to him. It has to be said that, at that time, homosexuality was criminal and that there was no contemporary comment on this aspect of the King's life. The King's court was always an open forum and deviations in sexual behaviour would not escape the eyes of those in the royal presence. Richard's curiously ambivalent confession in Sicily some years earlier of 'sins against nature' should not be ignored.

* * *

In August 1195, Richard finally released Alice, Philip's half-sister. This poor girl, whose life was blighted by being made a pawn in the political machinations of the time, was promptly and discreetly married off to the obscure Count of Ponthieu. Alice was by now thirty-five and could not have had any qualities of beauty left or developed any intellect. She had been immured in one castle after another with no amusements or facilities. She could only have become a middle-aged and unattractive pudding by the time she was released and history then lost sight of her. It would seem extremely unlikely that Henry II would have fallen for her charms and Richard, who was never too fussy, found it convenient to claim that she was damaged goods. The Alice affair had long become an embarrassment to all parties and this poor princess must have suffered deplorably. It would be nice to think that her husband was kind and considerate to her.

When Philip and Richard met and disposed of Alice, they still had to negotiate the outstanding matters of the return to Philip of the Vexin and Gisors. As in most of these parleys decisions were deferred, usually with irritation on both sides. Richard was not slow in pointing out that Philip had seized many of his estates during the period of his imprisonment. Other items on their agenda included the betrothal of Arthur of Brittany's sister (another Eleanor) to Philip's son, Louis, but this never came to pass.

Military operations during 1195 were low key but Richard was extremely active in reinforcing and rebuilding his many castles and frontier-zone defences. With the potential and imminent loss of the Vexin looming, Richard become aware of a considerable gap in his lines of defence. He remembered from his youth, when he wandered freely in Normandy and Aquitaine whilst hunting or fighting, the remarkable and strategically based interconnecting rocks on dominating heights situated on a bend of the River

353

Seine. This place was just above the pretty town of Les Andelys with existing fortifications within the walls. Richard, with his splendid eye for country and its military opportunities, immediately started plans for the most powerful fortress in Christendom. This place would lour over the upper reaches of the Seine and could be threatening to Paris itself, the capital of the Capetian kingdom. It would provide an impenetrable barrier to any invasion by Philip.

Richard had been bred in powerful castles throughout his realms from an early age, and had studied the massive constructions in Palestine which had been derived both from Saracen experience and crusader abilities. It might have been possible that he had seen the great Krak des Chevaliers in Syria but he would, in any case, have known of its plans and impregnable defences. The King threw himself into the planning of his new project with gusto and work started in earnest almost immediately. This involved much infrastructure work such as re-routing streams, digging ditches, throwing up walls, palisades and moats, building internal and interconnecting paths and constructing road access. Richard made frequent site visits to supervise progress and make the modifications which were inevitably required as the work progressed. Above all, he visited to galvanise activity and ensure his deadlines for completion were met. His life had a new focus and his step took on a new spring. Philip soon became aware of what was happening and was enraged.

Richard and Berengaria spent Christmas 1195 at Poitiers. Richard was now spending more time caring for his soul than he had ever done in the past. He had had the fright of his life following his severe illness during the spring and he was now a regular attendant at Mass. During the Christmas season he made substantial donations for charitable purposes and was much disturbed by the suffering of those unfortunates who had been seriously distressed by recent severe famines. It is probable that this new-found interest in matters spiritual was prompted by Berengaria.

There is one account in a lighter vein from this time recounted by Fulk de Neuilly when Richard was warned by a zealous preacher to marry at once his three most shameless daughters. The King responded sharply that this was a lie as it was well known that he had no daughters. The preacher replied, 'I do not lie for thou hast three most shameless daughters whose names are Pride, Avarice and Sensuality.'

'Give ear,' retorted Richard 'and bear witness. I give my daughter Pride to the Knights Templar; my daughter Avarice to the Cistercians; and my daughter Sensuality to the prelates of the Church.'

During 1195 Richard reinstated many of the estates that he had impounded from John following his disgraceful behaviour during his absence from England. The County of Mortain, the Earldom of Gloucester, the Honour of Eye and an annual pension of 8,000 pounds were restored to him.

In January 1196 the Treaty of Louviers was confirmed and this involved the return of the Vexin to Philip. The immense defence works in the Vexin, constructed over many decades and protecting the Norman capital of Rouen would now be exposed to depredations by the French. The preparatory work at Les Andelys, which was now called Chateau Gaillard (or the Saucy or Petulant Castle), would combat this problem and the farsightedness of Richard was an additional irritant to the devious French King who began to realise that he was being outmanoeuvred yet again by his adversary.

In a petulant rage Philip sneered at the works being thrown up with such speed and efficiency saying, 'Even if the walls were made of solid iron yet would I take them.'

Richard's response was sharp and to the point: 'By the throat of God, even if the walls were made of butter, yet would I hold them.'

Philip of France had given much encouragement to extending and developing Paris from the tiny, overcrowded and inconvenient city that it had been. The outskirts expanded dramatically and it was rapidly becoming a real centre for the French nation. A major setback occurred during the winter of 1196 which saw the most fearsome and terrifying flooding in the upper reaches of the Seine which caused considerable damage to wider Paris and its environs. Philip thought that this must be a visitation from God and retreated to higher ground with his entourage.

The chronicler William of Newburgh recorded three occasions when the sky went so red that it seemed to be on fire and caused much consternation. These phenomena are now believed to be the Aurora Borealis.

Other phenomena occurred. William of Newburgh also

355

reported that he saw a double sun from which he correctly foretold war between Richard and Philip.

In April Richard decided that he needed a greater involvement with his nephew, the ten-year-old Arthur of Brittany. At this time it was considered that Arthur was his putative heir and neither Eleanor nor the King had much opinion of his mother, the widow of his late younger brother Geoffrey, Count of Brittany. There was some dragging of feet so Richard marched into the county only to find that the birds had flown to Paris, where Philip announced that he was taking on full responsibility for Arthur's upbringing from now on. Richard was furious and the long-term results of this move were not to be happy ones for the unfortunate Arthur.

Prince John now became involved in the hostilities and took Gamaches in Ponthieu. On 19 May he seized Beauvais and captured its intensely belligerent and warlike bishop who was a cousin of Philip of France. This remarkable success reinstated him into favour with Richard and went a considerable way towards eliminating his treachery and lack of support during Richard's period of imprisonment. With a rare flair of ability, John also gave much needed support to his deputy in Ireland who was having a considerable disagreement with the Archbishop of Dublin. These activities were regarded as a mark of real gratitude following his financial rehabilitation during the previous year.

In October 1196, Richard's widowed sister, Joanna, she who was offered as a bride to their half-brother Saladin, was wed in Rouen to Count Raymond of Toulouse. Richard and Berengaria were present. It seems probable that Eleanor would have attended this felicitous family ceremony although it is not recorded in the annals. Eleanor had for many years regarded Raymond as an usurper, but was by now reconciled to her new son-in-law's position. The marriage was not to be a happy and blissful one as Raymond had already had three wives and had already been excommunicated for a bigamous marriage some years earlier. This bigamous bride, who was a rare beauty, was unceremoniously incarcerated in an austere nunnery later on. Raymond also maintained a lively harem, so Joanna was faced with more problems than she should have been. But Richard got on well with her new husband and he needed his active support.

The year 1197 saw a number of developments. Chateau

356

Gaillard was completed in record time and Richard now used it as his advance headquarters. He enjoyed sitting there, poised over the French King and waiting to pounce at the first opportune moment. The advanced methods of construction with curvilinear and concentric walls giving such excellent fields of fire with no concealment for attacking forces were far in advance of any contemporary plans. The internal and interconnecting roads and bridges gave a superb advantage to the defenders who were able to redeploy speedily in response to any change in direction of attack from below. The approaches were hazardous and the deep ditches were masterly deterrents. The views dominated the surrounding countryside and gave ample warning of danger from any direction. The site was chosen with a brilliant knowledge of control of communications. Richard was rightly proud of this, his masterpiece.

Hubert, Archbishop of Canterbury and the able administrator of England, nearly died but fortunately recovered fully. William Longchamp, the paedophilic and loathed Bishop of Ely, did die. Do we read anything into the close friendship between the King and this prelate?

The spring saw a resumption of hostilities. Richard destroyed the castle at St Valery and devastated the adjoining countryside. He also seized a number of supply ships. As always Richard needed money to finance his military expenditure and he had to put pressure on Hubert to squeeze yet more contributions from his English kingdom. The tax collection system in England was far more efficient and effective than in Normandy and Hubert was able to respond. Both the 'saintly' Bishop Hugh of Lincoln and Bishop Herbert of Salisbury dug their toes in and objected. The financial resources of the Plantagenets were much greater than those of the Capets and this was a commanding advantage to them in the incessant wars that continued.

That spring, the English countryside was inundated with torrential rain which caused much distress, dismay and damage.

Philip certainly had some successes as he took Aumale and forced Richard to retreat from Arras, but Richard devastated huge areas of countryside, seizing much booty. He also continued to recover many areas that had been so perniciously seized by Philip during his absence abroad. Richard's diplomacy also neutralised several of Philip's traditional allies and others switched their active allegiance to the Plantagenet cause. Richard was steadily getting the upper hand and all these things forced Philip to sue for a truce.

In September 1197, Emperor Henry of Germany died and this released Richard from the oaths extracted from him under duress at the end of his imprisonment. The succession in Germany was now obscure with many contenders for the throne. This would take many months to resolve and the two warring kings in France would be watching the outcome with much nervousness.

Richard's expenditure continued to soar and his need for funds was becoming embarrassing. The truce that had been negotiated on military grounds by Philip was just as important for the English King from the financial point of view, but being the astute commander that he was he was not going to reveal his weakness to his adversary. He was beginning to get the upper hand and a further campaign might tip the balance finally towards him.

Richard spent Christmas in his capital of Rouen with Berengaria.

* * *

During the winter of 1198 Hubert of Canterbury summoned a council at Oxford to address the matter of further funding as well as reinforcements for the French campaigns. Both the barons and the bishops were asked to provide 300 knights for a year at their expense. The senior bishop, Richard of London, gave his support and commended all those present to concur. Hugh of Lincoln took some time to consider his position and then refused to give any support, saying that he would prefer to retire from his bishopric and return to his native land. Hubert was furious and asked Herbert of Salisbury for his view, and he gave his unqualified support to his brother of Lincoln. Hubert angrily dismissed the council and sent messengers to the King with the dire news.

Richard became exceedingly angry and gave instructions for all the possessions of the recalcitrant bishops to be confiscated. Salisbury went to the King and was roundly rebuked before capitulating. He achieved Richard's forgiveness only by buying his estates back from the King for a large sum of money. The power and reputation of Hugh of Lincoln was such that nobody dared implement the King's orders. The exchequer officials were rebuffed and withdrew in discomfort.

Hugh then travelled to Les Andelys to see Richard who initially refused to admit him to his presence. Hugh pressed himself into the royal presence and Richard still rejected his advance and turned his face away. Hugh took him by the lapels and shook him, demanding a kiss of peace. Still the King refused and again Hugh shook him to the terror and trepidation of the bystanders. Richard was, like all Plantagenets, prone to violent rages. A third time the King was vigorously shaken, this time by his cloak and Hugh said, 'You owe me this kiss as I have come a long way for it.' To the surprise of all, the King relented and gave him the kiss of peace with a smile.

Bishop Hugh gave the King a good account of his stand against him. He argued that he had been misrepresented in the archbishop's letters and that he had always been utterly loyal and truthful in the best interests of his King. Hugh then returned to the matters that he had raised the year before and questioned whether Richard's morals had really taken a turn for the better. He also asked whether the King's appointments were always in the best interests of his realm and the Church or whether the King might not accept unwarranted payments for preferments and take too little account of merit. Hugh reminded Richard that he was speaking to him as his spiritual father. The King's reply denied many of these accusations but publicly praised Hugh for his honour, bravery, honesty and, above all, holiness and wished that others would profit by his example. It is not clear whether Bishop Hugh ever did fulfil his obligations to provide material support for Richard's cause, but they parted in amity and mutual respect.

Eleanor's old friend, the aged Pope Celestine, died at a ripe old age. He could have given more support to the Plantagenet problems than he did, but he was relatively powerless against Emperor Henry and, at his age, was coasting towards a quieter and less controversial life. His successor was elected on 9 January and enthroned as Pope Innocent III on 21 February. He was to play a crucial and vital role in the years to come. Innocent was a far more formidable occupant of the throne of St Peter.

On 8 May Chateau Gaillard was drenched in a heavy shower of what seemed like blood which was taken by many to be an ominous sign.

Otto of Germany, a nephew of Richard, seized Aachen on 10 July, married his seven-year-old bride on the following day and on the day after was crowned Emperor of Germany. Richard now had a most valuable ally but Philip was mortified at this development. The power struggle in France was steadily and inexorably moving towards the English King's advantage.

Count Baldwin of Flanders laid siege to St Omer in early September and surrendered a few days later. Richard invaded the French King's lands on 27 September and took the castles of Courcelles, Burriz and Sirefontaine. Philip advanced from Mantes with a strong force intending to support Courcelles, which unknown to him had already fallen. Richard counter-attacked and routed the French, seizing many prisoners and much booty. He pursued them and broke the bridge at Gisors before the French could escape, before taking the town. Richard was delighted to relate that the fleeing Philip fell into this stream and for refreshment on a hot and dusty day had to drink river water.

The new Pope started to flex his muscles and demanded the immediate release of the brigandly Bishop of Beauvais who had been captured by John earlier and who was a valuable prisoner. Richard dismissed the Pope's legate, telling him to remind Innocent that papal intervention when he had been imprisoned, despite the safeguards of the Truce of God, had been worse than useless. Eleanor realised that Innocent was not a man to be crossed and could become a most dangerous adversary. She bribed the bishop's gaolers to let him escape, gave this dreadful prelate asylum in her own domains and let it be known that Richard had graciously acceded to the Pope's request.

Although Richard was not a king to be crossed lightly, his mother's support and advice were always acceptable, sooner if not later. Other affairs were looming. Richard was obviously not now likely to beget an heir and John's marriage was also barren, although he had strewn a number of bastards around in his time, so was obviously fertile. Neither John nor Eleanor were fond of Isabella, but her estates and wealth were an important factor in the scheme of things. The couple's transparent incompatibility was becoming a matter of increasing concern. In the autumn of 1198, John became more active in supporting his brother's military activities. He burnt Neufbourg and captured a number of French knights.

On 21 December Richard issued a confirmation charter to Flaxley Abbey reciting many of the clauses given by Henry II with some important additions and clarifications. This confirmed his continuing and close interest in the Abbey and its activities.

* * *

The Welsh Marches still continued, from time to time, to flare into insurgency. During the period of the anarchy, fifty years earlier, the Earls Robert and Milo had made sure that this back door to the realm was secured and Milo's Welsh wife, Sybilla, continued to keep all her contacts in good repair. Her grandson, William de Braose, had nearly wrecked any remaining goodwill when he slaughtered many of the Welsh chieftains and their entourage on the joint Christmas Day feasting in 1175. Since then de Braose had struggled to maintain order but during 1198 his forces were enticed into a desperate battle at Painscastle in the Welsh foothills. After some vicissitudes and a timely reinforcement, the better armed and mounted Normans were able to rout the Welsh, capturing much booty. De Braose had been moving towards more important assignments and was becoming a valuable member of the King's entourage. In 1192 he was Sheriff of Herefordshire, in 1195 he joined Richard in his court in Normandy and in 1196 he became Justice of Staffordshire. During the following year he secured Barnstaple and Totnes in Devon from an insurrection. Earl Milo had been an uncle to Rosamond and therefore through his mother, Milo's daughter, he was a cousin once removed to the late King's mistress and a second cousin to Geoffrey Plantagenet and William Longspee. The interrelationships of the leading families and the friendships between them all were all important in the wider families of the time and the rewards for service were valuable. Sometimes relations could become strained or even dire, as William de Braose was to discover later on.

Another emerging knight and lawyer was beginning to gain prominence, not to mention immense wealth. William Brewer had come to Richard's notice in the mid-1180s and became Sheriff of Devon in 1187. In 1189 he became one of the investigating lawyers instructed to report on the Geoffrey Plantagenet problem when he first became Archbishop of York. In 1191 he became justiciar instead of William Longchamp. By 1198 he had

361

become Lord of Somborne in Hampshire and, in addition to Devon had acquired the shrievalties of Oxford, Buckingham, Berkshire, Nottingham and Derbyshire. To assuage his conscience and to insure his future in the afterlife he founded the Abbeys of Torre (in what is now Torquay) and Dunkerswell, both in Devonshire, and Mottisfont in Hampshire. His daughter, Graecia, married William de Braose's son Reginald, thus cementing yet another family connection. Both de Braose and Brewer were close to Richard and, in due course, close to John.

* * *

William Longspee's activities since the release of Richard are obscure but he must have been involved in vital and invaluable matters, since in 1198 Richard rewarded him with the hand of Ela, the only child and heiress of William D'Evereux, second Earl of Salisbury. Ela's grandfather, Patrick, the first earl, was one of the heroes of the early part of Henry II's reign and was slain by Guy de Lusignan in 1167 when Eleanor and her escort fell into an ambush. Ela, by virtue of her impeccable family background and parentage, and her huge wealth, was the prime catch in England and she was in the wardship of the King. It was a compliment of the highest order for William Longspee to have been accorded this supreme honour and it was a matter of love and respect to Rosamond's memory. At the same time William succeeded in his own right as Earl of Salisbury. It seems probable that at the time of their marriage Ela was only ten years old.

Richard also had to tackle the recalcitrance of his other half-brother, Geoffrey of York, who had now been in Rome for two years. Both Geoffrey and the canons of York were summoned by the King to meet in Normandy with the intention of instructing them to heal their differences and make peace. These events could only have started to take place early in 1198. Geoffrey arrived first and was given full restitution but was then dispatched back to Rome on 'the King's business and his own'. The canons then appeared and were able to negotiate with Richard that this restoration would not take place until Geoffrey returned from Rome. Geoffrey then returned and they all met at Les Andelys, but, needless to say, an agreement did not materialise. Geoffrey then returned to Rome to lay his case before the new Pope who supported Geoffrey and remonstrated with Richard to make further

362

moves for a reconciliation. Geoffrey would not accept any conditions unless ratified by the Pope. Innocent insisted upon Geoffrey's restoration without any conditions and threatened that unless this was now implemented he would interdict firstly the province of York and subsequently the whole kingdom of England. By the time that this papal letter arrived in the spring of 1199, Richard was dead. The affair of York now had to be tackled in the next reign. It is not unreasonable to assume that there was not only a meeting of minds between Innocent and Geoffrey, but, had anything untoward happened to Innocent, that Geoffrey could well have been a candidate for the papal throne. Richard's power and connections would then have become quite overwhelming.

It would have been apposite if Geoffrey had officiated at William and Ela's wedding in a family party consisting of Richard, Berengaria, John and Eleanor, but history is silent on this matter.

During that year, two of Eleanor's daughters from the time of her marriage to Louis VII died: Alice and Marie. Eleanor was particularly close to Marie who was so much a part of her court life in Poitiers during her years of estrangement from Henry and before her imprisonment. It may be that Marie may have been conceived during Eleanor's torrid parting from Ayub, before she returned to France after the Second Crusade. This would go some way towards explaining her attachment to Marie. Richard spent Christmas at Domfront.

1199 was to be a crucial year for the Plantagenet dynasty. On 13 January Richard and Philip met on the River Seine just below the brooding Chateau Gaillard. Richard upstaged Philip adroitly by staying in his river vessel whilst the French King was stranded on the river bank. Philip had few grounds for negotiation as Richard had now recovered all his territories stolen by the French King and had impregnable defences against any incursions. He had returned the Vexin as he was under an obligation so to do. He had rounded off some of his borders. Philip had to concede defeat and they signed a five-year truce with each side keeping what they now held. The French King retired duly mortified and full of rancour.

But before the two kings parted, Philip was able to plant a viper in Richard's bosom. He told him that John had approached him and requested an alliance against the English King. Although

John had behaved with remarkable and consistent propriety since Richard's return from Germany, this was so much in character that Richard believed the story. John swore that it was an entire fabrication but Richard seized some of his possessions as a token for good behaviour. John considered it to be wiser for the time being to visit his nephew, Arthur of Brittany, but this withdrawal was thought to be suspicious.

Richard's coffers were always nigh on empty if not often bare. One of his greatest strengths had always been his vastly superior financial resources and he now needed to replenish these as soon as possible. A rumour reached him that a huge cache of gold had been dug up in a field near to the small castle of Chalus. This hoard had been sequestrated by Achard, lord of Chalus, who in turn was obligated to surrender half to his overlord, Count Adhemar of Limoges.

This was too good an opportunity to miss. Chalus Castle was lightly defended and to one of Richard's ability and experience easy to subdue. Richard's advisers warned him that the story was uncorroborated and probably untrue. But Richard took his leading commander, Mercadier, and a strong force to seize the stronghold with its treasures. Philip of Cognac, Richard's young bastard son, accompanied his father's force to gain experience.

On 4 March Richard arrived and proceeded to undermine the walls. Just over three weeks later, on a quiet spring evening, Richard and Mercadier rode out to reconnoitre the walls, preparatory to the planning of the imminent assault. Unwisely, Richard was virtually unprotected and when a defending arbalister, one Bertram, loosed a well-aimed arrow the King was wounded in the upper arm.

In extraordinary pain he returned to their quarters where Mercadier tried to extract the deeply embedded shaft. In trying to wrench it out he contrived to break the wooden shaft leaving the arrowhead even more deeply in the wound. By now the King was in agony and urgent measures were becoming necessary. Mercadier finally and brutally managed to extract the arrowhead, causing far more flesh damage and immense suffering to Richard. Within two days the wound suppurated, festered and rapidly became gangrenous with blood poisoning setting in.

Whilst all this was happening, the assault started and the castle soon surrendered. The King ordered that all the defenders be hanged save Bertram whose fate was expected to be even more dire.

It was now apparent that the King was dying and an urgent message was sent to Eleanor to come at once. As always in a crisis she rose to the occasion: she sent a message of warning to Berengaria and summoned John, who was still unwisely extending his visit to Arthur, to return at once and secure the royal treasure in store at Chinon. She then travelled faster than the wind to reach Chalus which was over a hundred miles away to arrive at Richard's bedside on 6 April, only just in time to see him alive.

Meanwhile, Bertram was summoned to Richard's bedside and the King asked him, 'What have I done to you that you have killed me?'

'Sire,' replied Bertram boldly, 'you slew my father and my two brothers with your own hand, and you now intend to kill me. Take any revenge that you may think fit, for I will readily endure the greatest torments that you can devise, so long as you have met your end, having inflicted evils so many and so great upon the world.'

Richard was so moved and impressed by the archer's speech that he forgave him and ordered him to be released and given a hundred English shillings. Sadly there was not to be a happy ending for Bertram. After Richard's death, Mercadier had Bertram re-arrested, flayed him alive and then had him hanged. It is alleged that Mercadier was encouraged to do this by Richard's sister Joanna, but this is impossible as she was nowhere near Chalus at this time. Philip of Cognac is more likely to have influenced this deed as any prospects that he might have expected had now evaporated. Later on, Philip, holding Count Adhemar of Limoges to blame for his father's death, sought him out and murdered him.

* * *

Philip of Cognac only appears once again in history in 1201 when he sold his lordship in England to King John. He then disappears from all annals. It is not unreasonable to assume that he may have been liquidated on John's orders. There is yet another uncanny coincidence in this story. My headmaster, he who evacuated his school to Flaxley

Abbey in 1940 and hence introduced the author as a young boy to that magical place, had as his most unusual Christian name 'Adhemar'!

* * *

Richard died on the evening of 6 April 1199. He was only forty-one years old. Probably at the instigation of Eleanor, he nominated John to the throne. The matter of the succession was fraught with difficulty. In primogeniture terms, Arthur was the successor since his father was an elder brother of John. But Arthur was still just a child and much under the influence of both his tiresome mother and Philip of France who had arrogated to himself the upbringing of this princeling. The infighting started straightaway.

But first Richard had to be buried. His body was taken by barge to Fontevraud. Bishop Hugh of Lincoln was *en route* for a visit to Rome, no doubt to put his views on Geoffrey's problems to the Pope. He was intercepted and immediately changed his plans and went to Beaufort near Fontevraud to give consolation to the distraught Berengaria. He was then asked to conduct the funeral which he was glad to do. Richard was duly interred with appropriate ceremony at the foot of his father, as he had requested. His heart was sent to Rouen and his brain and intestines to Chalus. The two queens led the mourners and a large number of robed bishops, abbots and clergy, including the papal cardinal legate, were present.

* * *

Thus passed away the King of England in the prime of his life. Richard had recovered all that had been squandered so recklessly and was poised to consolidate and perhaps to expand. History has summed him up in a multitude of ways. He has been called 'a bad son, a bad brother and a bad king'. He was remarkably well educated and could speak Latin and write verse both in French and Provençal. He was a brilliant and innovative soldier and an inspiring leader of men. He chose his subordinates well and allowed them to get on with their jobs without interference. He was not, by inclination, an administrator or involved in the niceties of the law or justice, but during his reign calmness and sense prevailed in England and his French possessions. His diplomacy was remarkably successful and he kept all his alliances in good working repair and order. He was poised, by the time of his death, to surround his deadly and crafty enemy, Philip of France, with close support from Germany and Flanders. He was loyal to all his extensive family connections including, above all, those from Rosamond's relations.

He was extraordinarily generous and forgiving, although occasionally a 'noble savage' and brutal when it was considered necessary. Surprisingly he was not called 'the Lionheart' in his lifetime. This most apposite accolade was accorded to him first in a thirteenth-century French romance repeated in the English story of the fourteenth century. The legend is alleged to come from a story that he seized the heart out of the breast of a living lion.

His restlessness may well have led to a premature downfall. His death was caused by an indescribably foolhardy escapade which left a trail of disaster.

From now on the Plantagenet presence in France inexorably diminished. If Richard had continued to live and prosper the whole of history might have been astonishingly different. Richard was a much underrated king who was cut off in the prime of his life and success.

16

As instructed by Eleanor, John hurried to Chinon to take possession of the treasury, an essential prerequisite to consolidating his claim to the throne. He arrived on 14 April and then hurried on to Fontevraud and demanded immediate access to the crypt where his brother now lay buried at the feet of his father. The Abbess had forbidden anyone to enter but John was not to be forbidden and battered on the door in rage. Bishop Hugh persuaded him to desist from this unseemly behaviour at this distressing time, but promised to approach the Abbess for special leave for him to enter. This was conceded by her, and the Bishop escorted the Prince down.

Bishop Hugh regarded the marriage of Henry and Eleanor as adulterous and refused to give his support to John's accession since he could not be regarded as legitimate. John attended Mass on the following Sunday which was Easter Day but, as usual, refused to receive the sacrament. Bishop Hugh preached an inordinately long sermon which irritated John, who sent three messages for the Bishop to bring his homily to an immediate conclusion as he was famished. After the service Hugh showed the King a Last Judgement relief with the righteous ascending into heaven but John expressed a strong preference to join the damned descending into purgatory.

Support for John's accession was by no means universal. Arthur had a better claim and Philip of France immediately recognised his succession to the Angevin empire. Constance, Arthur's mother, had by now married a third husband who was a vassal of Eleanor and his territory would now become a centre of disaffection. Arthur marched on Angers which surrendered with no resistance. Maine and Touraine now declared for Arthur.

Eleanor was furious and instructed an immediate counter-attack on Angers which was mercilessly sacked. Arthur and Constance only just managed to escape and fled to join Philip near Le Mans. John now demanded the surrender of Le Mans which was contemptuously refused. John then retreated to Normandy and Philip entered Le Mans in triumph and Arthur swore fealty to him.

The English advisers were also not unanimous. William Marshal, the ageing agent for the King in England, was in Normandy when the dire news of Richard's death reached him. He immediately went to Hubert Walter of Canterbury who was staying nearby. They conferred in sorrow and distress with William opting for John and the archbishop for Arthur. They agreed with many reservations that Arthur would not be the best option and John with all his faults was the better choice.

'You may come to regret this decision more than any other that you have made William,' said Walter.

'Perhaps,' replied the honest William, 'but I believe it to be the best.'

Eleanor had now outlived all but three of her children. The apple of her eye was now no more, but Eleanor was not allowing herself to be immersed in sorrow and grief. Life was still for living, her energy was still prodigious and her matriarchal influence undimmed. Her choice of succession was quite clear and she had persuaded Richard to nominate the last of her brood to inherit the Plantagenet dynasty and she galvanised herself yet again, at the ripe old age of seventy-eight, into action to see that this was fulfilled. John may have been full of character defects but he was by far the most intelligent of her sons and when he could bestir himself into action was very effective. Arthur was a lightweight. Eleanor had always recognised quality when she saw it and backed her judgement when the choices were sparse.

John was duly invested as Duke of Normandy in Rouen by Walter of Coutances on 25 April. He behaved disgracefully by laughing and chattering to those around him during the ceremony and carelessly dropped his ducal lance at a critical moment.

John then marched upon Le Mans to punish that city for its earlier lack of cooperation and courtesy. Philip and Arthur made a tactical withdrawal to Paris so John wreaked his vengeance upon Le Mans' defences and citizens.

369

Eleanor now embarked upon a lengthy tour of her domains with a view to consolidating her hold on her possessions. On 29 April she was in Loudon. On 4 May she was in Poitiers where she confirmed a charter to the monastery of St John and on the next day travelled to Niort where she was joined by her daughter, Joanna, who was heavily pregnant. Joanna was in desperate straits, having a husband who was behaving despicably and having been involved in defending a revolt in Cassee. She had escaped from a disaster and needed support. Eleanor sent her, for solace, comfort and medical treatment, to the nuns at Fontevraud.

Eleanor now went to Andilly, La Rochelle, Oleron, Rochefort, St Jean d'Angely and then to Saintes. Everywhere she went she heard petitions, disputes, rendered justice and corrected wrongs. She issued charters, made grants, confirmed positions of authority in her towns and cities and generally improved the good order of affairs. She demanded renewed oaths of allegiance from her vassals and rewarded many with largesse. She also paid particular attention to religious foundations and charitable causes, re-issuing charters and regularising the affairs of abbeys and convents. It was an incredible journey which produced a period of stability and prosperity.

Eleanor was now confident that she had consolidated her control over Aquitaine and decided, in June, break off from her trip to return to Tours and meet Philip. She renewed her fealty to him for her possessions and they exchanged the kiss of peace. Philip realised that Eleanor had outmanoeuvred him and that he would be most unwise to go onto the offensive for the time being. Thus it was that Eleanor discouraged the French King from his tactics of openly supporting Arthur who was not invited to the meeting.

Eleanor then continued her royal progress by returning to Bordeaux for three days and started her return journey northwards, visiting Soulac and Royan and stopping for a few days at her haven at Fontevraud before arriving at Rouen on 30 July to meet John. This most remarkable woman had covered over a thousand miles in three months. Allowing for the several days that she spent at (at least) thirteen of her important cities, she must have averaged about twenty miles a day on horseback. An amazing feat for a lady of seventy-eight.

Whilst his mother was making her royal progress, John returned very briefly to England to be crowned at Westminster on 27 May, again refusing communion. He made a pilgrimage to the shrine of St Thomas at Canterbury, travelled to Bury St Edmunds and spent Whitsun at Northampton, before returning to France on 19 June. He now became immersed in his divorce from Isabella, who had not been crowned queen, on the grounds of consanguinity. They were far too closely related and it is surprising that they were permitted to marry in the first place.

Children were now desperately needed for the tenuous succession. By the end of August John's marriage was finally annulled and he now put his mind towards finding a suitable bride. The Pope was much incensed by this decision and it has been suggested that John fraudulently obtained a papal sanction in support of his petition.

Meanwhile Geoffrey Plantagenet having achieved the full support of the Pope over his reinstatement in his York archdiocese, returned from Rome and had a most friendly and cordial meeting with his half-brother on 22 June in Rouen. All now looked set for an amicable return for Geoffrey but Hubert Walter immediately interfered with the support of the chief justiciar of England. John was persuaded not to allow Geoffrey to travel on his own but only in the company of the King. So Geoffrey had to continue kicking his heels in France for an indeterminate time and his seething continued to build up.

Poor Joanna was now at death's door at Fontevraud. She was heavily pregnant and demanded that she be veiled as a nun immediately. This caused consternation as she was a married woman and about to give birth and her request was outside canonical law. The Abbess was summoned to give the necessary dispensation but was far away and not available. Joanna's life was rapidly ebbing away, so Hubert Walter, Archbishop of Canterbury, being at Rouen, was persuaded to come. He too tried to divert Joanna from her wish but failed. Hubert was duly impressed by Joanna's fervour and demeanour, so waived the rules and veiled her in the order of nuns just before she died. Minutes afterwards a son was born, cut from her lifeless body, who survived long enough to be baptised with the name of Richard.

Eleanor now formally announced, in September, that John was to be her heir to her Aquitainean possessions, as she was entitled to do. Philip of France was again outmanoeuvred as Eleanor had given due homage and he was faced with a potentially powerful adversary when John succeeded.

There is now some divergence in the interplay of contacts between Arthur, Philip and John. One source states that Arthur came to John and promised him his support and collaboration. John unwisely rejected this and dismissed Arthur from his presence, who then fled to Philip where he was welcomed. Another source states that a rift had occurred between Philip and Arthur over the garrisoning of certain castles and that Arthur left Paris to return to Brittany. Philip was much annoyed as this occurred at about the same time that he was having a dispute with the Pope over his own matrimonial problems. It is quite probable that both these sources are right since no dates are given. The first episode could have taken place in the autumn of 1199 and the second in the following year.

However, John did make a truce with Philip on 24 June 1199, until 16 August – a few weeks only. There followed a parley near Le Goulet. John was in a position to refuse any concessions and warfare broke out with minor successes on each side with some commanders switching sides. In September, Arthur and his mother were delivered into the custody of John. Arthur was warned that his uncle would imprison him so he and his mother managed to escape during the night of 22 September and flee to Paris.

John and Philip made a further truce in October and discussions were resumed at Les Andelys on 3 January 1200 when the latter was far more conciliatory. Philip negotiated a marriage agreement between his son, Louis, and one of John's Castilean nieces. These were two suitable daughters of Eleanor's sole surviving daughter, also Eleanor, who had been happily married for many years to the King of Castile. John made a number of concessions to Philip in honour of this agreement which opened him to considerable opprobrium for being so unnecessarily generous. So it was that, in the middle of the winter, the indefatigable Eleanor of Aquitaine set off for Spain to bring her choice of granddaughter back to the Capetian marriage bed.

Eleanor's journey was not without excitement as she was ambushed yet again by a de Lusignan. It will be recalled that in 1168 Guy de Lusignan tried to do the same thing but then the

Queen was fortunate to escape. Guy subsequently became King of Jerusalem. This time it was Hugh, who had achieved some distinction in the Third Crusade and had been a friend of Richard, but the de Lusignans were always troublesome vassals of Eleanor and Hugh needed some valuable concessions before he would release the Queen. Eleanor had more important matters to attend to so, on this occasion, she acceded to the blackmail.

Eleanor crossed the Pyrenees in the January snows and proceeded at her usual rapid pace through Navarre reaching either Toledo or Burgos by the end of that month. Now she rested for two months and re-established relations with her youngest and sole surviving daughter, Eleanor, whom she had not seen for thirty years. There were two daughters who were both eminently eligible. Both were beautiful, talented and distinguished. Normally the elder, Urraca, should have been the choice, but Eleanor chose the younger, Blanche, for no other reason than the elder's name was harsh and had an alien sound whereas Blanche was euphonious and more likely to be acceptable to the French court. Eleanor, as always, chose well and she returned after Easter with this girl.

Their adventures were not over though. Richard's loyal and able chief of staff, Mercadier, was to be in command of Eleanor's escort from Bordeaux. Whilst Eleanor was resting there, Mercadier was involved in an unseemly brawl and was murdered. This loss was to have serious military repercussions in the years to come. Following the fatigues of her journey and coupled with this disaster, Eleanor now took her time to return home and she was unable to go further than Fontevraud, where she stayed. From there the Archbishop of Bordeaux delivered Blanche to Philip on 23 May and she was married very shortly afterwards. Both Blanche and another of her sisters were to become mothers of saints.

During Eleanor's journey to Castile, John returned to England in February 1200 accompanied by his prickly brother, Geoffrey who was, by now, in a fever of impatience to put the affairs of his archdiocese in order. There was a solemn reconciliation between Geoffrey and his chapter in Westminster and he went north to put affairs in order. It was not long before he had upset the entire chapter with his abrupt and arrogant manner and it would not be long before an eruption would take place.

John had come north too to impose various taxes to pay for his commitments towards Blanche's dowry and these demands were to add to Geoffrey's problems. John then retired to France in April and concluded his treaty with Philip at Le Goulet on 22 May. It now appeared that there was a real chance of peace and stability.

John dispatched an emissary to the King of Portugal to solicit one of his daughters in marriage but this came to naught. In June or July John paid a visit to Ralph de Lusignan to ratify his mother's agreement with his brother, Hugh, made during the winter. Among those present in the castle was the extremely beautiful and vivacious Isabella d'Angouleme, a thirteen-year-old who was betrothed to Hugh. John was completely smitten with this lovely damsel and the girl's parents recognised that a marriage with a king was far more advantageous than a union with an obscure count. John persuaded the unsuspecting Hugh to undertake a mission on his behalf in England and the coast was clear. Isabella's parents connived quite disgracefully and the girl was spirited home upon some specious pretext where she was told of her fate to her mortification. Within days she was dispatched to Bordeaux where, on 24 August she and John were married, Philip of France having given his cynical consent, realising that the de Lusignans would never accept this insult to their family. It was ironic that 24 August was the very date that had been originally intended for Isabella's marriage to Hugh.

As predicted the enmity engendered by the de Lusignans festered and John would rue the day of his virtual kidnapping of this valuable bride.

John pleasured his new bride to his own entire satisfaction but seemingly not to hers and took a more than leisurely time taking her northwards. Eleanor had not considered Isabella as a prospective wife but she approved of her and was particularly pleased that she was a lively and talented Poitevin from her own province. Isabella was endowed by her mother-in-law with Niort and Saintes as a token of her love and esteem. The Queen's health thereupon improved. On the 8 October Isabella was crowned Queen in Westminster Abbey by Hubert Walter.

John visited the saintly Bishop Hugh on his deathbed and was covered in contrition, so much so that he acted as a pallbearer at the funeral. The Bishop was buried on 23 October at Lincoln.

John dedicated land and arranged for a Cistercian monastery to be built in the Bishop's honour at Beaulieu in Hampshire.

John was determined to extract taxes from both archdioceses to fulfil his obligations to Philip of France. Geoffrey had been suspended earlier in the year for failing to contribute. His estates had been impounded so he responded by excommunicating all those who had seized his property. In October John and Geoffrey were again reconciled and the latter's estates released from bondage. The terms of the peace were soon in dispute and by January 1201 the King, whilst staying with one of these excommunicants, arrested many of Geoffrey's servants. In March 1201 a further compromise was achieved.

These two brothers were so often so close that it could be an interesting speculation as to whether Geoffrey might have been better employed as John's military commander in Normandy. Geoffrey had been a brilliant soldier during the latter part of his father's reign. He was not noted for saintly qualities and was patently misemployed, even underemployed, as an Archbishop. Geoffrey was an excellent administrator and organiser and with the catastrophic death of Mercadier, John needed a commander of immense energy and capability. But all this did not come to pass and so the inspirational opportunity went by default.

Early in 1201 John confiscated part of the Lusignan estates and Hugh promptly complained to Philip of France. Philip was still in dispute with the Pope so sat on the fence but there was little doubt where his sympathies lay. In the spring of 1201, Eleanor was again not at all well and was becoming more and more disturbed by the machinations in France so summoned a loyal vassal from Thouars to restore some order in Poitou. Thouars responded sensibly and creditably and Eleanor's health again improved. The Queen summoned Arthur to appear before her at Fontevraud and made him promise to preserve peace in Aquitaine and Poitou. Next Eleanor impressed upon John that he needed to return to France quickly, and he did so in June.

An amicable meeting took place between the two kings at Les Andelys and immediately afterwards John visited Philip in Paris on 1 July and was well entertained.

Richard's queen, Berengaria, had been left with very restricted means. John had inherited most of his brother's estates, or had sequestered them. Berengaria had initially moved to Fontevraud and remained close to Eleanor but later moved to Le Mans, living in seclusion and retirement. From time to time John made provision for her so that she was able to live in decent style as befitted a dowager queen of England. On occasions she stayed with John and Isabella and in particular she was with them at Chinon during the summer of 1201. In 1200 she founded a Cistercian monastery near Le Mans. It is recorded that she was in England in 1216 and in 1220 travelled to Canterbury when Becket's bones were moved to a new shrine. In 1230 she took the veil to become a nun and died some few years afterwards, much beloved for her good works and care of the poor and destitute. She was never considered for remarriage.

In 1201 John was plundering the Lusignan properties who were now in open and active revolt. In July Philip's mistress died and the main obstacle to Philip's reconciliation with the Pope over his marital complications was removed. It was now an ominous moment for the Plantagenets as Philip was still a scheming and vindictive adversary.

During the autumn Philip was ready to flex his muscles and summoned John to Paris to account for his behaviour to the de Lusignans. John prevaricated and postponed meeting after meeting. On 25 March 1202 the two kings met at Le Goulet and Philip ordered John to give up all his Continental possessions, excluding only Normandy, to Arthur. On 28 April Philip again summoned his vassal John, in his capacity as Duke of Normandy but not as King of England, to appear before him to respond for his treatment of the de Lusignans. John's response was to offer to meet him on the borders of Normandy. Philip duly appeared with strong forces but John was absent because his troops from England had not arrived. The loss of Mercadier, who was a past master at raising reinforcements, was now becoming crucial and no adequate substitute had been found. Philip declared the truce broken and went into the attack. He bypassed the castles and camped at Arques just outside Rouen which was now under real threat. He then wheeled back and seized the bypassed castles of Gournay and Aumale. Arques was now under siege as well. This was no longer fighting with the Lionheart – it was knocking over the tyro with contempt.

Philip then knighted Arthur in the field and provided him with 200 mounted cavalry and told him to take possession of his lands.

Arthur joined up with the de Lusignans and their forces. John was faced with fighting on two fronts. Eleanor was outraged at these developments and realised that she was exposed to capture as the abbey of Fontevraud was not secure in this sort of warfare. Her value as a hostage was immeasurable so with a small escort she moved rapidly towards the safety of Poitiers. She stopped overnight in a small but decayed castle at Mirebeau, which was also inadequately provisioned. Unfortunately for her, Arthur, who was at Tours, learnt of her plans and set off in hot pursuit to capture his grandmother and use her, as she feared, as a pawn in his scheme. He battered down the town gate and occupied the town. Eleanor and her escort retreated to the keep. Eleanor, aware of what was about to happen, sent two messengers to both John and the castellan of Chinon to come at once and rescue her.

Arthur suggested that Eleanor should surrender and that he would honour her intended movements. Eleanor played for time and replied with much asperity that she was appalled at his behaviour and that he should immediately withdraw and attack any other of the plentiful castles in the vicinity. She also objected to the presence of Poitevins in his forces who owed her loyalty as liegemen.

John, displaying a rare sense of urgency, covered eighty miles in forty-eight hours and combined with the Chinon garrison to make a formidable force, arriving on 1 August. The Chinon castellan, William des Roches, made a stipulation that Arthur should not be executed and John gave his solemn word. Surprise was on their side. Arthur and the de Lusignans were totally unprepared. They had left the town gates open for supplies to arrive. They were breakfasting on roast pigeon and their troops were undressed and without their arms. It was a complete rout. William de Braose personally took Arthur prisoner and the two de Lusignans were also captured with 250 knights and all their accoutrements. It was a stunning victory and proof that John could be a good warrior when he put his mind to it. Philip was devastated and withdrew from all his conquests, pausing only to sack Tours, then returned to Paris where he spent the rest of the year.

The aftermath of this was a disaster for John. He treated his prisoners abominably and incarcerated them in chains in his dungeons starving twenty-two of them to death in Corfe Castle, and overall lost the opportunity for substantial ransoms. He did release the de Lusignans for a considerable sum and a solemn undertaking that they would not bear arms against him again. Arthur's sister, Eleanor, was imprisoned for forty years and moved from castle to castle in the West Country albeit that she was treated with some courtesy. Eleanor implored John that Arthur should be treated honourably and this he promised to do. In the autumn of 1202, William des Roches recaptured Angers.

The fate of Arthur has been shrouded in mystery and has been regarded as a major blot on the life of John. John instructed his chamberlain, Hubert de Burgh, to imprison Arthur in the formidable fortress at Falaise where his custodians included William de Braose. There was considerable nervousness amongst all the nobles both in Normandy and France regarding this prince's safety. In particular William des Roches and William de Braose had extracted from John vows for Arthur's well-being which had been reinforced by Eleanor. Arthur was now fifteen years old and a precocious lad who had been encouraged by Philip of France to regard himself as the rightful heir to his Uncle Richard. Indeed until Richard was on his deathbed Arthur had been his nominated successor. But since John's succession things had changed and Arthur was under a feudal oath to his uncle and had now committed treason. John was well aware however that Arthur commanded huge support from his own county of Brittany as well as receiving continuous and pernicious encouragement from Philip. Arthur was not entirely trustworthy and whatever he pledged would almost certainly not be fulfilled.

From October 1202 William des Roches and many others became so disturbed that they withdrew their allegiance from John. John had now lost one of his best commanders who was privy to the King's plans and military thinking. The de Lusignans who had been released now reneged on their pledges of neutrality. In December Philip of France demanded to be reassured but John prevaricated. Isabella, John's new wife, had been nearly captured but managed to escape. John descended into sloth, neglecting all his duties.

In January Arthur was presented with an ultimatum by John at Falaise. He demanded that Arthur separate himself from the French King and give irrevocable fealty to himself. Arthur would enjoy his domains of Brittany and other honours were included to sweeten the pill. It was generally considered that John was not only generous but exceedingly affable to his nephew. Arthur's reply was an utter and contemptuous rejection and a demand that the King give up all that he had inherited from Richard: the kingdom of England, Poitou, Aquitaine and Maine. Arthur left nothing out of his catalogue. John was shattered by his nephew's arrogance and greed and this was all the more bizarre considering that the lad was his prisoner.

John took council and the advice given was that he would have no peace whilst Arthur lived or could be active and disruptive. The suggestion of maiming and blinding him and removing his manhood so as to render him incapable of rule was considered. John ordered three servitors to perform these deeds but when they confronted Arthur he piteously begged them not to proceed. Two of them desisted and Hubert having just learnt of the plan intervened and stopped the outrage. Hubert hoped that John would reconsider once his anger had cooled and then spread the rumour that Arthur had died in captivity. But John was not so easily moved and the rumour was not believed.

In February Arthur was moved to Rouen. The seneschal of Rouen, Robert, was now made responsible for Arthur and rewarded with two castles in Westmorland. On 2 April 1203 William de Braose formally relinquished his guardianship of Arthur saying, 'I know not what fate awaits your nephew, whose faithful guardian I have been. I return him to your hands in good health and *sound in all his members*. Put him, I pray you, in some other happier custody.'

The whereabouts of Arthur from now on is obscure. William de Braose was patron of the Cistercian monastery of Margam in South Wales and the annals of that monastery report that 'after dinner on 3 April, John, drunk with wine and possessed of the Devil, slew Arthur with his own hand and tying a heavy stone to the body, cast it into the Seine. It was brought up by fishermen, identified and secretly buried... In Notre-Dame des Pres, a priory of Bec.'

After Easter (the Sunday being 7 April) Arthur was never seen again. On 16 April, John wrote an extant letter addressed to his mother and others in her entourage at Poitiers telling her that a monk, one John, 'will apprise you of our situation. Put faith in him respecting those things whereof he will inform you.' This letter, signed by John, was witnessed by William de Braose.

Eleanor had been at Poitiers since her escape from Mirebeau and was no longer in a fit state to return to her beloved Fontevraud. She was eighty-one and her exertions over the past few years had taken their toll. Her visit to Castile in the midwinter of 1202 had been most debilitating and she had never fully recovered. Her flight from Fontevraud to Mirebeau the previous summer had been exhausting and she was appalled at the rapid disintegration of her French possessions that she and Henry II had consolidated and which Richard had recovered so brilliantly. Now John had squandered so much through disgraceful treatment of so many who had been loyal for so long to the Plantagenets. She listened to the dire news from Falaise and knew that worse was to come. From now on she could only wait for the dread summons from the Reaper, calling her to final account with her Maker.

Philip moved with precision. On 9 April William des Roches took Beaufort so very near Fontevraud. Then Philip took Saumur, but found resistance at Chinon so deviated northwards through Maine and the Plantagenet heartland of Anjou. He seized with astonishing ease Sees, Conches, Le Mans (so beloved by Henry II), Falaise (William the Conqueror's great fortress), Domfront, Coutances, Bayeux, Lisieux, Caen and Avranches. The heart had been ripped out of the English Crown's proud possessions in France all through a total lack of defence. Henry and Richard must have been turning in their graves and Eleanor weeping at this dishonour.

John sent Hubert Walter, the great William Marshal and the Earl of Leicester to sue for a truce. But Philip was now on the crest of a wave and could extract much more juice from this lemon. His terms were completely unacceptable and had to be rejected. John's barons were forsaking him in droves.

It was Chateau Gaillard that Philip now really wanted. He was however not going to make any direct assault. He used his brains rather than his brawn. His sappers mined the outer works which controlled the moats. The breakwaters in the Seine controlling the river traffic were destroyed. Connecting paths and outer roads of the fortress were isolated and overlooked by embankments which Philip threw up. Now he harassed the citizens of

Les Andelys so that they besought the garrison commander to admit them into safety. Many of the garrison troops had wives, children and relations in the lower town and their morale and loyalty needed buttressing. Philip allowed these refugees easy access realising that 500 extra mouths would make quicker inroads into the reserve supplies held in the castle. Philip had time on his side and waited patiently as winter approached.

John scuttled about with no coherent plan. He changed his mind endlessly and infuriated his commanders who could get no decision or directive. When pressed he would boast, 'Let me alone. When the time comes, I will shortly recover all that I have lost.' These empty words reassured no one.

In December John fled ignominiously from Barfleur and landed at Portsmouth. He now made a show of visiting various centres trying in a desultory way to raise men and money to rescue his losses. But the English baronage and clergy had heard it all before and were in no mood to help him again. The rumours regarding Arthur were rampant and John's treatment of his prisoners, especially those incarcerated at Corfe, discredited him even further.

On 6 March 1204 the gallant castellan of Chateau Gaillard had no choice but to surrender. His supplies had now run out. The impregnable fortress had finally succumbed.

Eleanor's life then ebbed away. In her moments of lucidity, she reflected on her long life and all its vicissitudes. She remembered all her passions, all her children, all her successes and failures, all her virtues and vices and all those who loved her and who hated her. She smiled at the tender memories of her favourite son, the incomparable Richard, who had thrown his life away with such irresponsibility. She recalled how that trollop, Rosamond, had had so much more influence on John and how pernicious that had been. It is ironic that Henry died with a broken heart over John's perfidy. So too did Eleanor die, on 1 April 1204, from a broken heart over John's cruelty, stupidity and above all his disloyalty. There is doubt as to whether she died in Poitiers or whether her attendants were able to move her to Fontevraud as she had so dearly wished.

She was buried quietly with no pomp at Fontevraud in a fine tomb between Henry II and her most beloved son Richard the Lionheart.

*   *   *

Whatever one may say or think of Eleanor, she had a major influence on the twelfth century and on English and French development. Her blood coursed in the veins of every royal house in Europe. She was the great-grandmother of two saints. Was she a paragon? Did she destroy what she loved? Her passing went not with a bang but with a whimper. The Angevin line was descended from Fulques the Black who originated the family legend which says, 'From the devil they came to the devil they will go'. Both Henry II and Eleanor were descended from Fulques the Black so both equally shared the Plantagenet strain of demonic ancestry and neither had done much to redeem this satanic curse. It is perhaps unfortunate that this curse may have originated from the first wife of Fulques the Black, Elizabeth of Vendome, who was burnt as a witch in the year 1000. Henry and Eleanor were descended from the second wife, Hildegarde, who was not alleged to be demonic. Perhaps Fulques was infected by his first wife.

So the Tigress died leaving her indelible mark upon history.

382

EPILOGUE

King John and Queen Isabella

John was now on his own. He had never been close to Eleanor but since he was the last survivor of her brood of sons she had been the source of much sense and wisdom and gave him a valuable dimension and stability to his erratic life. He did not attend her funeral because he was too far away, in England, to get there in time.

During Lent 1204 peace overtures were made towards Philip, but the French King was in an unforgiving mood. For one thing his military successes were paying dividends and he had not yet finished. Secondly, Philip was aware that John had no heir and, if Arthur was still alive (and no one knew whether he was or not) then the Plantagenet succession would be under his powerful influence. If Arthur was dead, then Eleanor (Arthur's sister) would be the successor and Philip was in an even more powerful position to control her and her marriage to one of his choice. Thirdly, Philip was as certain as he could be that John had murdered his nephew and this was a heinous crime which invalidated John's right not only to the throne of England but also to his titles in France for which he owed fealty to the French King. Philip would only grant a truce on the condition that both Arthur and his sister were released to him alive. The net was closing in on John.

Philip attacked Falaise at Easter which soon surrendered. He then took Caen, Barfleur and Cherbourg. La Rochelle, Chinon and Loches gave stubborn resistance. Rouen, Verneuil and Arques bought a truce for forty days and sent a cry for help to John. John would give no assistance partly because he had no sources readily available and partly because he did not trust his allies. The three cities thereupon surrendered to Philip. Thus all Normandy had gone within weeks. John's indifference was remarkable and he was heard to boast, 'Let Philip go on; whatever he takes, I shall retake in a single day.'

In 1205 John made plans to assemble a strong army and a mighty fleet to invade France. Hubert, the Archbishop of Canterbury, and William Marshal both made powerful representations that this expedition would be doomed to failure mainly because John had been too late to react. John agreed to abort his invasion with much reluctance, although the French forces now on the coast of Normandy made some withdrawals for safety. On 23 June Chinon surrendered.

On 13 July the aged Hubert suddenly and unexpectedly died and extraordinary negotiations now started to take place concerning the election of his successor. These would soon escalate into a major confrontation. John was now bereft of another valuable and sensible adviser albeit that he seldom wished to listen to or act upon Hubert's words of wisdom and sense. John went to Canterbury to enforce his own candidate John de Grey, the Bishop of Norwich, for the archbishopric but the monks had already dispatched a deputation to Rome proposing their own sub-prior. John overturned this election. Pope Innocent III overturned both candidates and imposed his own selection, Stephen Langton. During 1206 both parties continued to quarrel and on 17 June 1207 the Pope consecrated Stephen in Rome as Archbishop. The Canterbury chapter had, by now, been persuaded to endorse the Pope's choice. The Pope instructed the Bishops of London, Ely and Worcester to resolve the impasse but they failed whereupon they fled to France. They were immediately followed by Geoffrey Plantagenet, Archbishop of York and the Bishops of Chester and Hereford. The Bishops of Rochester and Salisbury now found safety in Scotland. Meanwhile the Bishops of Durham, Lincoln and Chichester had died. This only left Winchester and Norwich who were loyal to the King and the latter had much to occupy him in Ireland. The Church in England was in dire straits and John seized as much of the revenues as he could lay his hands on.

In July 1206, John mounted his delayed invasion of France, having with some astute diplomacy, secured the support of some of his erstwhile vassals who were now disillusioned with the French King. He landed at La Rochelle and took Angers and Montauban and then ravaged Anjou, Nantes, Rennes and La Mee. Philip counter-attacked by laying waste the county of Thouars. A two-year truce was agreed from October and John returned to England having achieved limited success.

John's succession problems were eased during 1207 with the birth of Henry, the first of his legitimate children. It is curious that it should have taken the nubile Isabella no less than five years to produce a child for her lord and master. It was transparently obvious that the uxorious King could hardly keep his hands off her during these early years of their marriage.

In 1208 the King indicated that he would climb down on the ecclesiastical front, but when the Pope's deputation arrived he reneged and the kingdom was promptly placed under an interdict. Many clergy fled for safety in France.

John's relationship with Isabella deteriorated and she was imprisoned in Corfe Castle to cool her heels. It is probable that she was developing a roving eye and had learnt this from her faithless husband with whom no woman was safe. Despite this, she produced him a second son, Richard, in the following year, 1209.

In 1209 the row with the Church continued unabated and the bishops excommunicated John, which had no effect whatsoever upon his godless nature. John's need for money never ceased and the barons were becoming increasingly uneasy. Many fled the country. John responded by demanding hostages, imprisoning many, torturing and blinding others and putting several to death. In 1210 the King now turned to an easier target, the Jews, whom he treated with bestiality.

In that same year, he mounted a campaign against Ireland, the scene of his youthful failure during his father's reign, with the intention of subjugating the power and wealth of the Lacys who ran that country entirely independently from England. It was here that John achieved perhaps the only real military success of his reign. He then wished to wreak vengeance upon his erstwhile friend and supporter William de Braose who just managed to escape his clutches although his wife, Maud and eldest son were captured and incarcerated.

In the following year, 1211, John led a successful expedition into Wales with the assistance of William Longspee. There was a further inconclusive meeting with the papal legates but John was still feeling comfortable enough to raid the ecclesiastical coffers not only of the vacant sees but also the revenues accruing during the absence of most of the bishops.

In 1212 the Pope himself now excommunicated John and declared that his throne was forfeit. Philip of France was instructed to implement this decision and preparations were now made by him to invade but John's naval strength was superior to that of France. The barons in England who had been deprived of so many of their estates in France following the disasters of earlier years were now so dissatisfied that they were pressing for far more autonomy in their affairs in England.

The north Welsh King, Llewellyn, who had suffered reverses in the previous year, was preparing for a counter attack and achieved some success. John's illegitimate daughter by the so-called 'Queen Clementina' was married to Llewellyn and managed to send a warning to her father. John slew twenty-eight Welsh youths whom he was holding hostage as a reprisal. One of John's ablest ordained advisers, Geoffrey, the Bishop of Norwich, withdrew his services since he could not continue to serve an excommunicate and was unhappy over the King's behaviour. John imprisoned him at Bristol enclosing him in a leaden cope until he repented but the poor man soon died of starvation and deprivation in extreme misery.

In 1213 John was considering an invasion of France, but many of his nobles now invited Philip to take the throne of England. In May John made his submission to the Pope and the agreement was signed by Ascension Day. He accepted Stephen Langton as archbishop and agreed to make full restitution to all exiled bishops and clergy. He placed England under the Pope's direct suzerainty in the belief that Philip could not now invade and take the throne from a vassal of the Pope. A hermit, one Peter of Pomfret, had foretold that John would lose his crown by Ascension Day 1213 and there were many who believed him. John was much worried by Peter's prophecy and had imprisoned the hermit at Corfe. On the day after Ascension he caused the seer to be hanged for the flagrant inaccuracy of his forecast. There were many who considered that John ceased to be king when he became the Pope's subject and that Peter had been technically correct.

In 1214 the long awaited invasion of France took place. William Longspee led the forces to Flanders with an alliance of the German emperor, Otto, and the Counts of Boulogne, Holland and Flanders. John landed at La Rochelle and with Poitevin help achieved some initial successes taking Anjou, Angers and Nantes. All now seemed set fair for a much needed victory. Philip's son, Louis, advanced to relieve a siege at Roche-aux-Moins. John then realised that his Poitevin allies were about to desert him so he retired in haste and confusion to Rochelle whilst Louis recovered all that had been taken. Thus instead of a pincer movement being imposed upon the French King, the latter was now able to reinforce his northern armies with Louis' forces from the successful southern front. The critical battle of Bouvines took place on 27 July and Philip won a resounding victory taking many illustrious prisoners including the redoubtable Longspee. John's allies continued to desert in droves and Philip granted the English King a five-year truce in mid-September.

John returned to England in November to find that his nobles were not only disillusioned but verging on open rebellion. The promised success in France had been a disaster and the spoils and rewards were non-existent. The nobles demanded a charter similar to that granted by Henry I otherwise they would have no alternative but to resort to arms. Early in 1215 their mood hardened. John played for time and made many specious promises.

During the early part of that year, both sides made threatening moves and there were many who were desperately trying to conciliate. Finally on 15 June the parties met in the meadow of Runnymede and the King was forced to sign the historic Magna Carta, known throughout the world as the first charter to guard the liberties of all classes and above all to impose upon the King his own subjection to the law. This was a huge step forward in justice and human dignity. The immediate effect was far more limited and protected only the interests of the Church and the nobility.

John immediately regretted his submission and had a prolonged Plantagenet rage. The Pope was horrified at what had happened and directed that John's enemies should be immediately excommunicated. The warfare that the Charter was intended to avoid broke out soon afterwards.

In February 1216, Louis landed in England intending to depose

John. He reached London and took many castles in southern England. John was campaigning through the Midlands and the north. Louis was then excommunicated.

John established a base in Norfolk and decided to move into Lincolnshire to harry the Scots and plunder as much as he was able. He made an unwise decision to hurry across a causeway of the Wash and the tide came in faster than he anticipated. His baggage train and his treasure were all engulfed in the quicksand and lost. John took refuge in the abbey of Swineshead where he partook excessively of peaches or pears and too much new cider. He began to suffer from what seemed to be a nasty attack of dysentery which turned to a fever. He was moved to Sleaford and then to Newark but his condition deteriorated daily despite being bled. His illness lasted for a fortnight and he died in much pain on 19 October 1216. It is probable that the real cause of his death was peritonitis following a burst duodenal ulcer, a hazard of those days, the cure for which was not known. John's unpopularity was such that he was accused of dying as a consequence of gluttony but this is unlikely as he took so long to succumb with increasing pain and weakness. Other legends have suggested that he was poisoned by a monk at Swineshead to prevent him ravishing a nun who had taken his fancy.

John was buried in a fine tomb in Worcester Cathedral, probably because this was a relatively safe place for his burial. As he lay dying he had had time to nominate his nine-year-old son, Henry, as his successor.

*   *   *

When John was first married to Isabella, his lust knew no bounds but as the years went by he seems to have grown to loathe her, feelings which were heartily reciprocated. There is the most curious delay in the arrival of their first-born to be considered. John had had no less than seven (perhaps eight) illegitimate children before he came to the throne and he was always randy, but there is no record of later bastards. So he may have become infertile. At forty, he very badly needed an heir. There are three alternative scenarios. The first is the accepted historical explanation that, at long last, Isabella did her dynastic duty and conceived. Secondly he may have swallowed his pride and persuaded a suitable close associate to impregnate his wife. Isabella, having become increasingly disillusioned with her boorish husband, may have accepted this with more relish than John might have wished. The third alternative is that Isabella herself pre-empted this solution by taking unto herself a suitable lover and thus she was able to fulfil her dynastic duty. John was increasingly edgy and imprisoned her in 1209 in Bristol and again in December 1214. Isabella bore five children during John's reign: Henry and Richard were born in 1207 and 1209; Joan was born in 1210 and married King Alexander of Scotland and is buried at Tarrant Crawford in Dorset; Isabella was born in 1214 and Eleanor in 1215. It is also reported that Isabella took many lovers and that John reacted by hanging these gallants over her bed so that she could relish the sight of her erstwhile bedfellows swinging gently from the beams over her head. Matthew Paris writes that he was told by an eye-witness that 'Isabella turned into an evil-minded, adulterous and dangerous woman'. There is no record of who any of these gallants were, which has to cast some element of doubt on the story. But Matthew Paris' version makes sense: if Isabella did take unto herself a paramour, it did solve the Plantagenet succession. She was twenty-one years younger than her husband and married him when she was only fifteen.

After John's death Isabella travelled to Lusignan with the intention of negotiating a marriage between her erstwhile betrothed Hugh IX and her daughter Joan but promptly married him herself and bore him four sons. She seems to have reverted to being a dutiful and loyal wife. One source however suggests that she married Hugh X de Lusignan the son of Hugh IX who must have been some twenty or more years younger than she was. This seems most unlikely. Isabella died in 1246 and is buried at Fontevraud.

John is the most vilified king in English history. No subsequent king has ever been called John and the name is regarded as unlucky by royal families. It was certainly fortunate for England that John died suddenly when he did. He was a small, dark, thick-set man who suffered from periodic rages like his father, when he would fall to the ground, kicking, screaming and chewing the rushes. He was erratic in activity and when inertia overtook him nothing whatsoever was done. But when he put his mind to things he was excellent. He took much interest in administration and in legal affairs. But he was intrinsically untrustworthy and needlessly cruel and vicious. He had some longstanding friends including Longspee, William Brewer, William Marshal and Hubert de Burgh who stood by him at all times and he badly needed their support.

William de Braose and his family

At Richard's death, William was one of the ardent supporters for John's accession. They had all been youngsters together and had enjoyed many happy days at Flaxley under the benign influence of Rosamond to whom they were all devoted. But after William asked to be relieved of responsibility for Arthur's safety in 1202 some suspicion of disloyalty began to creep into the scheming mind of John. However, William and his family were powerful on the Welsh frontier and John needed the west of his kingdom to be guarded. William was rewarded with the castle of Limerick but failed to pay for this privilege and fell several years in arrears. John then put a distraint upon William's English estates and William later surrendered three castles to the King in compensation. In due course de Braose and his family fled to Ireland where they were harboured by the Lacys. The falling out between the families seems to have been financial and John was squeezing his barons excessively. John resorted to his usual tactic of demanding hostages as surety. William's tough wife, Maud, was having none of this. She was heard to comment that she did not trust John and knew all too well what he did to hostages, including poor little Arthur. The timings now becomes obscure since John did not invade Ireland until 1212, but William was under threat whilst in Wales in 1210 and managed to escape via Shoreham to France where he died soon afterwards.

Maud, and their eldest son, another William, were captured in Ireland by John and imprisoned in Corfe Castle. John devised a singularly unpleasant torture for these unfortunates. They were fed with a sheaf of wheat and a flitch of salty bacon and totally deprived of water. They died in agony within eleven days. Another source gives their prison as Windsor Castle.

William Brewer

Brewer was an up and coming lawyer who served Henry II, Richard and John with increasing authority and responsibility and with rewards commensurate. In 1206 he was a witness to the discreditable treaty of Thouars between Philip and John. He tried to mediate in the reconciliation between the King and Archbishop

Langton in 1209. In 1210 he was party to the extortion put upon the Church, especially the Cistercians, and was described as an evil councillor of the King. In 1212 he signed the treaty with the Count of Boulogne and signed the charter of submission between John and the Pope. Prior to the submission of the King at Runnymede he was a steadfast supporter of John. In the fighting in 1216 he was actively involved in the defence of the King's interest and assisted in the crowning of the child king, Henry III. He became a close councillor in his upbringing, but not regarded as a good influence.

In 1223 Henry was required to confirm the provisions of the Magna Carta and Brewer answered for the King: 'the liberties that you ask for ought not to be observed, for they were extorted by force'. Langton, the Archbishop, rebuked him angrily: 'William, if you loved the King, you would not disturb the peace of the kingdom'. Brewer gave way.

He acquired many huge estates and became extremely wealthy and was not only very loyal to John but gave him much support and advice. Brewer was one of those men who kept close to the powerbase, albeit misguidedly and was duly rewarded. He founded many abbeys to assuage his soul: Torre in 1196, Dunkerswell five years later, and Pilso, all these being in Devon, and Mottisfont in Hampshire in 1201. He married Beatrice de Valle by whom he had several sons and daughters one of whom was Graecia who married Reginald de Braose as his first wife. He died in 1226 and was buried in his abbey at Dunkerswell, allegedly having taken the garb of a monk.

Geoffrey Plantagenet

Geoffrey was last seen having endless rows with everyone and losing his friends when he was beginning to need them more and more. He had been reinstated by John in 1201 subject to recovery of his revenues sequestrated whilst the archbishop been abroad and a 'reinstatement fine' imposed by and payable to the King of 1,000 pounds.

In 1203, Geoffrey had not recovered his revenues and presumably was not able to pay the King. Disputes within the chapter aggravated his relationships. In 1204, John came to York to protect the chapter from their archbishop. In 1205 the Bishop of Durham petitioned the Pope to have the excommunication imposed by Geoffrey lifted. In January 1207 Geoffrey and John were reconciled but the truce only lasted for a few weeks as in February the King laid a tax on all clergy. Geoffrey then forbade the clergy to pay this imposition on pain of excommunication. The clergy were caught in a cleft stick. In despair, Geoffrey fled overseas for safety and all his revenues were again seized by John. Geoffrey appealed to the Pope who interfered energetically on behalf of the archbishop, placing an interdict upon the primacy of York but to no avail. Pope Innocent was always a friend and supporter of Geoffrey.

Nothing more was heard of Geoffrey until he died, probably in December 1212 and was buried in Notre-Dame-du-Parc a favourite place of his father, Henry II.

* * *

Geoffrey was at the zenith of his powers and influence during the last years of Henry II's reign. He was an excellent administrator and a fine soldier. His church career was disappointing primarily because he was in no way devout. He had an intractable self-will and his father's ungovernable temper but he was honest and much more use could have been made of his loyalty and ability. He was the only son who stood by his father through thick and thin. He had no diplomacy or deviousness. There was no breath of sexual scandal connected with him. As he got older, like all Plantagenets, he put on weight and was unable to pursue his sporting interests of riding and hunting. He died embittered, lonely and sad. His career is in so many ways similar to Becket. They both left complete dissension and confusion in their respective provinces. Pope Innocent had a great regard for him and had Geoffrey lived longer he might have been reinstated fully to York after the submission of John to the Pope in the following year.

Morgan de Bloet

Morgan was born early in the 1180s, being the son of Henry II and Nest de Bloet who was married to a knight from the North one Ralph de Bloet. Ralph and his wife agreed to bring Morgan up as one of their children and the King promised to look after the subsequent career of this lovechild. In 1201 Morgan became provost of Beverley, being then not much more than twenty years old. His more senior half brother, Geoffrey Plantagenet, eased this preferment through his influence, no doubt remembering that their mutual father had helped him considerably during his own youth.

In 1213 Morgan was proposed by the Durham chapter to become their bishop-elect, one of the most senior positions in the northern province. By this time Geoffrey was dead and the Church in England was under an interdict from the much stricter Pope Innocent III. Innocent was not at all sympathetic to promoting another royal bastard and would not countenance giving his support. Morgan made a hasty visit to Rome to petition the Pope who became more understanding and cooperative as well as much moved by Morgan's presentation of his case and the earnestness of the man. Innocent gave his informal and conditional support. If Morgan was to swear that his parents were really Ralph and Nest de Bloet then he would be confirmed as Prince Bishop of Durham. But if he continued to insist that he was the son of Henry II then his bastardy precluded this promotion.

Poor Morgan felt that life really was unfair. Geoffrey had become Bishop of Lincoln when he was twenty and then Archbishop of York. Morgan was far more devout and zealous in his priestly duties than his senior half-brother. Morgan took the decision that he was unable to deny his father and would have to renounce his application. He presumably ended his days as a worthy provost of Beverley.

William Marshal, Earl of Pembroke

One of the most steadfast and honourable nobles of those times, he had rescued Eleanor as a young knight when she was ambushed. He was then a mentor to the young King but failed to achieve any success in stiffening that youth's character. William was a leading jouster in tournaments and was able to amass some considerable wealth in prize money. Henry II received his staunch support and when Richard came the throne, William promised him his devotion. Similarly, when John succeeded this was transferred to give that prince the benefit of his experience and wisdom.

Richard I rewarded him with the hand of Isabel de Clare, the wealthiest heiress in the kingdom. By this time William was a grizzled veteran and his bride a mere slip of a girl. Theirs was an idyllic love-match blessed with five sons and five daughters. On the death of John, William became one of the trusty guardians of the nine-year-old King. The kingdom was rent asunder with the rebellion of the barons, the so-called ignominious climbdown and signing of the Magna Carta and the invasion of England by the French King's son, Louis, who was intent on seizing the throne. Marshal steered a firm and courageous course through all these stormy and treacherous currents, and the kingdom settled down to a necessary stability.

William died in 1219. Each of his five sons succeeded to the earldom in turn and although four of them were married, none of them had any issue so the title became extinct on the death of the fifth son who was the sixth Earl of Pembroke. All five daughters married well, the youngest being Eve who had wed William de Braose.

It was said by William: 'By God's word, if all abandoned the King, do you know what I would do? I would carry him on my shoulders step by step, from island to island, from country to country, and I would not fail him, not even by begging my bread.'

Nowhere in the annals of the English kingdom have so many sovereigns been served by a man of such honour, loyalty, integrity, wisdom and ability.

William Longspee, Earl of Salisbury

It is difficult to get the full measure of Longspee and the contribution that he made to this period. He seems to have been a late developer although he was an exact contemporary of Richard. The first mention of him is in 1188 when he was granted Appleby in Lincolnshire. Next he was given the hand of the heiress Ela, Countess of Salisbury, by his brother Richard which was an immense honour and reward at the same time being created Earl of Salisbury. William Longspee seems to have kept himself firmly in the shadow of firstly Richard and then

John, and been utterly loyal. He must have accompanied Richard on the Third Crusade and had his own adventures whilst returning. Once Richard resumed control of his kingdom, Longspee was at his side but seldom mentioned. He received Pontorson castle in Normandy in 1198 and exchanged it a year or two later, then received it back in 1203. But these are all secondary matters. He became Sheriff of Wiltshire in 1200 and was involved in diplomatic matters with John in 1201 and 1202. He received other responsibilities and the important castle of Eye in Suffolk. All these are rewards but we do not know what he was doing. John had a good sense of administration and it seems that Longspee implemented many of these important changes and undertook many diplomatic negotiations. He commanded the Welsh and Irish campaigns in 1210 and 1212. During John's period of excommunication Longspee was accounted as one of the King's evil counsellors. In 1213 he defeated Philip of France in a naval engagement at Damme thus causing the French King to abandon an intended invasion of England. In 1214 he was captured by Philip after the battle of Bouvines and exchanged with a prisoner of equal rank. In 1215 Longspee supported the King in his resistance to the Magna Carta. In 1216 he seems to have deserted the King's cause and supported the invasion by Louis of France, probably because he regarded John's cause as hopeless – a rare act of disobedience. However, after the death of John he switched back to supporting the cause of his nephew, the boy king Henry III.

He was much involved over the next two years in the fighting both military and naval, and in various peace initiatives. He is then reputed to have taken the Cross for the Fourth Crusade and become involved in the abortive siege of Damietta in Egypt although the evidence for this is inconclusive.

In 1220 he was present when the foundation stone of the new cathedral of Salisbury was laid by a papal legate. In 1222 he was involved in a campaign in Wales and in 1224 he became Sheriff of Hampshire. In 1225 he was involved in a campaign in Gascony.

During the voyage back after Longspee's Gascon campaign the vessel hit violent and stormy weather and they all feared for their lives – so much so that William jettisoned his apparel and money overboard. It is not recorded whether this was to appease the gods of the deep or to lighten his load prior to jumping. As they were poised to abandon ship they observed 'a mighty taper of wax, burning bright at the prow of the ship, and a beautiful woman standing by it, who preserved it from wind and rain, so that it gave a clear and bright lustre. Upon sight of which heavenly vision both himself and the mariners concluded of their future security, but everyone there being ignorant of what this vision might portend except the earl; he however attributed it to the benignity of the blessed virgin'. Thus was saved William Longspee by this divine intervention.

However, a rumour reached England that the earl was lost so Hubert de Burgh, with the agreement of the King, provided a suitor, his nephew as it happened, for the widowed Ela, who rejected this premature and far too hasty suggestion with much indignation. The baked meats for the wake had not been cooked let alone grown cold. Upon Longspee's return he reproached de Burgh with much wrath and was persuaded to join the King and Hubert at Marlborough for a feast of reconciliation. William fell sick immediately afterwards and it was considered that Hubert tried to poison him. However it is more likely that the earl still suffered from the privations of his voyage which led to his decline. Longspee just managed to return to his castle at Salisbury where his health continued to decline quickly. He received absolution from Richard le Poore, the Bishop of Sarum and died on 7 March 1226. He was buried in a fine tomb in his new cathedral which is still in excellent condition.

When Longspee's tomb in Salisbury Cathedral was opened some years ago, the desiccated carcass of a rat was discovered in his skull which contained evidence of arsenic. This may well indicate that Longspee was in fact poisoned as legend has suggested. *This rat is exhibited as a somewhat macabre relic in the Salisbury museum and proves to be most popular with children.*

Longspee was constant in his support for both John and his nephew Henry III, other than a brief aberration just before John's death. His involvement in the affairs of state became much more intense and useful without ever reaching the major contributions made by the great William Marshal and the increasingly powerful Hubert de Burgh. He was devoted to Henry III and was closely and much involved in the boy's upbringing. If there is a probable candidate for a nobleman of quality to be the real father of Henry it has to be William Longspee. William had

Henry II's blood line in his veins and was more royal than anyone else in the kingdom. He could therefore continue the Plantagenet succession more appropriately than anyone else. Whether it was with John's connivance it cannot be known but Isabella chose well, and kept her attachment to herself. William was a much nicer man than his brother and there was more to life than rampant sex with John. And how ironic that Rosamond's bloodline should be preferred in the Plantagenet succession from Henry III rather than that from Eleanor. *Later on Edward I married Eleanor of Castile who was descended from Eleanor, so the genes of the Tigress re-emerge in the royal succession.*

There are two other vignettes in William Longspee's life. Some time during the early years of Henry's reign he had a court case against Roger of Akeny concerning property. There had been a continuing needle between this son of Hikenai and William. It is almost certain that Geoffrey Plantagenet had been generous and helpful to this man during his life and after his death Roger became more aggressive. After all, Hikenai had been Geoffrey's wet nurse and been most useful in those very early days when Henry II and Rosamond needed to keep their relationship quiet. Hikenai had been with child at about the same time. When Roger was born (at about the same time as Geoffrey) he had been in the Clifford household and his mother had been well looked after. Roger had always been resentful that his mother's rewards had not been considerably larger and more generous and had always been antagonistic to William and the affair had been simmering for many years. The outcome of this case is not known.

The young boy king was very close to his uncle William and was always asking for stories about his youth and upbringing and wanting to know more of Rosamond and Eleanor as well as his fabled uncle Richard. William told him about their exploits on the Third Crusade and the famous Saracen leader, Saladin. He also related stories of his grandmother Eleanor who went on the Second Crusade with her Amazon army of women to combat the infidel and win Jerusalem back for the Christians. He told him about the maze at Everswell and the extended family's happy school holidays at Flaxley and the hunting and games that they had all had there as children under Rosamond's relaxed regime. He mentioned the swords made at the arsenal at Flaxley and how

397

he got his name of Longspee from wielding and fighting with his huge swords made there.

One day Henry told his uncle that he wished to rebuild his grandfather's fortified castle at Clarendon and make it into a pleasure palace for relaxation, hunting and sport and to include many mementoes and memorabilia to commemorate the exploits of his immediate ancestors for posterity to admire.

'I should like you, Uncle William, to guide me and tell me all. Let us tell the truth and leave some riddles for those who come after us to enjoy and work out.'

Thus it was that Henry designed an Antioch chamber in memory of his grandmother's honourable uncle Raymond from Antioch and Eleanor's fulfilling visit there. Then he floored that chamber with locally-made tiles depicting his uncles Richard and Saladin back to back in memory of the two most famous sons of his redoubtable grandmother as an enigmatic tribute to her and her exploits.

Longspee's eldest son, also William Longspee, married Maud Clifford his second cousin once removed. Maud was a great-granddaughter of Rosamond's father, Walter Clifford.

* * *

Why should Clarendon Palace include an Antioch chamber and these tiles? It is an astonishing irrelevance otherwise. It has to be said that it is unlikely that William Longspee would cast any doubts about the identity of Henry III's father! Some historians claim that this disproves the elder Longspee's descent from Rosamond as this later marriage was within the forbidden bands of consanguinity and there is no record of a dispensation. Whilst this is a valid argument, there were plenty of such marriages at that time, including both of Eleanor's trips to the altar.

Flaxley Abbey until 1377

Isabella produced their first born son at Gloucester Castle in 1207 whilst John relaxed at Flaxley by indulging in several days' hunting. Following William Longspee's stunning naval victory over the French in 1212, he and John attended a thanksgiving service at Flaxley after which they presented a sword made at Flaxley and blessed by Abbot Richard to the mayor and burgesses of Newnham which is now in Gloucester Museum. The King much preferred the hunting at Flaxley to that of Windsor.

On 13 November 1213 John deviated from Monmouth to St Briavels and thence to Flaxley before arriving at Gloucester. It was here that he hanged two of Isabella's lovers over her bed. John, after he had enjoyed his hunting, maintained an establishment at Staure farm in Westbury for those court ladies that took his fancy. The records of Flaxley show frequent hunting visits by John during the years of 1212, 1213 and 1214 but he was an expensive guest and mean in his offers for reimbursement so the Abbey suffered financially during this period.

In 1216 the King also wrote from Lincoln to remind his constable that breeding boars from the forest should not be disturbed by wandering cattle from Flaxley, an astonishing attention to detail but one that must have been near to his heart. It seems to indicate that the King was intending to visit Flaxley during that winter but he died suddenly before he could come.

John had very many happy memories of Flaxley during his life and his visits were frequent and enjoyable. He assigned the manor of Newnham to Humphrey de Bohun whose father had married one of Milo's daughters.

The slight and puny Henry III was crowned at Gloucester Abbey where his mother had been imprisoned and just released. The ceremony was modest and undertaken by the papal legate, Gallo, in the presence of William Marshal and three bishops. The royal regalia had just been lost in the Wash so Isabella removed a gold bangle from her wrist with which the boy King was crowned.

King Henry became the second largest benefactor to Flaxley although managing to impoverish the Abbey by the time he died fifty-six years later. Royal letters were frequent, reinforcing the Abbey's rights and privileges despite frequent and vexatious harassments from the constable of St Briavels. In 1218 Henry III granted Newnham manor to William Longspee. There are numerous legal documents issued during Henry III's reign extending the rights and privileges of Flaxley and its abbot. A confirmatory charter of 1227 was issued.

The King made many hunting trips to the forests and stayed in the king's lodgings there with his extensive retinues. He also demanded from time to time huge quantities of game to be sent from Flaxley to Windsor and Westminster. One such request asked for fifty-eight harts, 615 bucks and 512 wild boar, involving fifty-four journeys.

By 1227 the King achieved his majority and dismissed his regent, Hubert de Burgh, and the younger William Marshal who had succeeded his famous father. Henry III now fell under the pernicious influence of Isabella who had married Hugh de Lusignan and who had surrounded herself by Poitevin advisers whose advice was of doubtful quality. William Longspee had died in 1226 followed shortly afterwards by Stephen Langton, the archbishop, both of whom had been sensible and stabilising influences.

Arising from these troubles a major insurrection took place in the West Country. Richard Marshal and Hubert were being pursued and harried. At one time they sought refuge at Tintern Abbey but they had to leave and fled to Flaxley which had stronger defences. A siege started on 20 February 1234 followed by an order from the King dated 6 March demanding that those against him and in refuge should surrender and stand trial. The peace of the Vale of Castiard was being rudely shattered and efforts to starve the Abbey and its refugees were ineffectual. The powerful Cistercian movement was horrified at this appalling development and the King was heading for excommunication. Hugh Foliot, Bishop of Hereford, and a kinsman of an earlier bishop, Gilbert, was asked to mediate. His first foray was unsuccessful. A King's writ was issued on 15 March instructing the Sheriff of Gloucester to keep watch on Flaxley. Presumably this was to prevent supplies from entering the besieged Abbey. The bishop returned to negotiate further and found that the sheriff had been aggressive. Events were getting ugly. It was obvious that there was a back gate through which supplies were passing easily. Bishop Foliot persuaded the King to back down and allow his erstwhile, trusted and loyal advisers a peaceful release and to repair the unauthorised damage to the Abbey and its stables.

The King was having problems on a wider scale as his Poitevins were excessively profligate and the nobility were threatening serious trouble, but this episode at Flaxley was a flashpoint.

In 1258 Henry granted Flaxley 930 acres of prime woodland near Littledean. But his extravagant visits during his reign were no compensation for the increasing expenses of the Abbey. Sheriffs, nobles and justices with their huge retinues had abused the hospitality of abbeys which had led to financial crisis. At the time of Henry's death in 1272 the Abbey was obliged to mortgage itself to Jewish moneylenders.

When Edward I came to the throne he found the country had been virtually bankrupted by his profligate father. He set about restoring the finances everywhere and in particular those Church organisations who were in dire straits and impoverished. Edward instructed that no sheriff or minister should be allowed to be lodged at Flaxley without special royal licence. By 1277 the Abbey had rid itself of its burden to the moneylenders. There is no record of Edward I ever visiting the Abbey or hunting in its woods, but he saved it from impending disaster. In 1282 he also recognised the value of the forges and iron works of Flaxley and reinforced its military activity.

Edward II was a wastrel who abused the facilities that Flaxley and the king's lodgings offered. His favourites were allowed free reign and treated the abbot and the monks with scant respect and contempt. Hugh Despencer, a favourite, was even granted, by a royal charter of 1316 an extensive tranche of land for his use in perpetuity. Abbeys were acquisitors of land not providers of their property to dubious and pernicious friends of sovereigns with doubtful morals. Flaxley was now again in decline.

Edward III was a passionate hunter and made frequent visits. The King's famous military victories in France owed much of their success to the weapons tipped with Flaxley iron and the swords and shields wrought in the furnaces of the Vale. The foresters of Dean made their name by sapping and mining at the siege of Berwick and in return were given the perpetual freedom of mining in the Forest of Dean. In 1353 Edward refurbished the upper chamber of the king's lodging at his expense and put in a gothic window and modelled the room on the Jerusalem chamber of Westminster Abbey, so that it would be more becoming for the King to use.

The Flaxley finances were at last in good order, although Edward III was the last royal patron of Flaxley continuing a tradition lasting for 225 years. The iron works continued their activities until 1938 but became obsolete and run down during the later years.

401

After the death of Edward III no other sovereign took an interest in the Abbey or used the spacious and gracious king's lodgings to the west of the cloister garth. Neither did anyone use the hunting facilities of the Vale of Castiard. Flaxley went to sleep and the Cistercians reverted to their intensive pastoral activities.

On 4 February 1536 Abbot Thomas Ware surrendered the Abbey to Anthony Kingston the son of Sir William Kingston who represented the king's commissioners. Abbot Ware received Anthony graciously, offering him hot cider and handing over the keys inside the refectory door. Abbot Ware left accompanied by his nine remaining brethren singing the Nunc Dimittis. Ware went to live at Aston Rowant in Oxfordshire and died in 1545. Most of the dispossessed monks either accepted livings in the reformed church or were pensioned off with dignity.

Sir William was the man who arrested Cardinal Wolsey and supervised the execution of Queen Anne Boleyn. He received as his reward the grant of Flaxley Abbey on 26 March 1547 but died three years later being succeeded by his son Anthony. Sir Anthony was known as the 'terrible marshall' for crushing insurrections in the West Country. Sir Anthony turned his coat during Queen Mary's reign and was instructed to arrest and burn Bishop Hooper of Gloucester at the stake, which he did. Sir Anthony decided to turn his coat back again and with turbulent Welsh colleagues was ready to replace Mary with Elizabeth. He was arrested and sent to London to face trial. He had watched Bishop Hooper burn so, *en route*, drove his horse over a bridge at Wallingford and was drowned. The Kingston successors demolished the building of the Abbey and cloister and built themselves a fine new house at Littledean with the salvaged stone. The west wing, or the King's apartments used as the royal hunting lodge for so long, stays to this day largely in its original form.

The Boevey brothers, originally from Holland, acquired Flaxley Abbey from the Kingstons in 1647 as a residence for their widowed sister who lived there until her death in 1670. Her son Abraham Clarke succeeded. In 1685 William Boevey married Catharina Riches and the pair then inherited Flaxley. William died in 1692 and Catharina then lived in considerable style until her death in 1726. She appeared as the 'perverse widow' pursued by Sir Roger de Coverley in *The Spectator* published by Addison. She was much admired for her wit, intelligence, charity and liberality. She has a fine monument in Westminster Abbey. She took much interest in the iron works. During her time, about 1687, the non-juring Bishop Frampton of Gloucester had to escape persecution from James II and hid until it was safe in the secret room underneath the abbot's parlour.

After Catharina's death the Abbey passed to her relative Thomas Crawley-Boevey. In 1777 a disastrous fire destroyed the south wing of the cloisters, mercifully not touching the twelfth-century west wing. This part of the building was reconstructed under Anthony Keck in the Jacobean style and still stands today. In 1788 a vault was uncovered in the middle of the old chapter house, containing seven coffin lids presumably holding the remains of abbots. When the monks fled they had carefully hidden these remains. In 1784 the Crawley-Boeveys were created baronets and owned the Abbey until 1960 when Mr and Mrs Baden Watkins acquired the property. The Watkins family were much involved from the sixteenth century in iron ore and coal mines in the Forest of Dean and more recently owned engineering works in Coleford.

Abbot Ware must have removed in 1536 the Flaxley cartulary when he departed. Half of this came into the possession of Sir Thomas Bartholomew who died in 1872. In 1958 it was sold and acquired by the British Museum.

The twelfth-century buildings of Flaxley Abbey today

The present Abbey comprises an L-shaped building. The southern, and newer part, was rebuilt after a fire in 1777 and is in the Georgian style albeit with, to my eye anyway, some Jacobean influence and almost Dutch overtones. This may have been due to the then owners, the Crawley-Boeveys, being partly of Dutch origin.

My school lived in the west wing and this is what really matters. The main rooms are transparently miscalled today for reasons that I shall explain. The main ground floor room is the refectory, 65' long by 25' wide, built in 1150 and consists of five vaulted bays with simple groin ribs intersecting the diagonal vaulting. The ribs spring from plain corbels situated about 5' from the ground level. The walls vary in width from about 5' to 8.5', which incidentally make it warm in winter and cool in summer. There are three Gothick windows on the west side which are seventeenth century and probably due to repairs then needed and enlargements made for convenience. The floor paving is worn but largely original. On the east side is a fine thirteenth-century arch, originally an outside entrance but now leading to an impressive internal Jacobean staircase. There is a door leading to what was probably a monk's cell, perhaps used for punishment purposes. Next to this is the site of what was a pulpit (a later addition). At the north end were the necessaries – a delightfully expressive description of what they really were – more usually called the lavatorium, a slip of a room parallel to the main refectory and obviously containing the 'necessary' fitments. Baden Watkins suggests that this room is probably the finest twelfth-century unspoilt Cistercian building in existence and I would agree with him. And what an appropriate place to use as a school dining room! At the northern end a Victorian extension had been built and this was used by us as classrooms.

Upstairs there were several rooms that were part of the original structure over the refectory. I am certain these have been modified and altered over the years but not to any exceptional extent. Certainly I slept in one of these rooms as a dormitory and, undoubtedly, this was its original use. And who, may one ask, slept in these rooms all those centuries ago?

At the south end of the first floor corridor is the second gem in this building. The so-called Abbot's Guest Room running east-west, 40' long by 16' wide and 20' high has arched bracing ceiling timbers with double rows of cusped wind braces springing from the wall. At the west end is a large and handsome eighteenth-century replacement Gothic window in the original style. The ceiling is original and the twelfth-century craftsmen were subsequently transferred to Westminster Abbey and, in exactly the same style, and according to Philip Watkins, erected a ceiling in the Litlyngton Chamber off the western cloister. Baden however says that the duplicate roof was erected over the Westminster 'Jerusalem' chamber. However, neither of these statements can be proved as Henry III reconstructed Westminster Abbey entirely in the following century. The ceiling at Flaxley is of superb quality and is an integral part of a room used for those of the highest status – not just for the use of an obscure abbot and his guests who may have called at this seemingly out of the way abbey.

Of the Abbey church itself hardly a stone remains. The building was completely razed to the ground and the site is now the most attractive gardens to the newer house. The cloister bases, now part of a summerhouse are almost certainly original but are hardly higher than ground level.* There is the original well, with wellhead complete, which provided the entire water supply to the house until the 1960s.

Christmas Eve 1995

The Vale of Castiard in the weak evening sunshine of the winter's gloaming. Two harts come out of the Flaxley woods and are grazing by the stream. One of them raises its head and warily sniffs the air. It remains poised for flight. Suddenly the second also stops grazing.

The descendant of Milo, Henry, Eleanor and Rosamond is driving by.

---

*A blocked up doorway in the northern wing of the cloister is the sole remaining evidence of an original entrance to the Abbey.

AUTHOR'S NOTE

May 1940

The kindling of my involvement in this extraordinary story was really sparked in May 1940, when I was twelve years old. The Nazi hordes had, without any warning whatsoever, invaded the Low Countries. During the preceding few months of World War II the French were, so they thought, safely ensconced behind the impregnable Maginot Line. Sadly this stopped short of the French/Belgian border and within days the German tanks were sweeping round its edge through France, and the French promptly capitulated. Thus for the next four years most of Europe suffered under the jackboot of the German Army and its Gestapo.

My prep school was in Felixstowe and, in common with almost all other East Anglian schools was instructed, at only a very few days notice, to find safer accommodation elsewhere. Our headmaster was told to look in Gloucestershire. A place of sufficient size was found, a mutilated telegram had arrived giving incorrect information, no telephones were working and all we knew was that we should get to Gloucester station as soon as possible. A minuscule advance party departed and the rest followed the next day. I cannot now remember anything of that journey. We certainly would not have been allowed to go through London as it was likely to be bombed at any moment. We probably went by coach to perhaps Cambridge, train to Oxford, change to Didcot, change for Gloucester and then a coach with a packet of wartime sandwiches and the odd cup of tea *en route*. A very long day compensated for by having had no lessons for the time being.

Thus it was that I arrived with thirty other little boys in the gloaming of a long summer evening and saw for the very first time the magical outlines of the west wing of Flaxley Abbey.

To a boy steeped in the romance of history a whole new experience burst into flower. I was actually going to live, eat, sleep and work in a twelfth-century building which had hardly altered since it had been built. History, as it was then taught at prep schools and, for all I know, is still taught, does not tell you anything about what really happened and it certainly didn't tell us anything about Henry II and Rosamond and what they got up to and why. And to think that I now know that they first met here at Flaxley and it took me years to find that out.

In the 1940s the Abbey was owned by the Crawley-Boevey family who had been there since 1647.

Christmas Eve 1995

My wife, Sheila, and I were to spend Christmas at the Speech House in the Forest of Dean, a lovely Carolean house in the middle of the forest, once the Verderer's Court, the dining room of which is still the courtroom when so convened. I never go near Flaxley without making a detour and going down the road to Mitcheldean off the A48, the Gloucester to Chepstow road. We had a thermos of tea at the top of the drive and looked, as we have so often done, at the west front of the cloistral mediaeval building of the Abbey. The misty gloaming of that December evening in the evocative Vale of Castiard could be so full of ghosts and spirits of the past.

I am simply not built that way. But Sheila is.

That evening, as we settled in at the Speech House, we reopened Baden Watkins' book *The Story of Flaxley Abbey and the Cistercian Monks in the Forest of Dean*. We read that on Christmas Eve 852 years ago Milo, Earl of Hereford, a leading opposition leader to King Stephen, was murdered in that very place and his lifeless body was placed in a poor man's cart which slowly trundled its way over the muddy and rutted tracks back to the castle that he had built in Gloucester. A humble litter for his last journey in this world.

I have Forest of Dean ancestors. A great-great-great-grandfather, John Williams, was a freeminer who married Hester

407

Morgan from the Forest of Dean; their son, James, married Harriet Nayler, the youngest daughter of the governor of the Littledean Bridewell. From the Williams and Morgans I have pure Decanian bloodlines. Decanians are distinctly odd people and when I am in the forest my roots feel at home.

In a light moment Sheila asked me if I could find her a descent from the murdered Milo. I said that I would try. Genealogy is my hobby and it would be fun to see if we shared my love of Flaxley with her ancestral background.

Spring 1996

During the ensuing winter I struck not lead, not silver, but gold – pure gold.

Baden Watkins had bought Flaxley in 1961. Some say he paid £15,000 for it, others £21,000. It doesn't matter what he paid but he had to spend an arm and a leg to put the Abbey into good order and thereby hangs another tale. He was enthralled by Flaxley and his enthusiasm comes bubbling through in his book about the Abbey. However, the book is not the easiest read as his time sequence jumps around and he repeats himself as he leaps from year to year and back again and from century to century. An index is something he cannot be bothered with and he gives hardly any references. But he has done more homework than he may have been given credit for, although he has obfuscated so much in his telling of the story and has barely scratched the surface of the wider tale in his obsession for Flaxley.

There is a gem of a complex and multi-faceted story emanating from those involved with the Abbey which spreads throughout all the early Plantagenet kings. But first I had to try and go back and see the Flaxley that I knew after a fifty-four years' absence. I had spent sixteen months there when my school had been evacuated, and I was smitten with the building then and am still captivated and enthralled by its aura and ambience.

In 1972 I wrote to Baden and asked him if he would be agreeable to my visiting the Abbey. He didn't answer so I rang him up. 'No,' he said, 'the Abbey is never open and I never ask anyone to come round.' And he put the phone down.

After Christmas 1995, I learnt that Baden had died some time

408

ago and that his grandson, Philip, now lived at the Abbey. So I wrote to Philip and asked him if he would, perchance, be agreeable to Sheila and me coming over to see the Abbey. He wrote a charming reply and said he would welcome us, although he too stressed that the Abbey was never open but that he would make a special exception for us.

Thus it was, in the spring of 1996, that we went to Flaxley and all my schoolboy memories came flooding back. Philip was especially understanding and interested in an elderly man's walk down memory lane.

We went into the garden and identified the approximate site of the high altar, now a raised grassy bank. I asked Sheila to pose at that very spot where Milo, her twenty-four times great-grandfather, had been killed in 1143. Five yards behind her was the position of the Abbey crossing, where no less than nine of her ancestors in the direct line had been sitting on the day of consecration and dedication in September 1151.

* * *

Robert, Earl of Gloucester, was the eldest, albeit illegitimate, son of Henry I and was the stabilising influence during the tumultuous problems following Stephen's accession to the throne in 1135. Robert was a soldier, statesman and scholar and with some dexterity negotiated for the prince's succession to the kingship. Luckily for the nation he also became the effective guardian of the young Henry and undertook a sensible training regime. It was Robert who was the instigator of the Flaxley Abbey foundation as a memorial to his colleague and friend, the murdered Earl Milo of Hereford who had shared so many of his aspirations for the future. Quite apart from the Cistercian expertise in developing agriculture which was hugely important for the growing population, the Flaxley hamlet contained the site of an antiquated and run-down Roman iron smelting complex. Ore was available from the Forest of Dean and there was ample charcoal that could be manufactured from the nearby extensive woods. Iron was a vital added dimension of strategic and military importance and to update and reinforce this facility would provide the sinews of war over the following decades – and ensuing centuries as it turned out. The iron smelting works actually only closed down in 1938, just two years before my own arrival.

Lastly, and never to be ignored, the Normans were enthusiastic hunters and the Earls Robert and Milo and their entourages were no exceptions. Prince Henry was being brought up as he should be brought up and his taste for the chase was becoming as avid as his mentors'. Robert therefore incorporated in his Abbey plans for a luxurious hunting lodge to the west of the claustral range which was to be used as a royal Plantagenet sporting retreat, or country cottage if you wish, for the king's sport and relaxation. They could also keep a beady eye on the raw materials for their arsenals and make sure that supplies of ore and charcoal were forthcoming.

All the kings from Henry II until Edward III made considerable use of this facility – a period lasting well over 200 years. When royalty gave up coming, the Abbey absorbed these vacated buildings into conventual use. Thus it was that the kings' private apartments and the dining facilities for their attendants came to be called the Abbot's Parlour and the Monks' Refectory. Originally these Abbey facilities would have been within the cloistral complex and not, as they later became, so far outside the precincts.

We are going back over 800 years and details of what happened then are not to be confirmed as easily as all that, but I have found in my genealogical researches that family legends and stories often have a nub of truth. The Henrician stories are generally dismissed as being unlikely and have been contemptuously discounted. What I have tried to do is to see if some of these legends can be made to interlock and make sense in the context of the times. Henry II and his queen, Eleanor, were a most quarrelsome pair and their sons had an extraordinary love/hate relationship with their father. Their mother encouraged all to rebel. But Eleanor became, in her old age, a much respected and responsible elder stateswoman. We have this awful tendency to classify the kings and queens of that era, in the *1066 and All That* tradition, as 'good' eggs or 'bad' eggs. None of them were all good or all bad – not even King John, whom we all love to hate.

The Rosamond story is fascinating. When did it start? When was Rosamond born? Was she murdered by Eleanor at Woodstock and, if not, what happened and why does that story persist and still strike our imagination so? Did they have any children?

410

What happened to them and how did they get on with the Henry/Eleanor brood? And is there any curious and inexplicable evidence which could fill in our gaps in the fragmentary knowledge? Why, when she died, was she buried (and indeed venerated) in a convent dedicated to chastity?

Tom James, an expert on Plantagenet palaces and an eminent historian, has said that Rosamond appeared on the scene as Henry's mistress in 1170 when she was seventeen, and died in 1175 or 1176, and there are many sources which support this contention. Hugh Clifford, in his book *The House of Clifford* considers that the Henry/Rosamond affair started much earlier and that Rosamond, baptised Jane, was born in about 1138. There is also extraordinary and confirmatory evidence from the Clifford family still living at Frampton and descended directly from Rosamond's brother. Curiously, several sources give 'Jane' as her real name but Lord Clifford actually records her name as 'Joan'. I have used Jane, a name that I much prefer to Joan, quite apart from the general weight of evidence for Jane.

Baden confuses the issue in his book by telling us that Walter Clifford's daughters were Jane the elder and Rosamond the younger. Why did the saintly Bishop Hugh of Lincoln object to the siting of Rosamond's tomb and instruct its removal? And why did Prince John subsequently re-embellish her tomb so sumptuously?

Was Henry devoted exclusively to her over a long period of time? Only three names appear as possible paramours: one a degraded character called Hikenai, the second the wife of Ralf Bloeth and the third Ida, Countess of Boulogne. Was Henry as promiscuous as his grandfather Henry I who, mark you, had no less than thirty-five mistresses and left nine sons and eleven daughters born on the wrong side of the blanket?

Was Milo assassinated? And why? And why did they build Flaxley Abbey in his memory on the very spot that he fell? They did not erect an abbey on the spot where William Rufus was shot. Why did Richard I fulfil his father's dying wish to appoint Geoffrey Plantagenet to the Archbishopric of York? What did Eleanor get up to on the Second Crusade when she was married to Louis VII? And why was the ensuing divorce so messy? How does Thomas Becket fit into all this and why did Richard I found in Acre the hospital dedicated to St Thomas Acon just after he

411

met Saladin? The alleged reason for this was that it was an expiation by Richard for his part in the Becket murder but Richard had no such involvement and Thomas Becket had no obvious connection with Acre. Why did Richard Coeur de Lion and Saladin get on so well together, as well as look alike – allegedly they could easily have been mistaken for brothers. And does that most charming German poem about the Saracen lady who fell in love with her father's captive, loosed his chains to free him and then came to England to find him knowing only two words of English ('London' and 'Gilbert') have any bearing on this story?

I have also woven the involvement of the four Becket murderers into the story. Baden, in his book, refers to his daughter Bertha's noble betrothed being present at Milo's assassination and disappearing immediately afterwards in suspicious circumstances. I cannot find his source and he does not give a name. I have identified a singularly obnoxious earl, the elder Geoffrey de Mandeville, an ardent supporter of Stephen, who had switched his allegiance between Stephen and the Empress Maud depending on the value of the bribes that each had made.

Geoffrey had a son, one Ernulph, who never married and died the year after Milo's murder. I have used him as the 'noble betrothed'. The father of Reginald FitzUrse (a Becket murderer) had dealings with Geoffrey. Here one of Sheila's family legends comes into play. Her mother was a Mahon who have claimed to be descended from the MacMahons in Ireland, and who have alleged that they have a descent from Reginald FitzUrse on the somewhat specious grounds that 'MacMahon' and 'FitzUrse' both mean 'Son of the Bear'. This legend has been repeated, in some sources, that FitzUrse did indeed flee to Ireland. But Sheila's great-grandfather, the Rev. George William Mahon, left a diary, now in our possession and written in 1835, which suggests that the Mahons are also descended from 'King Ernulphus'. I have never found in any reference book a king called Ernulphus. But here we have Reginald's father being involved with an earl whose son was called Ernulph. It is such a coincidence that I felt that it was only right that I should weave this into this story, but I freely admit that this a real shot in the dark which does not have any vital bearing on my theme. Morville signed the Constitutions of Clarendon. Tracy had lands in Devon and Gloucestershire. I have to interpolate another extraordinary coincidence here that

Liz Mascall, who lives in my village and who has given me much hope and encouragement, is a Le Breton by birth. Is Liz perchance descended from the fourth murderer of Becket, Le Breton, a man about whom very little is known? It is not unreasonable to assume that the Becket assassins were all heavily involved over many years with the Henrician court and that they all had something to prove, which meant living down some inherited problems from their pasts.

This is not the tale of Flaxley, although it may have started as such and may have been inspired by Baden's book. I should say here that there is an added dimension to our interest in that Mr and Mrs Baden Watkins retained Oliver Messel to refurbish the Abbey and his work both in the house and the gardens is not only quite stunning but treats everything with enormous sympathy and understanding. Sheila's sister-in-law's mother's cousin was Oliver Messel. Quite close in fact, I suppose, but an incredible coincidence to us.

This is a story not only about Rosamond and her influence on the early Plantagenets, but also her rival, Eleanor. If Rosamond had not died when she did, what might have happened? Henry was virtually committed to divorcing Eleanor in 1174 and making Rosamond his queen. Rosamond was in the mould of those royal paramours who were intensely loyal, keeping a low profile, but who gave a stability, a real and genuine love and a family comfort to their partners and those close to them.

I have tried to address all these threads, and this has involved much research and detective work, all of which has been both enthralling and fascinating. I will also admit to a quantum leap or two in making the odd assumption. But there are so many coincidences and so many loose ends that tie up that I am convinced that several or most of these stories could be far more true than we have realised.

Oh yes, I did discover that Sheila is twice directly descended not only from two of Milo's daughters, Margery (de Bohun) and Berthe (de Braose), but also from both Eleanor and Rosamond.

As Winston Churchill once said, if it isn't all true, it ought to be.

BIBLIOGRAPHY

Ali, Tariq, *The Book of Saladin* (Verso, 1998)

Bradbury, Jim, *Stephen and Matilda* (Sutton, 1998)

Bradner, Sir Joseph, *History of Monmouthshire* (Academy Books, 1991)

Brewer, Clifford, *The Death of Kings* (Abson, 2000)

Burke, *Dormant and Extinct Peerages* (Genealogical Publishing & Burke's Peerage, 1978)

Clifford, Lord of Chudleigh, *The House of Clifford* (Phillimore, 1987)

Davies, R R, *The Age of Conquest 1063–1415* (Oxford University Press, 1987)

Fenwick, Kenneth, *Third Crusade* (Folio Society, 1958)

Fraser, Antonia, *The Lives of the Kings and Queens of England* (Weidenfeld & Nicholson, 1975)

Given-Wilson, Chris and Curteis, Alice, *Royal Bastards* (Routledge, 1984)

Hallam, Elizabeth, ed., *The Plantagenet Chronicles* (Guild Publishing, 1986)

Howse, W H, *Radnor Old and New* (Mid-Border Books, 1989)

James, T Beaumont, *The Palaces of Medieval England* (Seaby, 1990)

James, T Beaumont and Robinson, A M, *Clarendon Palace* (Society of Antiquaries, 1988)

Jones, Thomas, *Chronicles of the Princes* (University of Wales Press, 1955)

Kelly, Amy, *Eleanor of Aquitaine and the Four Kings* (Harvard University Press, 1950)

Meade, Marion, *Eleanor of Aquitaine* (Frederick Muller, 1978)

Mitchell, Mairin, *Berengaria* (A Wright, 1986)

Nicolle, David, *Saladin and the Saracens* (Osprey, 1986)

414

Olding, Frank, *Abergavenny Castle* (Monmouthshire Museum Service, 1998)

Owen, D D R, *Eleanor of Aquitaine* (Blackwell, 1993)

Penman, Sharon, *When Christ and his Saints Slept* (Penguin, 1995)

Poole, A L, *Doomsday Book to Magna Carta 1087–1216* (Oxford University Press, 1951)

Runciman, Steven, *The History of the Crusades Vols 2 & 3* (Penguin, 1990)

Stahl, E L (ed), *The Oxford Book of German Verse* (Oxford University Press, 1967)

Thorp, Lewis, *Gerald of Wales* (Penguin, 1978)

Watkins, Baden, *The Story of Flaxley Abbey* (Alan Sutton, 1985)

Weir, Alison, *Eleanor of Aquitaine* (Jonathan Cape, 1999)